Schwarz auf weiß

Writing German for GCSE

William Rowlinson

Oxford University Press 1989

Oxford University Press, Walton Street, Oxford OX2 6DP

Oxford   New York   Toronto
Delhi   Bombay   Calcutta   Madras   Karachi
Petaling Jaya   Singapore   Hong Kong   Tokyo
Nairobi   Dar es Salaam   Cape Town
Melbourne   Auckland

and associated companies in
Berlin   Ibadan

Oxford is a trade mark of Oxford University Press
© Oxford University Press 1989

First published 1989

ISBN 0 19 912104 4

Acknowledgements

The author is most grateful, as so often in the past, to Kath Williams, Head
of Modern Languages at Silverdale Comprehensive School, Sheffield, and
to Lilo Lehnigk, for their constructive criticism and help, and to his OUP
editors for their continued patience and encouragement.

The publishers would like to thank the following for permission to
reproduce photographs:

Austrian Tourist Board p.38; Barnaby's Picture Library p.35 (both);
Berolina Travel Limited p.58; J Allan Cash p.11 (right); Tony Mays p.11
(left).

Illustrations are by Penny Dann, Gecko Limited, Mark Hackett and
Christine Roche.

Thanks are also due to the Headmaster, staff and students of The German
School, Richmond.

The publishers would like to thank *Bravo* magazine (p.65) for permission to
reproduce copyright material.

Although every effort has been made to contact copyright holders, a few
have been impossible to trace. The publishers apologize to anyone whose
copyright has been unwittingly infringed.

Typeset by Tradespools Ltd, Frome, Somerset

Printed and bound in Great Britain by Scotprint Ltd., Musselburgh, Scotland

Preface

Schwarz auf weiß is a textbook aimed at developing the writing skills needed for GCSE German, that can be used throughout the GCSE course. It offers a large and varied collection of authentic written exercises directly aimed at the syllabuses of the five boards, divided into twelve topic areas and graded at three levels of difficulty.

This is not a course to be worked through text by text, but a resource book to turn to for materials that will prepare for the written element of the examination. A realistic stimulus for the writing is offered in every case, often based on authentic German material, and all tasks are genuinely communicative – pupils are never asked to undertake merely formal work. At the head of each topic area there is a short general vocabulary of basic and immediately useful words and structures, and where necessary stimulus material is also accompanied by a specific German-English side vocabulary so that comprehension does not present too great a hurdle. For simpler exercises guidelines to the answer are given, by providing a form to complete, a set of questions to respond to, a framework to model the answer on, or one or two useful words and phrases (marked with a ●) to indicate a direction in which the answer may develop. Most exercises however are left fairly open-ended so that students may use their own German rather than be forced into a strait-jacket.

Considerable oral and pair work related to these writing exercises is possible. In the early stages a preparatory oral discussion of each exercise in class (with blackboard notes on possible versions, part versions or beginnings of versions) is both comforting and productive; many of the items too will benefit from pair discussion before individual writing and some items can be written jointly by pairs. 'Prepared telephone message' exercises can usefully be followed by oral classwork, with individual pupils transmitting the prepared message to the teacher as receiver. The symbol ◢ is used to indicate the possibility of pair discussion or joint writing.

There is a full English-German vocabulary based on the German vocabulary set by the examining boards; it also has some additional words that may be needed for specific tasks set in this book. The vocabulary cannot of course include everything that every student might wish to look up in the course of his or her writing; however, bearing in mind that this may be the only English-German vocabulary to which some students will have ready access, care has been taken to make it as full and as explanatory as possible. A strong-verb list is also provided.

Symbols are used to differentiate Basic and Higher Level material. Where no symbol is used this indicates suitability for Basic Level; the symbol ▶ indicates suitability for either level (with more extended responses looked for from Higher Level students), and ▶▶ is used to indicate Higher Level material.

The topic areas and the language content set by the various boards show a considerable degree of unanimity, which has made the production of this book a less daunting task than it might have been. Where boards do differ from one another, often quite sharply, is in the length (and occasionally the type) of task which they see as appropriate to the different levels of the examination. At the time of writing, letter-writing exercises for instance vary greatly in length from board to board, and not all boards include them at Basic Level. However, messages, postcards, instructions, and letters are common to the boards at one level or another, and only a few tasks are specific to particular boards.

All this means that teachers will need to make a choice of exercises suited to their own course and to the level at which individual pupils are working, and to stipulate lengths of answer accordingly. All teachers of GCSE German will however find here in *Schwarz auf weiß* material that is exactly appropriate to their syllabus and, we hope, suitably stimulating to their students.

No symbol = suitable for basic (general) level GCSE and foundation/general level Standard Grade

▶ = suitable for both basic (general) and higher levels of GCSE and foundation, general and credit levels of Standard Grade

▶▶ = suitable for higher (extended) level of GCSE and general/credit level of Standard Grade only

◪ = suitable for pair discussion or joint writing

● = useful words and phrases to help with answers

Contents

Lovely rension sheet!

Useful hints

These hints should make the tasks in this book easier to
tackle and improve your written work.

Postcards

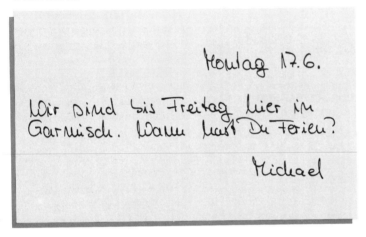

These don't need formal openings or endings – just the date
and if necessary the town you're sending the card from at
the beginning and your name with or without **Dein(e)** in
front of it at the end. Most postcards will use **du** rather than
the more formal **Sie**. Remember that **du, dich, dir, dein**
and **ihr, euch, euer** all have capitals (**Du, Ihr** etc.) on
postcards and in letters.

Messages

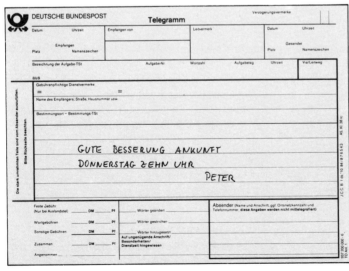

Remember that messages and
telegrams don't need complete
sentences; they do need to be
understandable though – don't
sacrifice understandability to
save a few Pfennige at the
Postamt!

Informal letters

Köln, den 26. März

Liebe Ilse!

Ich habe erst gestern Deinen letzten Brief bekommen

schon vorgestern angekommen!

Herzliche Grüße,

Dein Hans

These should have the town of origin followed by the date, in the form **(Montag,) den 7ten** (or **7.**) **April** at the top right.

They should have **Liebe(r) …** as greeting, followed by either a comma or an exclamation mark; paragraphs aren't indented in German.

Common useful letter endings are **Es grüßt Dich** or **Herzliche Grüße**, followed by **Dein(e)** and your name.

Most informal letters will use the **du** form (remember that **du** etc. and its plural forms **ihr** etc. all take capitals in letters). Some informal letters, though, for instance to friends' parents, may use the **Sie** form.

Formal letters

```
                27 Runcorn Street,
                Widnes WD4 6FE,
                England.

                den 17ten Oktober

Esderts und Klein GmbH,
Erdinger Str. 17,
Frankfurt/Main.

Sehr geehrte Damen und Herren,
ich bedanke mich herzlich für Ihr Schreiben vom
12. Oktober.  Ich habe Ihren Vorschlag genau
überlegt, und...
```

```
auf Ihre Antwort.

              Mit hochachtungsvollen Grüßen,

                   Peter Washington  .

                   Peter WASHINGTON
```

These may just give town of origin plus date, as in the informal letter (in Germany the sender's address appears either on the back of the envelope or at the upper left-hand corner of the front of the envelope); but it is better to give your full address, with the date on a separate line.

The letter starts **Sehr geehrter Herr X., Sehr geehrte Frau X,** (the latter is nowadays used even if you know the woman is unmarried). If they don't know the name or sex of the people they're writing to, many people begin **Sehr geehrte Herren**; however, **Sehr geehrte Damen und Herren** is now becoming more common and avoids any appearance of sexism.

There are a number of possible endings, but the simplest (and very common) are **Hochachtungsvoll** or **Mit hochachtungsvollen Grüßen**, or (less formal) **Mit freundlichen Grüßen**.

General hints

– Make sure you answer all the questions that are asked if you're replying to a letter or a section of a letter;
– don't be afraid to ask questions yourself in your reply;
– don't be afraid to use exclamations **(wie schade! wie schön! unglaublich! . . .)** – they're lively and easy;
– don't be too ambitious – keep to German you know is right;
– reuse wherever you can the German you are given in the letter, questionnaire etc. that you are replying to;
– collect in a notebook useful expressions from the texts and phrases you are given in this book and reuse them wherever possible in your own work;
– when you've finished writing go back and check each of your *verbs* individually to make sure it's in the right tense and the right place.

1 LEUTE UND TIERE

In this unit you will be asked to describe and write about yourself, your family, other people and the odd animal.

People are ...

nice **nett**
beautiful/handsome **schön**
old **alt**
young **jung**
friendly **freundlich**
stupid **dumm**
pretty **hübsch**
fat **dick**
slim **schlank**
tall **groß**
short **klein**
shy **schüchtern**
funny **komisch**
(un) pleasant **(un)angenehm**
awful **schrecklich**
polite **höflich**
fair **blond**

dark(-haired) **dunkel (haarig)**
lazy **faul**
hard-working **fleißig**

Animals can be some of these things too!

Asking about people (and animals) ...

what does she look like? **wie sieht sie aus?**
how old is he? **wie alt ist er?**
have you any pets? **hast du Haustiere?**
where does she live? **wo wohnt sie?**
have they got brothers and sisters? **haben sie Geschwister?**
do you like ... ? **hast du ... gern?**
do you like swimming? **schwimmst du gern?**

◢ **1 a** Make a list of your own characteristics to send to your new German pen-friend. Some of the words in the box at the beginning of the unit may help you. Don't be too modest!

◢ **b** Make a similar list to describe your pet animal. If you don't own one, decide what animal you would like to have and list the characteristics you would like it to possess.

◢ **2** Make a list of the characteristics of someone you don't like in order to describe him/her to your German pen-friend. When you've made the list give it to your partner and see if s/he can guess who you are describing!

3 You have arrived in Germany to study. To get the very valuable student discounts you have to fill in a form about yourself:

Zur sofortigen Ausfüllung bei Ankunft in der Schule

FAMILIENNAME ....

VORNAME(N) ....

ANSCHRIFT ....

POSTLEITZAHL ....

GESCHLECHT ....

STAATSANGEHÖRIGKEIT ....

GEBOREN AM ....

ALTER ....

PASSNUMMER ....

SCHULE ODER UNIVERSITÄT ....

FAMILIENSTAND ....

BESONDERE KENNZEICHEN ....

....

DATUM .... UNTERSCHRIFT ....

sofortig immediate
die Ankunft arrival
die Anschrift address
das Geschlecht sex
das Alter age
das Kennzeichen distinguishing mark

- **männlich** male
- **weiblich** female
- **ledig (= unverheiratet)** unmarried

4 You are looking for a summer job working in a south German holiday hotel. You see an advertisement in a German paper which asks for a letter of application to the manageress giving personal details. Use the skeleton opposite to apply:

sich bewerben um apply for
der Trimesterschluß end of term
einzuholen available

```
                          ..... , den ...... 19..
Frau Renate Böll,
Direktorin,
Hotel Goldener Adler
D-7759 Immenstadt.


Sehr geehrte Frau Böll,

ich möchte mich hiermit um eine Stelle als
Hotelangestellte(r) bewerben (Die Welt, 1.4.19..).

Ich bin ...... Jahre alt und bin in ...... geboren.
Ich habe ...... Jahre Deutsch studiert.  Im
Augenblick studiere ich auch ...... .

Ich bin nach dem Trimesterschluß (am ........ 19..)
frei.  Referenzen sind bei meinem Schuldirektor
(meiner Schuldirektorin) einzuholen.


Hochachtungsvoll,


......
```

5 ... ome town of your German ... nts have suggested ... to visit them ... of ...

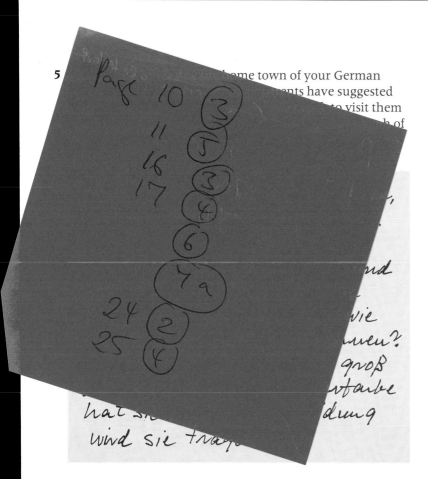

freuen please
abholen meet
erkennen recognise
aussehen look like

Page 10 ③
11 ⑤
16 ③
17 ④
6
7a
24
25 ②
④

...nd... vie ...wen? groß ...farbe hat si... ...dung wird sie tra...

6

Your family has just acquired a new dog/a new cat. On the back of the above photo there is room for only about 30 words of description of this charming animal. What would you write on the back of the copy of the photo you are sending to a German friend?

▶ **7** Reply to this advertisement by a German television station which you have found in an English magazine. After giving the details requested add a final sentence saying why you think you should be especially considered.

Süddeutsches Fernsehen sucht sechs deutschsprechende sechzehn-jährige Engländer(innen) für Jugendsendung über England. Kein Honorar, aber der Flug nach Stuttgart, Unterkunft und alle sonstige Unkosten werden vom Sender bezahlt. Schreiben Sie bitte an Ulrike Graf, Süd-deutsches Fernsehen, Stuttgart, mit Bild und folgenden Einzelheiten: Geburtsdatum; Geschlecht; Wohnort; Jahren Deutschstudien; Lieblings-schulfächern; Freizeitsinteressen.

die Jugendsendung youth broadcast
das Honorar fee
der Flug flight
die Unterkunft accommodation
sonstig other
die Unkosten expenses
der Sender radio/TV station
die Einzelheit detail

▶ **8** You have just been allocated an exchange partner for a school exchange to Germany. Write him/her a short letter:
 – introducing and describing yourself
 – mentioning what you're interested in or what your hobbies are
 – giving details of your family – how many, how old (where appropriate), what they do
 – mentioning any pets you may have.

◢ **9**

You are staying with the family of your German friend. Whilst they are all out this man (opposite) arrives and asks for your friend's father, Herr Müller. When you tell him there is no-one in except you he says 'Na ja, da komm' ich heute abend wieder vorbei – etwa gegen halb acht, ja?'

You have to go out to meet your German friend at the youth club, so leave a message for Herr Müller explaining what happened and describing the caller.

vorbeikommen come round

● **allein im Haus** alone in the house
● **er wünschte Sie zu sprechen** he asked for you; he wanted to speak to you

12

▶ 10

Ich habe seit Monaten keine Nachricht von Dir. Wie geht es Dir und Deiner Familie?
Uli

die Nachrichten news

Well ... in fact the most awful things have been happening to all the members of your family – your uncle Archibald, your little sister, your grandmother and even the hamster. Write a short note to Uli explaining your predicament.

Lieber Uli,
entschuldige, daß ich so lange nicht geschrieben habe, aber mein Onkel Archibald – du kennst ihn, nicht? – also, mein Onkel Archibald ... .

◢ **11 a** Your German teacher has applied to become a spy for the
▶▶ West German government. All spies are, of course, positively vetted and questionnaires are sent to people who know the candidate well. You have received the questionnaire below, and are required to complete it as accurately as possible.

Name des Kandidaten/der Kandidatin: ....

Wohnort (Stadt): ....

Beschreiben Sie bitte seine/ihre Person: ....

Wie ist sein/ihr Charakter? (ruhig? lebhaft? zurückgezogen?

gesellig?) ....

Hat er/sie besondere gute Eigenschaften? ....

....

Hat er/sie besondere schlechte Eigenschaften? ....

....

Ist er/sie völlig zuverlässig? ....

Wie sind seine/ihre Deutschkenntnisse? (mangelhaft? ausreichend?

hervorragend?) ....

ruhig quiet
lebhaft lively
zurückgezogen withdrawn
gesellig sociable
die Eigenschaft quality
zuverlässig reliable
mangelhaft unsatisfactory
ausreichend adequate
hervorragend outstanding

▶▶ **b** Add a further paragraph explaining why s/he would/ would not be successful as a spy.

● **meines Erachtens ...** in my opinion

13

12 Your mother has just presented you with a new baby sister/ brother (or both!). Send a postcard to your German pen-friend telling him/her the news and describing the new arrival.

▶▶ **13** A friend of your German pen-friend is organising a summer sailing holiday in the Adriatic on a six-berth yacht. Your pen-friend, who is going on the trip, thinks that if you can sell yourself well enough as a tough, reliable, independent type, you could get in on the holiday too, even though you have had no/not much sailing experience on a boat of this size. Complete this letter, therefore, to your pen-friend's friend:

die Segeltour sailing trip
die Besatzung crew

> 82 Rosemead Drive
> LICHFIELD
> WS13 9XY
> den. 17 Oktober
>
> Lieber Uwe,
> Mein guter Freund Peter Beckmann hat mir von Ihrer kommenden Segeltour der Adria erzählt und meint, daß Sie vielleicht auch für mich Platz bei der Besatzung haben würden.
> Ich bin

● **nicht viel Erfahrung** not much experience

▶ **14** You see the following competition in a German teenage magazine:

die Geschwister (pl.) brother(s) and sister(s)
gelitten (*from* **leiden**) suffered

> ## Oh, die Geschwister!
>
> Erzähl uns in 100 Worten, wie und warum dein Bruder oder deine Schwester so absolut unmöglich ist: wer unter seinen Geschwistern am meisten gelitten hat, wird eine CD-Platte als Preis bekommen!

You decide to try to write the paragraph, (a) because you think that as a foreigner you might stand a chance of the prize, since you'll at least be different from the other contestants and (b) because you have the most awful brother/sister in the world.

14

2 WOHNUNG UND STADT

In this unit you will be asked to write about your own home and your own room, about your town or village and about other towns and cities you know. You will also practise asking about and describing other people's homes and their contents, and writing exact directions for getting to places.

Your house or flat...

entrance **der Eingang (ˇe)**
front door **die Eingangstür (-en)**
garden **der Garten (ˇ)**
garage **die Garage (-n)**
storey, floor **der Stock (-)**
on the first floor **im ersten Stock**
ground floor **das Erdgeschoß**
lift **der Fahrstuhl (ˇe)**
stairs **die Treppe** (*sing.*)

Its rooms...

living room **das Wohnzimmer (-)**
dining room **das Eßzimmer (-)**
kitchen **die Küche (-n)**
bedroom **das Schlafzimmer (-)**
bathroom **das Badezimmer (-)**
lavatory **die Toilette (-n)**
hall **der Flur (-e)**
cellar **der Keller (-)**
loft **der Dachboden (ˇ)**

In the house...

appliance **das Gerät (-e)**
tape recorder **das Tonbandgerät**

hi-fi **die HiFi-Anlage (-n)**
video **das Videogerät (-e)**
compact disc player **der CD-Plattenspieler (-)**
central heating **die Heizung**
radiator **der Heizkörper (-)**
plug **der Stecker (-)**
switch **der Schalter (-)**
freezer **die Kühltruhe (-n)**
microwave **der Mikrowellenherd (-e)**
washing machine **die Waschmaschine (-n)**
vacuum cleaner **der Staubsauger (-)**
fridge **der Kühlschrank (ˇe)**
dishwasher **die Spülmaschine (-n)**
dustbin **der Mülleimer (-)**

Around the town...

(bus) station **der (Bus)bahnhof (ˇe)**
town hall **das Rathaus**
market square **der Marktplatz**
pedestrian precinct **die Fußgängerzone**
department store **das Warenhaus (ˇer)**
straight on **geradeaus**
to turn left/right **links/rechts abbiegen**
to get on/off **ein-/aussteigen**
to change (*buses etc.*) **umsteigen**
first on the right/left **die erste Straße rechts/ links**

1 a Imagine you've just moved into your present house or flat and you're going to describe it to your German penfriend. Make a preliminary list of all the rooms and such things as garage or garden.

b Now write a postcard to your German friend describing the house or flat. Things you might want to mention:

— How many rooms are there?
— Is there a garden and garage?
— What are its surroundings like – are there trees, is there a lot of traffic?
— How far away are shops, cinema, school, park?

● **nicht allzu weit weg** not too far away

2 Your town twinning committee has asked for volunteers to put up members of a group of young people visiting your town, and your parents have been allocated Fräulein Ilse Bartols. Use this skeleton letter to tell her something about your house and to welcome her.

```
                              ......, den ...... 19..

Liebe Ilse,

meine Eltern und ich heißen Sie herzlich
willkommen in unserem Haus!

Wir wohnen in der ......[street, road],
Nummer ...... . Am besten nehmen Sie ein Taxi
vom Bahnhof: es ist ein ziemlich langer Weg./ Vom
Bahnhof ist das Haus zu Fuß leicht zu erreichen
(Plan anbei!).
Unser Haus werden Sie liecht erkennen: es ...... .
Sie werden ein eigenes Zimmer im ...... Stock/ im
Erdgeschoß haben, und Sie werden natürlich auch
alle Mahlzeiten in der Familie einnehmen.

Wir erwarten Sie also am ...... (wissen Sie noch,
wann Ihr Zug ankommt?), und wir freuen uns sehr
auf Ihren Besuch.

Mit freundlichen Grüßen,

......
```

willkommen heißen welcome
erreichen reach
anbei attached
erkennen recognize
der Stock storey
das Erdgeschoß ground floor
die Mahlzeit meal
erwarten expect
sich freuen auf look forward to

▶ 3 Your family are exchanging houses with a German family for the Easter holidays. Your parents have written a welcoming letter to them in English, which is to have a short German enclosure (produced by you) with the following information:
  a Describe your house to them in general terms (for example, where it's situated; number and type of rooms; garden; heating system).
  b They are coming by car from Germany. Explain how they reach your house from the motorway or main road, or from the town centre.
  c They don't know your town at all. Give them some useful information – perhaps where the shops, pubs, restaurants are, what there is to do in and around the town.

4 You are staying with your Swiss friend and are alone in the house when your father rings up from England to say that he's found the ideal holiday home in Devon for your friend's family (they've been looking for one to rent for the summer for some time). You're to tell them the following points:

- It's not far from Bude.
- It has a living room, a big kitchen that you can eat in, three bedrooms and a bathroom.
- It's near the sea and the view is terrific.
- It's amazingly cheap.
- If they're interested they should ring him back as soon as possible.

Since you're going out you leave a message for your pen-friend's mother with all this information in it.

- **hat angerufen** has rung up
- **so bald wie möglich** as soon as possible

5

You have just moved house and have acquired a new bedroom. Write a note to your German pen-friend describing it in detail. (Why not take this opportunity to make imaginative improvements to your present room? What about a four-poster bed – **das Himmelbett** – for instance . . .?)

6 Your German friend is staying with you and has offered to do some food shopping whilst you are at school. Make notes for him/her on how to get to the supermarket (if s/he needs to take a bus, make notes on how to reach the stop where s/he gets on, the number and destination of the bus, where to get off and how to get from there to the supermarket).

- **Linie Nummer ...** route number
- **in Richtung ...** going towards

Du gehst ....

7 a Your father's/mother's job is taking you all to Germany for three years. A flat has been offered for the family to rent and you have been told you may take as much furniture as you like with you. However, it isn't too clear how big the flat is and whether there will be enough room for all your present furniture. Draft a letter for your father/mother to the owner of the flat, in which you enquire about the size of the rooms in it and list the furniture you would like to take if there is room for it.

- **und zwar folgendes:** to be precise, the following:

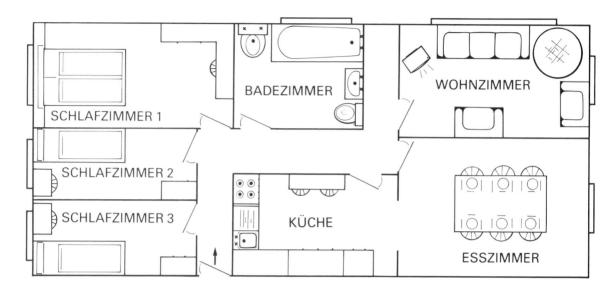

SCHLAFZIMMER 1 / SCHLAFZIMMER 2 / SCHLAFZIMMER 3 / BADEZIMMER / WOHNZIMMER / KÜCHE / ESSZIMMER

▶ **b** You have arrived with the family in Germany for that three-year stay and moved into the flat shown in the plan above. Describe it room by room (in a letter to your pen-friend) using the pattern: 'Die Wohnung hat ein großes ... mit einem ... und einer ... Sie hat auch ...'

8 A friend of yours was annoyed on a recent holiday by the number of essential kitchen items that were missing from a rented Swiss villa, and which s/he either had to buy or do without. There were no fewer than twelve absolutely essential items missing. You are helping your friend to write a letter of complaint to the agency. Complete the letter below.

Sehr geehrte Herren,

Ich muß mich wirklich beschweren über die mangelhafte Einrichtung der „Villa Borghese" in Zermatt, die wir vorletzte Woche über Ihre Agentur gemietet haben. Vor allem fehlte eine ganze Menge Küchengeräte, und zwar folgende:

sich beschweren über complain about
mangelhaft insufficient
die Einrichtung equipment
mieten rent
fehlen be lacking
das Küchengerät kitchen tool
und zwar ... to be precise ...

9 Your German pen-friend writes to say that he's recently read an article in a German magazine about the city nearest to where you live. The article was very critical indeed of the shopping facilities there. Your friend asks if it is really that bad. Spring to its defence . . .! The letter below may help you.

Hallo Michael,
das, was Du gelesen hast über
. . . . . . stimmt wirklich nicht!
Dort sind allerlei Läden zu finden,
und man kann wirklich alles
dort kaufen. Zum Beispiel:

allerlei all kinds of

10 A German acquaintance has been asked by his school to conduct a survey amongst people of his own age answering the question 'Was hast du nicht zu Hause, was du gern besitzen möchtest?', and so he has written to you.
Your friend asks you to list ten items and to describe them. Apparently most people included 'ein großes Schwimmbad', and quite a lot have suggested 'einen privaten Tennisplatz'.

besitzen own

11 You have just moved to a new town or village (choose one you know!). Send your pen-friend in East Germany a postcard telling him/her some interesting facts about the town (size? pleasant/unpleasant? industry? shops? parks and gardens? entertainments?).

- **gerade eingezogen** just moved in
- **es ist (nicht) sehr viel los** there's (not) a lot going on

12 You receive the following letter from a German friend who is coming to stay with you in Britain:

Ich warte mit Ungeduld auf den Tag
meiner Abreise zu Euch nach
Großbritannien. Mein Zug kommt am 17ten
um 3 Uhr nachmittags am Liverpool
Street-Bahnhof an. Wird es möglich sein,
daß Du mich dort abholst? Oder soll ich
alleine weiterfahren? (Das wird kein
Problem sein, ich kenne mich ja in London
aus!)
                                Deine Gisela

die Ungeduld impatience
abholen collect/ pick up
sich auskennen know one's way around

You simply can't get to Liverpool Street to meet her. Write a letter to her apologizing and saying why you can't be there. Then give her these instructions:

- tell her which London station to go to (by tube) in order to get a train to the nearest mainline station to where you live
- tell her to ask when her train arrives at your station
- tell her to phone you from London (give your number) with that information
- tell her you'll be at the station to meet her.

- **es tut mir furchtbar leid** I'm dreadfully sorry
- **dort nimmst du die U-Bahn nach (Euston)** there you take the underground to (Euston)

13 Your town has decided to produce a new brochure advertising itself and its amenities. This will include a paragraph of about 100 words in French and the same in German to introduce the town to speakers of those languages. Write a 100-word paragraph that will really attract German speakers to your town.

14 a Friends of yours have bought a cottage near St Ives in Cornwall which they want to rent each summer to people from Europe. It has two bedrooms, sitting room, kitchen, bath. Design an advertisement for them to put in a German newspaper (keep it short to cut down the cost). The advertisements below may help.

das Cottage cottage
der Selbstversorger self-caterer
der Landschaftsgarten landscaped garden
sicher safe
der Strand beach
die FeWo = Ferienwohnung

- **unvergl. Aussichten auf ...** incomparable views of ...
- **preisgünstig** good value
- **aller Komfort** all mod. cons.

20

b Your friends also want a one-paragraph description in German of the location and amenities of the cottage, which they are going to photocopy and send off to any German-speakers who enquire. Write the paragraph for them using the map below. Avoid mentioning anything you think might detract from the cottage's attractions!

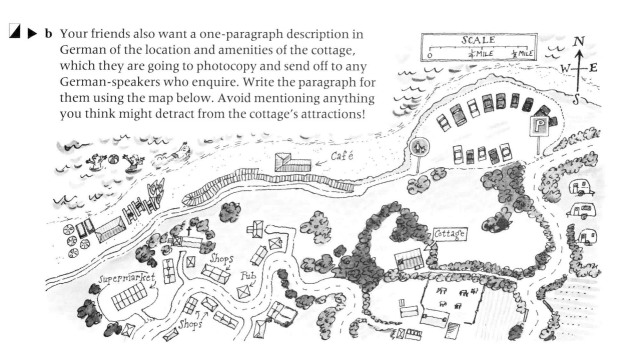

- **mittelalterlich** medieval
- **gute Badegelegenheiten** good bathing

15 A Swiss friend of the family is considering buying a holiday home in Britain. 'Where?' he writes.

Pass on some of the family's views to your Swiss friend, add your own comments and suggest where *you* think would be the best place to buy this holiday home.

- **das Seengebiet** Lake District
- **mein eigener Vorschlag wäre ...** my own suggestion would be ...

16 You are moving into your new flat in Germany and the first van load of furniture has just arrived. None of the family is there to receive it, but luckily it had occurred to you to provide the German delivery firm with a complete list of the furniture, which room each piece is to go in and where (in relation to other pieces, doors, windows or whatever) it is to stand. Use the drawings and plan of the flat below to produce that information.

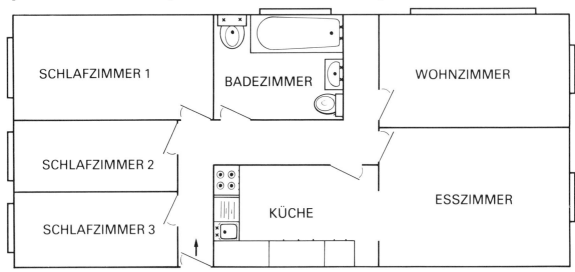

3 ALLTAGSLEBEN

In this unit you will be asked to write about everyday life in
town and country; about birthdays, Christmas,
November 5th, weddings; about everyday tasks, everyday
problems, everyday weather, ordinary and extraordinary
weekends . . .

Daily tasks . . .

wash up **abwaschen**
dry up **abtrocknen**
make the bed **das Bett machen**
lay the table **den Tisch decken**
clear the table **abdecken**
make coffee **Kaffee kochen**
peel **schälen**
empty **leeren**
tidy **in Ordnung bringen**
go shopping **einkaufen gehen**

When . . . ?

today **heute**
yesterday **gestern**
tomorrow **morgen**
the day before yesterday **vorgestern**
the day after tomorrow **übermorgen**
this morning **heute morgen**
tomorrow morning **morgen früh**
tonight **heute abend**
yesterday afternoon **gestern nachmittag**

Good and bad weather . . .

the sun's shining **die Sonne scheint**
it's raining **es regnet**
it's snowing **es schneit**
it's hailing **es hagelt**
it's cool, cold **es ist kühl/kalt**
it's warm/hot **es ist warm/heiß**
cloudy **wolkig**
windy **windig**
foggy **neblig**
bright **heiter**
stormy **stürmisch**

Events . . .

birthday **das Geburtstag**
(at) Christmas/Easter **(zu) Weihnachten/Ostern**
excursion **der Ausflug (¨e)**
stay **der Aufenthalt (-e)**
invitation **die Einladung (-en)**
go dancing **tanzen gehen**
go to the cinema **ins Kino gehen**
bonfire **das Freudenfeuer**
concert **das Konzert (-e)**
wedding **die Hochzeit (-en)**

1 a Your friend in Germany has asked you to
send a list of everything you would like for
Christmas. Make as full a list of possible
presents as you can – maybe s/he'll buy you
something from it!

b It's early January, and you're writing to your German friend to say thanks for the rather splendid Christmas present s/he sent. Use this skeleton letter to do it:

```
                              ...... , den ...... 19..


     Liebe/Lieber ......,


     herzlichen Dank für ......, d.. Du mir zu Weihnachten geschickt
     hast.  Es (er, sie) hat mir wirklich gut gefallen.

     Übrigens, hast Du ...... bekommen, d.. ich Dir geschickt habe?
     Schreib mir bald!


     Dein(e)

     ......
```

übrigens by the way
schicken send

2 You have just had a birthday. Your German friend has sent you a rather boring desk set, with paper, envelopes, and a couple of ballpoint pens. But at least it has given you the stimulus to write back, telling him/her about the terrific birthday party you had, and to mention some of the really interesting presents you got. Don't forget to thank him/her for the desk set!

- **die Geburtstagsfeier** birthday party
- **die Schreibtischgarnitur** desk set

3 a Your German friend's parents have somehow discovered that it's your birthday and sent you a portable radio-cassette player. You are overwhelmed by this gift and a little embarrassed. Write a letter of thanks in which

- you say how pleased you are with the present
- you tell them it's something out of the ordinary, the sort of thing that you are not used to receiving
- you say it's really too much for a birthday present, but that none the less you are very grateful indeed.

- **der Radio-Recorder** radio cassette-player
- **außergewöhnlich** out of the ordinary

b Then write to your friend telling him/her what you did on your birthday, and especially the effect that your new radio-cassette player had on all your friends.

4 The last letter you received from your German friend contained the following paragraph. Write a paragraph in reply demonstrating that s/he doesn't know how lucky s/he is when you consider the amount of work *you* have to do about the house. Some bending of the truth may be necessary!

> *Meine Mutter ist jetzt plötzlich der Meinung, daß ich nicht genügend Hausarbeit mache. Sie hat ganz neue Regeln eingeführt: jetzt muß ich nicht nur jeden Tag mein Bett machen und mein Zimmer in Ordnung bringen, ich muß auch noch dreimal in der Woche abwaschen, einmal in der Woche den Rasen mähen und einmal im Monat die Fenster putzen. Kannst Du Dir das vorstellen?!*

die Meinung opinion
genügend enough
die Regel rule
einführen introduce
der Rasen lawn

- **außerdem** as well as that
- **da muß ich noch ...** I also have to ...
- **das Allerschlimmste ist ...** the worst thing of all is ...

5 Your German friend's sister is getting married and all your family have received this invitation to the wedding. A note is enclosed offering accommodation for any members of your family coming.

UND WIR MEINTEN DOCH!

BARBARA BENSIEN + RÜDER AUER

STANDESAMTLICHE TRAUUNG:
16 JUNI
27 JUNI
SAMSTAG,
12⁰⁰ UHR : KIRCHLICHE TRAUUNG
S⁺ ALBERTUS MAGNUS
SUIBERT-HEIMBACH-PLATZ
18⁰⁰ UHR : GROSSES HOCHZEITSGARTEN SOMMERFEST
IN DER MAYENER S⁺ᴿ 5
U.A.W.G. BIS 31. MAI 1987 (16⁰⁰ UHR)

Write a formal reply to Barbara Bensien saying
- you're very pleased
- you will be very happy to accept
- the other members of your family are very sorry but they will not be able to be there
- you'll be arriving the day before the wedding (make sure you mention the date, and that you get the right one!).

heiraten marry
standesamtlich in the register office
die Trauung marriage ceremony
kirchlich in church
die Hochzeit wedding
u.A.w.g. (um Antwort wird gebeten) R.S.V.P.

- **es wird mich sehr freuen, die Einladung anzunehmen** I shall be very happy to accept the invitation

6 Frau Stein cleans the holiday flat you have rented each day, but she does not speak English. You are off for the day and your parents have asked you to leave a note for her in German asking her, when she arrives, if she can do the following things:

Clean the bathroom
Make beds
Sweep kitchen floor
Tidy up and vacuum sitting room
Put the washing in the washing machine
Empty rubbish bin

- **staubsaugen in** (+ *dat.*) vacuum

Helga,
wollen Sie
bitte folgendes
machen:

7 You receive a letter from your German friend that includes this paragraph:

Meine Eltern werden immer schlimmer. Du wirst es kaum glauben. Jetzt sagen sie nicht nur, daß ich jeden Tag bei der Hausarbeit helfen muß, sondern ich muß auch um zehn wieder zu Hause sein, wenn ich abends ausgehe. Und sie wollen andauernd wissen, wo ich war und mit wem! Ich bin doch schließlich sechzehn Jahre alt, ich bin doch kein Kind mehr! Findest Du das auch so unmöglich?

schlimm bad
andauernd continually
schließlich after all

- **den Standpunkt nicht verstehen** not understand the point of view

Do you? Write a reply giving your own opinions.

8

Prima Wochenende mit dem Motorradverein am Bodensee. Morgens geschwommen, nachmittags Tennis gespielt, abends getanzt. Habe auch ein Surfbrett gemietet – Klasse!
                    Deine Daniele

der Verein club
das Surfbrett sailboard
mieten hire
toll terrific

You have just received this postcard from a German friend. Write one back about your weekend, which was less impressive (you stayed at home, it rained, the television broke down and the cat was ill).

9 Your exchange partner who has just returned to Germany writes:

> und erst als ich alles ausgepackt hatte, habe ich bemerkt, daß mein rechter Hausschuh fehlte. Ich habe ihn bestimmt irgendwo bei Dir in meinem Zimmer liegen lassen, vielleicht steckt er unter dem Bett? Oder vielleicht im Badezimmer? Er ist aus grauem Wildleder.

Well, you've looked everywhere in the bedroom – under the bed, in the cupboard, in all the drawers. The slipper's not there, nor is it in the bathroom. You don't think the dog's taken it, but you certainly can't find it. Write a postcard explaining and apologizing.

- **überall gesucht** looked everywhere

10 Your German friend has asked you to write a report for his/her class magazine about Bonfire Night. Write an account of how Bonfire Night originated, and say how you yourself usually celebrate it.

- **das Feuerwerk** firework display
- **das Freudenfeuer** bonfire
- **das Komplott** plot
- **das Parlamentsgebäude** Houses of Parliament
- **in die Luft sprengen** blow up

11 You receive the following letter from your West German friend early in January. Write back describing how you yourself spent Christmas.

> Soweit ich weiß, feiert Ihr Weihnachten etwa so wie wir: mit Weihnachtskarten, Baum, Geschenken, viel Essen und Trinken am ersten Weihnachtstag und am zweiten einem Kater! Aber ich denke, wir machen mehr vorher (z.B., Adventskalender, Adventskranz), und vielleicht feiert Ihr länger nachher (wann fangt Ihr wieder zu arbeiten an? Erst am dritten Januar, habe ich gehört!). Schreib mir mal, wie Du selber Weihnachten gefeiert hast.

etwa so wie about like
der erste Weihnachtstag Christmas Day
der Kater hangover
vorher before
der Adventskalender Advent calendar
der Kranz wreath

12 You have received a letter from your friend in West Berlin with the following weather information:

> Du wirst es kaum glauben, aber es ist jetzt Mitte April und wir haben schon wieder Schnee. Und wie viel Schnee, 20 bis 30 Zentimeter hoch! Im Dezember wäre das schön gewesen, aber jetzt nach diesem langen, kalten Winter — nicht unbedingt. Dabei haben wir bald Mai!

wäre gewesen would have been
nicht unbedingt not necessarily

Well . . . they may have a lot of snow in Berlin, but in this last winter *you've* had snow, rain, fog, hailstorms, gales – and it's been very cold. Tell her all this, laying it on thick!

● **es wollte nicht aufhören**
   it wouldn't stop

13 You have just spent three weeks with friends of your family who have a farm in Shropshire. Write to your friend in Vienna telling him/her how much you enjoyed your stay in the country, contrasting life on this Shropshire farm with your normal life and mentioning some of the things that you did there.

14 Imagine yourself as either of the two people in the first of the pictures below and write the whole story, in the past tense, in about 100 words.

die Telefonzelle telephone kiosk
draußen outside
unbekümmert unconcerned
böse cross

durchnäßt soaked
aufhören stop
das schnurlose Telefon cordless phone
wütend furious

4 REISEN UND FERIEN

In this unit you'll be writing to ask for holiday information, to book campsites, youth hostel beds and hotel rooms, to retrieve lost property and to explain breakages . . . You'll also be writing about holidays, real and imaginary, and ways of reaching your holiday destination.

Holidays . . .

summer holidays **die Sommerferien**
on holiday **in/auf Urlaub**
camp **zelten**
campsite **der Campingplatz (⁻e)**
youth hostel **die Jugendherberge (-n)**
hotel **das Hotel (-s)**
caravan **der Wohnwagen (-)**

Booking it . . .

book **reservieren**
single/double room **das Einzelzimmer/
  Doppelzimmer**
with bath/shower/breakfast **mit Bad/Dusche/
  Frühstück**
adult **der Erwachsene** (*a.n.*)
how much is it per day/per person? **wieviel
  kostet es pro Tag/pro Person?**
further information **weitere Auskunft**
information office **das Verkehrsamt, das
  Verkehrsbüro**
ticket **die Fahrkarte (-n)**; (*tram, bus*) **der
  Fahrschein (-e)**
timetable **der Fahrplan (⁻e)**
brochure **die Broschüre (-n)**
map **die Karte (-n)**
sea **das Meer (-e); die See**

lake **der See (-n)**
in the country **auf dem Lande**

Getting there . . .

journey **die Reise (-n)**
luggage **das Gepäck**
departure **die Abfahrt**
hitch-hike **trampen**
cycle **radfahren**
go by train/car/bus/motorbike **mit dem Zug/
  Auto/Bus/Motorrad fahren**
by ferry **mit der Fähre**
fly **fliegen**
supplement **der Zuschlag (⁻e)**

Being there . . .

arrival **die Ankunft**
tourist **der Tourist (-en)**
spend (time) **(Zeit) verbringen**
stay (= *be staying*) **wohnen**
abroad **im Ausland**
beach **der Strand**
countryside (= *landscape*) **die Landschaft**
guide (*book*) **der Führer**;
  (*person*) **der Reiseleiter (-)**
camera **der Fotoapparat (-e)**

◢ 1 You are going on a camping holiday with your German friend and realise that there are quite a number of things you need (or would like) to take that you can share (one torch between the two of you, one tin-opener . . .). Make a list in German of all such items that you can think of so that you can decide who will bring what.

- **die Taschenlampe** torch
- **der Dosenöffner** tin-opener

2 You are going to visit friends in East Germany and are taking them some presents. Before setting off, for safety's sake you make a list in German of the things you are taking that you think might give you trouble at the DDR customs. The drawing here may give you some ideas; add some of your own if you can.

3 a You are going to telephone the information office at Freiburg to find out about a holiday in the Black Forest for your parents. Make preliminary notes in German of the things you will ask about (hotels? excursions? the weather? maps? . . . what else?).

b You decide to write instead. Use your telephone notes to write the letter, using this framework if you want to: ▶

```
                                            ......, den ......

Verkehrsamt,
Freiburg/Breisgau.

Sehr geehrte Herren,

meine Eltern haben vor, Ihre Osterferien im Schwarzwald zu
verbringen.  Können Sie mir bitte folgendes sagen:

......

Wollen Sie mir bitte auch folgendes schicken:

......


Hochachtungsvoll,

......
```

4 You are camping in Bavaria and you're hoping to hitch a lift there down the motorways. You have found the following advertisement in Europa-Camping. The site is not too far from the motorway and looks attractive as a stopping place before going further south, so you write a letter to book a stay there.

Campingplatz Estenfeld
Maidbronner Straße 38
8702 Estenfeld b.Würzburg
Inh. S. Strümper, Tel. 09305/228
Zwischenstation auf dem Weg in den Süden
Ruhig und sonnig gelegen –
Nur 3 km von der Autobahnabfahrt Wü-Estenfeld
Geänderte Zufahrt durch Umgehungsstraße.
Hinweisschilder beachten
– geöffnet 01.03.–31.10. –

gelegen situated
geändert changed
die Zufahrt access
die Umgehungsstraße bypass
das Hinweisschild sign
beachten observe; follow

There are two of you, you have two one-person tents and no car. You will arrive on August 3rd and intend to stay for two nights. You are not sure how late you will arrive on the 3rd – ask what is the latest time for booking in.

- **das Einmannzelt** one-person tent
- **die Anmeldezeit** booking-in time

5

Reisedienst
des
Fremdenverkehrsvereines
Mödling
Gästedienst im Rathaus
Postfach 34, 2340 Mödling, Tel. 02236/6727

Bitte Karte heraustrennen, ankreuzen und an
Hotel, Gasthof oder Privatzimmervermieter einsenden

☐ Ich würde gern Näheres über Ihr Hotel/Ihren Gasthof erfahren.
  Bitte senden Sie mir zunächst Ihren Prospekt, Preisliste usw.

☐ Ich bitte um Reservierung eines
☐ Doppel/   ☐ Einzelzimmers
  in der Zeit vom _____ bis _____

☐ Übernachtung/Frühstück
☐ Halbpension
☐ Vollpension

Bitte senden Sie mir Ihre Bestätigung bis _____

Ich bin telefonisch erreichbar unter Nr. _____

Hier abtrennen!

Bitte Ihren Absender nicht vergessen!

WERBEANTWORT   Bitte ausreichend frankieren

An Hotel/Gasthof

Postleitzahl

Some places make it very easy indeed to book a hotel room. The town of Mödling, near Vienna, offers you this card which can simply be ticked and sent off in next to no time.

Not everywhere is so helpful though. Use the Mödling card to help you write a letter to the Hotel zum Roten Löwen, Marktplatz, D-8803 Rothenburg ob der Tauber, booking three nights bed and breakfast in a single room from June 3rd to 6th. Ask for any further information they can give you about their hotel and their price list.

heraustrennen tear off
ankreuzen tick
der Vermieter renter; landlord
Näheres more details
zunächst initially
das Einzelzimmer single room
die Übernachtung accommodation (only)
die Halbpension half board (dinner, bed and breakfast)
die Bestätigung confirmation
erreichbar available; to be reached

▶ **6** You and your friend want to explore the Rheinland from the Youth Hostel at Burg Bacharach; you're going to get the train to Bacharach and walk or hitch to the castle from there. You want to be sure of at least one night's lodging when you get to the hostel, so write to the Herbergsvater asking

– can you book two beds for the night of August 19th?
– how long can you stay after that (ideally you'd like to stay there ten days)?
– do they do meals (evenings meals especially)?
– can you hire sleeping bags?
– what will it all cost?

• **einen Schlafsack leihen** hire a sleeping bag

▶ **7** You left the last campsite of your motoring and camping holiday in Germany on August 12th in the morning. The campsite was the Campingplatz Schöndorf in the Bremerhavener Straße in Worpswede. You drove to Hamburg, took the overnight ferry and got home on the 13th.

On arriving home you discovered that the tent, which you had carefully packed into its

blue bag, wasn't in the boot of the car. You must have left it on your pitch at the campsite, number 17. Write to the campsite asking

– if they've found it
– if they would be prepared to forward it
– how much it is going to cost.

• **der Zeltplatz** pitch (*for tent*)

▶ **8 a** Your ancient but terribly rich aunt has asked you to take her to Munich for four days (she'll pay for everything, and if all goes well she'll probably leave you a fortune in her will). She likes Beethoven, mediaeval art, antique shops, public parks and fish restaurants. She insists on her creature comforts but greatly dislikes hotels in modern buildings.

Write to the information office in Munich (address: Städtisches Verkehrsamt, München, Sendlinger Straße 2) to find out what the city has to offer that will appeal to her. Ask them to send you a city plan at the same time – you'll need it!

- **die mittelalterliche Kunst** mediaeval art
- **die Antiquitätenhandlung** antique shop
- **die öffentliche Anlage** public park

b Consider this advertisement from one of the brochures that the Munich information office sent in response to the letter of enquiry you wrote to prepare for your eccentric aunt's trip.

bekannt well known
die Zirbelstube room decorated with pine cladding
der Kamin fireplace
repräsentativ imposing; formal

Write booking two single rooms for September 1st–8th inclusive, making sure that your aunt's room has a private bathroom (*not* just a shower), a good view, large windows, heating and if possible a balcony. It must also be on the first floor (she hates heights).

- **im ... Stock** on the ... floor

c Your aunt (the same one) left her umbrella in the hotel where you were staying in Munich. It is green and yellow and she thinks she left it in the bathroom of her room (number 112). Write to the hotel to discover whether they have found it. Ask them to send it on, tell them that your aunt will pay all the costs and give them her address.

- **alle Unkosten** all costs

▶▶ **d** Write an account of the holiday in Munich with your aunt for your German friend. Include full details of all the awful problems and difficulties she gave you.

9 a You and your parents are spending your summer holiday in Austria at Bad Igls. You're going by car and you want to spend a night en route in Bavaria, at Garmisch. Write to the Hotel Habsburgerhof there.

  – Tell them their hotel was specially recommended by a friend of your father's.
  – Ask if they have a double room for your parents and a single room for you for the night of July 27th.
  – Your parents would like a room with bath (or shower), you yourself don't mind a room without bath.
  – Find out what it costs (with breakfast).

  ● **besonders empfohlen** especially recommended

▶ **b** You receive this letter in reply:

Hotel Habsburgerhof
Partenkirchener Straße
Garmisch 8100

Sehr geehrter Herr ....../geehrte Frau ......,

wir danken Ihnen für Ihr Schreiben vom 13. April und
bestätigen, daß wir Ihnen für die Nacht vom 27. Juli
ein Doppelzimmer und ein Einzelzimmer zur Verfügung
stellen können; beide sind leider ohne Bad.

Der Preis für das Doppelzimmer beträgt DM 62.- pro
Person, für das Einzelzimmer DM 64.-. Diese Preise
verstehen sich einschließlich Frühstück, Kurtaxe und
Mehrwertsteuer.

Wollen Sie uns bitte bis zum 1.7. mitteilen, ob diese
Zimmer Ihnen zusagen.

Hochachtungsvoll,

......

---

das Schreiben communication
**Ihnen zur Verfügung
  stellen** place at your disposal
betragen amount to; total
sich verstehen be reckoned
einschließlich inclusive of
die Kurtaxe visitor tax in spa
  towns
die Mehrwertsteuer VAT
zusagen be suitable

Your parents find these prices too high, and they really *did* want a room with a bathroom. Write back saying you're sorry, you don't want the rooms, tactfully giving the bathroom rather than the price as your reason.

10 Write a postcard to your rich and eccentric aunt, from Bad Igls in Austria where you are spending the summer holidays with your family. Remember the sort of things she's interested in (see above) and remember too that she'd cut you out of her will if she thought you were interested in anything else at all!

11 You're on a school group trip to Germany and have just spent three days in Karlsruhe. With the help of this town plan showing some of the local attractions, write an account of your visit for your Austrian pen-friend, saying where you stayed, and what you saw and did.

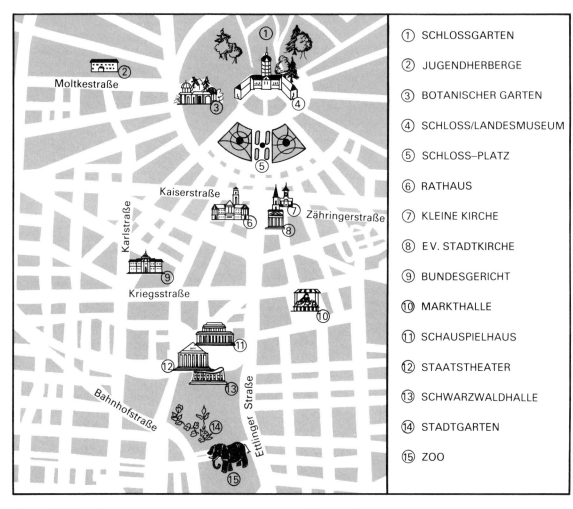

①	SCHLOSSGARTEN
②	JUGENDHERBERGE
③	BOTANISCHER GARTEN
④	SCHLOSS/LANDESMUSEUM
⑤	SCHLOSS–PLATZ
⑥	RATHAUS
⑦	KLEINE KIRCHE
⑧	EV. STADTKIRCHE
⑨	BUNDESGERICHT
⑩	MARKTHALLE
⑪	SCHAUSPIELHAUS
⑫	STAATSTHEATER
⑬	SCHWARZWALDHALLE
⑭	STADTGARTEN
⑮	ZOO

das Schloß castle
das Landesmuseum county museum
das Rathaus town hall
die ev(angelische) Stadtkirche municipal
  Protestant church

das Bundesgericht Federal Court
die Markthalle market hall
das Schauspielhaus playhouse
das Staatstheater state theatre

12 You're holidaying at St. Peter on the North Sea coast of Germany. You're about to leave the beach car park when you find the car won't start. You're going to have to leave the car and walk to a garage in town to get a mechanic to come down and fix it. The beach car park is over a mile from town and you've no parking time left.

Write a note to stick under the windscreen wiper explaining the situation to the policeman who's sure to appear the moment you leave the car ...

13 Your friend in Hamburg writes that the family has got
a new car:

> Du, unser neuer Wagen ist wirklich toll. Wir haben
> jetzt einen Porsche, der fährt so schnell, ich kann's kaum
> fassen. Viel besser, als der olle BMW, den wir früher
> hatten – der war wirklich etwas für die ganz Alten.
> Erstaunlich, daß mein Vater so was kaufen würde, er ist
> vielleicht doch nicht so uralt, wie man glaubt

fassen grasp; believe
olle (*N. Germ. colloq.*) old
uralt ancient; antique

Having looked at your old Austin outside your house, you
decide to write back explaining all the advantages of hitch-
hiking and all the disadvantages of owning a car – especially
a Porsche . . .! Start by making two lists (pro
hitch-hiking / anti car), then put each list together to make
two continuous paragraphs.

14 You've bought these two picture postcards of the area in
Wales where you're spending your summer holidays. Write
one to your North-German friend and one to Swiss friends
of your father, saying on each what is nice about the place.
Remember that they live in very different parts of the world
and so will probably appreciate different things.

- **wie bei Dir zu Hause** like you
  have at home

15 a You have been staying in an Austrian holiday flat for a
month with your family and unfortunately no fewer
than 20 items of equipment in it have been broken. Make
a list of the broken items for the owner of the flat, noting
also which member of your family was responsible for
each. (Curiously, you yourself don't seem to have broken
anything at all, as far as you can remember).

> die Fernsehantenne –
> meine Schwester

b Here's a picture of the Austrian holiday flats and a plan of the one in which you were staying. Write a letter to your German friend describing the flat and saying what you did on the holiday.

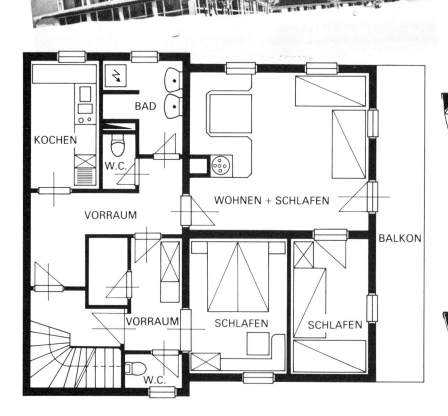

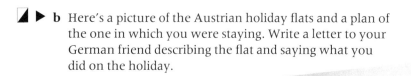

16 What did you *really* do on your last summer holiday? Use the following framework to write a paragraph about it:

Wo bist du hingefahren? – wie bist du gefahren? – mit oder ohne Familie? – wie lange bist du dort geblieben? – was hast du während deines Aufenthalts gemacht? (tagsüber? abends?) – was hat das alles gekostet?

5 AUFENTHALT BEI FREUNDEN

In this unit you will be writing about what you would like to do and what you might have done during a stay with friends in a German-speaking country. You will be organizing your arrival, considering alternative means of transport, making money arrangements, altering a travel booking, taking and transmitting phone messages, coping with emergencies, writing about your journey and writing to say thank you.

Likes and dislikes . . .

I (don't) like it **ich habe es (nicht) gern**
I prefer **ich habe lieber**
I don't like her **ich mag sie nicht**
I like swimming **ich schwimme gern**
I like chocolate **ich esse gern Schokolade**
I prefer tennis **ich spiele lieber Tennis**
I should like to go to the cinema **ich möchte ins Kino gehen**
I should like the smaller room **ich hätte gern das kleinere Zimmer**
I should prefer **ich hätte lieber**
I hate **ich hasse**

Things to do . . .

go for a walk **spazierengehen**
go for a walk round town **einen Stadtbummel machen**
go swimming/to the cinema/ shopping **schwimmen/ins Kino/einkaufen gehen**
to a party **auf eine Party (-s)**
cycle **radfahren**
sail **segeln**

fish **angeln**
go canoeing **Kanu** (*n.*) **fahren**
excursion **der Ausflug (¨e)**
visit (*e.g. cathedral*) **besichtigen**
museum **das Museum (-een)**
zoo **der Zoo (-s)**
theatre **das Theater (-)**
concert **das Konzert (-e)**

Things you need . . .

ticket **die Fahrkarte (-n)**
seat reservation **die Platzkarte (-n)**
traveller's cheque **der Reisescheck (-s)**
cash **das Bargeld**
change **das Kleingeld**
passport **der Paß (¨sse)**

Getting around . . .

tram **die (Straßen)bahn (-en)**
bus **der Bus (-se)**
taxi **das Taxi (-s)**
tip **das Trinkgeld (-er)**
ticket **der Fahrschein (-e)**
multiple ticket **die Sammelkarte (-n)**

◤ 1 You've just spent three days staying with friends in West Berlin. Make a record of what you did each morning and afternoon of your stay, in four columns thus:

die Geschäftsstraße shopping street
der See lake
die Mauer wall

TAG	ZEIT	WETTER	WAS ICH MACHTE
Montag	vormittags	Sonne	Kurfürstendamm, einkaufen

Here are some of the places you may have visited:

der Zoo;
der Kurfürstendamm (Hauptgeschäftsstraße);
der Wannsee (Schwimmen!);

die Mauer;
der Tiergarten (großer Park);
Ostberlin (Tagesausflug im Bus)

2 Your Swiss friend with whom you are about to spend a holiday has written to ask what sort of things you might like to do there. Make a list for him/her. The drawings may give you some ideas: add some of your own.

SPAZIERENGEHEN

3 Write a postcard in reply to this card from your Austrian pen-friend. It really is about time you visited the country:

HABE DIESE KARTE VOM SALZKAMMERGUT GERADE IN SCHREIBTISCH GEFUNDEN. WIR WAREN WÄHREND DER SOMMERFERIEN DORT - HERRLICH! NÄCHSTES JAHR WERDEN WIR DIE FERIEN IN NORDITALIEN AM GARDASEE VERBRINGEN. HAST DU SCHON PLÄNE? KOMMST DU ENDLICH MAL NACH ÖSTERREICH?

KARL

gerade just
der Schreibtisch desk
herrlich great

4 Your German friend and you are to spend a fortnight cycling in the Spessart. Your friend has done most of the planning, but you're not sure about the money arrangements. Write and ask

- how much money (in D-Marks) you should take altogether
- how much s/he thinks you should bring in cash and how much in traveller's cheques
- if it is a good idea to bring a little English money as well.

5 a You're going to stay with a German friend in Cologne and s/he's sent you the map below and suggested you make some notes on what you'd like to see on your first day there. Clearly you want to start with a general view of the town, so note down the places you'd like to go and see, and where appropriate say what you want to do there, e.g.:

Fußgängerzone (Schaufensterbummel)

der Fußgänger pedestrian
das Schaufenster shop window
der Bummel stroll
der Dom cathedral
der Rheindampfer Rhine steamer
die Altstadt old town
das Römisch-Germanische Museum
  Roman-Germanic Museum

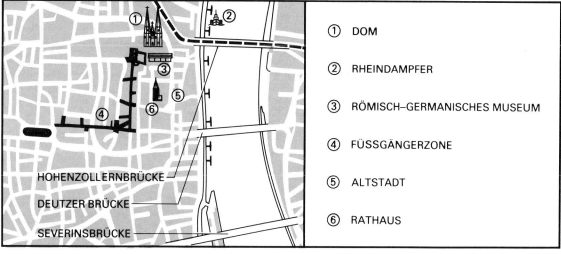

①	DOM
②	RHEINDAMPFER
③	RÖMISCH–GERMANISCHES MUSEUM
④	FÜSSGÄNGERZONE
⑤	ALTSTADT
⑥	RATHAUS

HOHENZOLLERNBRÜCKE
DEUTZER BRÜCKE
SEVERINSBRÜCKE

• **vom Wasser aus** from the water

b Your fortnight's stay with your German friend's family in Cologne is now imminent. Write a letter to them saying:

– you're looking forward to your trip
– you arrive at Cologne station on Thursday July 17th at 5.15 p.m.
– should you take a tram straight to their house or telephone from the station, or can they meet you there?
– your parents send their best wishes.

• **lassen herzlich grüßen** send best wishes

6 a Whilst you're staying in Cologne you're left in the house alone one morning and the phone never seems to stop ringing. Here are the notes you made on each of the calls: write them up entirely in German to produce comprehensible messages for your friend's mother, Frau Pförtner.

verspätet late; delayed
auch noch even
liefern deliver

Herr Pförtner rang - "etwas verspätet" - home about 8 p.m.

Frau Köhncke (Putzfrau) - coming tomorrow instead of Wednesday - here at 8.30

Tante Ilse - Auto will nicht starten - coming by bus but won't be here until 3.30 or "auch noch ein bißchen später"

Karstadt rang - ordered a new washing machine - "wird morgen nachmittag geliefert"

▶ **b** Again whilst you're alone in the house in
Cologne the phone rings: this time it's your friend who
wants you to meet her and two of *her* friends at the
'Weißen Löwen' in a quarter of an hour. You can make it
easily, your friend says, if you borrow her mother's
bicycle – her mother won't mind.

When you've put the phone down, though, you begin to
think that Frau Pförtner will wonder what has happened
to her bike when she gets back. Write a note for her,
explaining where you've gone, why you borrowed it . . .

der Löwe lion

- **ich sollte** I should (= *am to*)
- **leihen** (*past. part.*
  geliehen) borrow
- **es würde Ihnen nichts
  ausmachen** you wouldn't mind

7 a Your ticket back from Cologne to London is booked for
Thursday July 31st but your German friends have
persuaded you to stay two more days until Saturday
(there's a party on Friday night). You're going to have to
change the booking: your friends have found the phone
number of the travel agency, but they're leaving it to you
to make the change in booking ('ist gut für dein
Deutsch!'). Make some notes in German on what you're
going to say before making the phone call:

Present booking: 8.15 train from Cologne – London via
Hook (2nd class) on Thursday July 31st. You have no seat
reservation.

Booking required: same train two days later (Friday
August 2nd), seat reservation if possible.

- **ab** from
- **über** via
- **auf** (+ *acc.*) . . . **umlegen** change
  to . . .

▶ **b** After your stay in Cologne with the family of your
German friend you are writing to thank them. Tell them:

- you arrived home safely, and the time
- your parents are delighted with the present they sent
- they (your friend's parents) were most kind and
  generous and you had a marvellous time in Cologne
- you liked the Rhine steamer trip especially
- you hope the dog's better.

- **glücklich zu Hause
  ankommen** arrive home safely
- **begeistert (von)** delighted
  (with)
- **es geht ihm besser** he's feeling
  better

▶▶ **c** In fact, though your holiday in Cologne was excellent,
the trip back was terrible. Though you didn't like to go
into this in your thank-you letter to her parents, you are
now writing to your German friend to tell her about it . . .

- the train to the Hook of Holland arrived an hour late
- the boat had gone and the next boat wasn't
  until 11 p.m.
- you couldn't get a cabin
- the sea was very rough indeed and you were ill
- when you reached Harwich it was raining
- there was no buffet on the BR train and that arrived
  late as well.

- **war abgefahren** had gone

8 a You've been staying with a family friend in Potsdam, in East Germany, for a week; using the map below, write a postcard to your West German friend in Bremen telling her two or three things you have been doing or have seen.

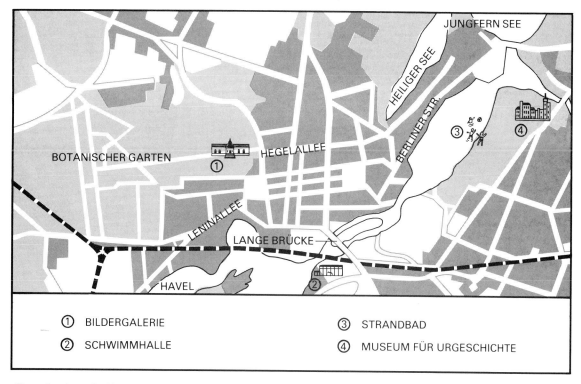

① BILDERGALERIE
② SCHWIMMHALLE
③ STRANDBAD
④ MUSEUM FÜR URGESCHICHTE

die Schwimmhalle indoor swimming pool
das Strandbad (*river, lake*) bathing place

die Bildergalerie Picture Gallery (name of this one; 'picture gallery' is normally **Gemäldegalerie**)

der Botanische Garten botanic gardens
das Museum für Urgeschichte museum of prehistory

b Your West German friend writes back;

> Ich bin wirklich erstaunt, daß Du in Potsdam etwas unternehmen konntest. Für meine Begriffe ist Potsdam kein Ferienort – früher war das ein Vorort von Berlin, jetzt ist es eine Großstadt für sich geworden … aber ein Ferienort? Wohl kaum!

für meine Begriffe as far as I can see
der Ferienort holiday resort
der Vorort suburb
für sich in its own right
wohl kaum I doubt it

Again using the Potsdam plan above, write a letter telling her at more length how wrong she is, and about all the things that one can do there on holiday.

• **alles Mögliche** all sorts of things

41

6 ESSEN UND TRINKEN

In this unit you'll be booking a restaurant, paying (or not paying) the bill, describing a special meal, making shopping lists, listing food and drink likes and dislikes, inventing a menu, complaining about the food . . .

In the restaurant

menu **die Speisekarte (-n)**
drinks menu **die Getränkekarte**
service **die Bedienung**
waiter **der Ober (-)**
waitress **die Serviererin (-nen)**
bill **die Rechnung (-en)**

What you're eating . . .

soup **die Suppe (-n)**
starter **die Vorspeise (-n)**
main dish **das Hauptgericht (-e)**
pudding **die Nachspeise (-n)**

What you're drinking . . .

orange/apple juice **der Orangen-/Apfelsaft**
a bottle of beer/wine **eine Flasche Bier/Wein**
milk **die Milch**
a pot of tea/coffee **eine Kanne Tee/Kaffee**
cola **die Cola**

Preparing it . . .

frying pan **die Bratpfanne (-n)**
saucepan **der Kochtopf (¨e)**
electric/gas cooker **der Elektro-/Gasherd**
colander **das Sieb**
to boil **kochen**
to fry **braten**
to bake **backen**
to grill **grillen**
to roast **rösten; braten**
to season **abschmecken**

How you find it . . .

enjoy your meal! **guten Appetit!**
how did you like it? **wie hat es dir geschmeckt?**
my favourite food/drink is . . . **am liebsten esse/ trinke ich . . .**
appetizing **appetitlich**
tasty **lecker**
too sweet/salty **zu süß/salzig**
hungry **hungrig**
thirsty **durstig**

1 You are going to stay with your German pen-friend on a visit and her parents have asked you to make a list of all the foods that you especially like. Make the list, starting . . .

Am liebsten esse ich . . . . .

2 You're going to Vienna on holiday, and you'll arrive in mid-afternoon. You want to celebrate your arrival by eating at a restaurant whose address has been given to you by a friend, with a strong recommendation. Write to book a table using this skeleton letter:

```
                          ...... , den ...... 19..


Restaurant Hübner,
Margaretenstraße 52,
Wien V,
Österreich.


Sehr geehrte Herren,

ich möchte, wenn möglich, fur den Abend vom ......
einen Tisch reservieren. Wir sind ...... Personen
und werden ...... Uhr ankommen.
Darf ich auch sagen, daß Ihr Restaurant uns von
einem guten Freund/einer guten Freundin, Herrn/Frau/
Fräulein ...... sehr empfohlen worden ist?


Hochachtungsvoll,

......
```

3 You and your younger brother are to spend a week with family friends in Austria. You, of course, eat anything, but there's a whole list of things that your brother won't eat, including:

bananas	dumplings
mushrooms	carrots
sauerkraut	mashed potatoes
black bread	veal

Write the appropriate paragraph to your letter, beginning:

Ich esse selbstverständlich alles, aber mein kleiner Bruder Kevin .....

If you remember anything else that Kevin won't eat, don't hesitate to add it to the list!

4 You are on holiday with your school in Germany and have just had a really terrific meal here in Witzenhausen at the Sommersberg Hotel where you are staying. Write a postcard to your German friend, telling him/her how great it was and what you chose from the menu below.

TAGESKARTE
23. MAI

TAGESSUPPE: Hausgemachte SPARGELCREMSUPPE
oder WILDKRAFTBRÜHE
oder FRUCHTKALTSCHALE

DESSERT: Nach Wahl vom DESSERTWAGEN oder
1 Tasse KAFFEE oder TEE

Zarter RAHMGOULASCH mit frischen
Champignonköpfen, Semmelknödeln und gemischter   17,80 DM
Salatteller

Schnitzel „HOLSTEINER ART", paniertes
Schweineschnitzel mit einem Spiegelei überbacken,
umlegt mit feinen Erbsen und Möhrchen, garniert mit
Fischhappen, Röstkartoffeln   22,80 DM

FRISCHE BACHFORELLE mit zerlassener Butter
und Sahnemeerrettich, Dampfkartoffeln u. gem.   24,80 DM
Salatteller

„ZWIEBELSTEAK", gut abgehangener Roastbeef
und ohne Schwarte mit gerösteten Zwiebelringen
überzogen, gratinierte Kartoffelscheiben, gemischter   28,80 DM
Salatteller

KALBSTEAK – vom Grill – mit ganzen
Champignonköpfen und Blumenkohl überzogen,
überbacken mit sauce hollandaise, pommes dauphinois   32,80 DM
und gemischter Salatteller

SEEZUNGENFILETS „CARDINALE" MIT
LACHS-MOUSSE gefüllt, Sauce Cardinale, Reis und   36,80 DM
gemischter Salatteller

hausgemacht home-made
der Spargel asparagus
das Wild game
die Kraftbrühe clear soup
die Kaltschale cold soup
zart tender
der Rahm cream
der Semmelknödel dumpling
paniert breadcrumbed
das Spiegelei fried egg
überbacken browned on top
umlegt mit surrounded by
die Erbse pea
das Möhrchen baby carrot
der Happen morsel
die Bachforelle river trout
zerlassen melted
der Sahnemeerrettich creamed
  horseradish
die Zwiebel onion
ohne Schwarte trimmed
die Scheibe slice
das Kalbsteak veal steak
der Blumenkohl cauliflower
die Seezunge sole
der Lachs salmon
das Reis rice

5 Here is a recipe which you are going to cook this evening in your rented villa in the Vorarlberg. Write a list of the things you need to buy. There's salt, pepper, butter and an onion in the kitchen already.

> ### KÄSENUDELN ÜBERBACKEN
>
> 250 g Nudeln 12 Minuten in 2 L Salzwasser kochen und in einem Sieb abtropfen lassen. 50 g durchwachsenen Speck und 1 Zwiebel würfeln und in der Pfanne leicht bräunen. Dann 4 geviertelte Tomaten und 1 große Dose Champignons (in Scheiben) zufügen. Gekochte Nudeln untermischen und alles zusammen in eine gefettete Auflaufform geben.
> ¼ L Milch und 2 Ecken Schmelzkäse unter Rühren erhitzen. Mit Salz und Pfeffer abschmecken und über den Auflauf gießen. Butterflöckchen daraufsetzen. 15 Minuten bei 225 Grad überbacken.

der durchwachsene Speck streaky bacon
würfeln dice
abtropfen drain
zufügen add
der Auflaufform pudding mould
die Ecke (triangular) piece
der Schmelzkäse processed cheese
rühren stir
gießen pour
das Flöckchen small pat

6 You and your partner are together staying with a German friend, and you have promised your friend's mother that you will prepare an English meal for the family; your friend's mother has offered to do the necessary shopping for you since you are out all day, provided that you make a list. Decide on the meal together, then make out a shopping list in German of all the necessary items.

7 Your East German pen-friend writes that s/he believes British eating habits to be very different from theirs and includes this sample list of a day's meals. Make a similar one of a typical day's meals of your own for comparison.

Frühstück (6 Uhr 30): Brot oder Brötchen, Marmelade, Kaffee
2. Frühstück (10 Uhr 30): Brot, Butter, vielleicht etwas Käse, Kaffee
Mittagessen (12 Uhr 30): Fisch mit Dampfkartoffeln, grüne Bohnen, Pudding
Kaffeepause (4 Uhr): Kaffee (!)
Abendbrot (7 Uhr): Brote mit Käse und Wurst, Obst, Bier oder Tee

die Dampfkartoffeln steamed or boiled potatoes
die Bohne bean

8 Your school's Home Economics department is cooking a different country's food each Monday. Make out a possible German menu, suggesting three alternative starters and three alternative puddings. (Only suggest things that you like, you're going to have to eat it!)

9 You are on a self-catering holiday in Germany with your family and have offered to do the cooking for a whole day (with a little help) and all the necessary shopping for it. Make out a shopping list for yourself in German listing the things you need for each meal. ➤

Frühstück:

Mittagessen:

Abendbrot:

10 Your German exchange partner is coming to stay with you the week after next and you want to welcome him/her with a typically English meal. You want it to be something s/he'll enjoy, so you're going to offer him/her the choice of three different meals. Work out three that you think s/he'll like (and that don't include anything you don't like!).

11 You are on a motoring holiday in Germany and you are going to do the shopping for a picnic lunch. Everyone wants something different (of course), so you'd better make a list – in German, since you'll be doing the shopping in German:

Your mother: Rye bread; butter; Emmenthal cheese; tomato; orange juice; banana

Your father: White bread; butter; sausage; potato salad; tomato; apple strudel; bottle of beer

Your sister: Rusks; low-fat cheese; yoghurt; apple juice

You: Make up your own mind!

- **das Roggenbrot** rye bread
- **der Zwieback (¨e)** rusk
- **der Quark** low-fat cheese

▶ **12** It serves you right for taking your eccentric aunt to an expensive restaurant during your holiday in Munich: she didn't like anything about it and now she wants you to write and complain. The following things especially were wrong for her:

- the table was right next to the kitchen door
- the service was very slow indeed
- the food was cold (especially the chips – they were very cold)
- so was the coffee
- your aunt's steak was tough, and her fork was dirty.

sich beschweren über (+ *acc.*) complain about

Start your letter:

> Sehr geehrte Herren,
> meine Tante und ich haben gestern abend in Ihrem Restaurant gegessen, und wir müssen uns leider über folgendes beschweren......

and end it:

> Wir sind noch bis zum 12. August im Hotel zum Weißen Rössel; ich erwarte mit Interesse Ihre Antwort auf diesen Brief.
> Hochachtungsvoll,

7 BEAMTE, BEHÖRDEN UND DIENSTLEISTUNGEN

In this unit you will be completing DDR entry and exit forms, reporting an accident to the police, completing East and West German telegram forms, explaining telephone procedure, using banks, dry cleaners and a lost property office, arranging car repairs, writing to the DDR Embassy, coping with a parking ticket, discovering postbus details...

Forms...

form **das Formular (-e)**
to fill in **ausfüllen**
block capitals **die Druckschrift**
signature **die Unterschrift**
declaration **die Erklärung**
description **die Bezeichnung**

Phones...

to lift/replace the receiver **den Hörer abnehmen/auflegen**
to dial **wählen**
to insert a coin **eine Münze einwerfen**
to press the button **den Knopf drücken**
to get back **zurückbekommen**
operator **der/die Telefonist(in)**
directory **das Telefonbuch (¨er)**
dialling code **die Vorwahl (-en)**

Banks...

to change **wechseln**
traveller's cheque (for ...) **der Reisescheck (-s) (über ... + acc.)**
to cash **einlösen**

note **der Schein (-e); die Banknote (-n)**
change **das Kleingeld**
rate of exchange **der Wechselkurs (-e)**
receipt **die Quittung (-en)**

Police...

investigation **die Untersuchung (-en)**
accident **der Unfall (¨e)**
has been stolen **ist gestohlen worden**
has been lost **ist verlorengegangen**
has been handed in **ist abgegeben worden**
made of... **aus...**
witness **der Zeuge (-n)**
involved (in it) **(daran) beteiligt**
forbidden **verboten**

Repairs...

to have something repaired **etwas reparieren lassen**
to service **überholen**
to check **kontrollieren**
to (dry) clean **reinigen**
broken **kaputt**
isn't working **funktioniert nicht**
torn **zerrissen**

1 The front of the form at the top of the next page has to be filled in as you enter the DDR. You have with you £25 and DM100 and you are bringing in as presents a soft toy, four cups and saucers and a pot of Scottish marmalade.

The second side of the form has to be completed as you leave the DDR. You are taking out £7, DM12 and are also taking back with you four books, two records, a bottle of wine and a DDR flag. ➤

Complete the forms.

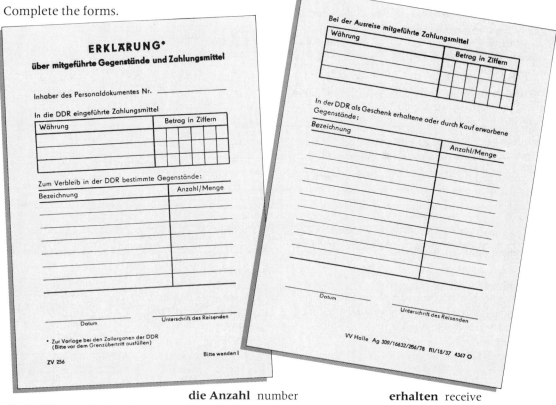

die Erklärung declaration
der Gegenstand object
das Zahlungsmittel means of payment

die Anzahl number
`der Inhaber` owner
die Währung (*type of*) currency
zum Verbleib bestimmt intended to remain

erhalten receive
erwerben obtain

- **das Stofftier** soft toy
- **die Fahne** flag

2 a In Mainz, on August 17th at 5.30 p.m. in clear weather, at the junction of Stadthausstraße and Emmeransstraße, you saw a road accident. A car came out of the side street, Stadthausstraße, without stopping, attempted to turn left and hit a (male) motorcyclist coming from the right on the main road. The car, a red Opel Ascona, was being driven by an elderly man, and was clearly in the wrong.

The police have asked you to give an account of the accident in your own words, as simply as possible.

b You were on your way from Mainz to Munich, but as a result of the above accident, and then being involved with the police as witness, you missed your train. You will not arrive in Munich until the 18th at about 2 p.m. Use the form below to send a telegram to your friends who are expecting you (they're called Otto, they live at Schwabinger Str. 19).

Tell them:
– you won't arrive until tomorrow at 2 p.m.
– it's because of an accident
– you were not personally involved in the accident.

Write your message using the minimum of words.

stark umrahmt within the heavily printed frame
der Absender sender
der Empfänger recipient

3 You are going to spend a walking holiday in Austria and have been told that the way to get to good walking spots in the mountains is by postbus. Friends have recommended the area in the Salzkammergut (das) around Bad Ischl.

Write to the postbus information service (Postamt 4820 Bad Ischl/Postverkehrsbüro) saying that you would like to spend a holiday in the Salzkammergut using postbuses and
– could they send you a route map and time table?
– could they give you some examples of fares?

- **der Streckenplan** route map
- **der Postbus (-se)** postbus
- **der Fahrpreis (-e)** fare

4 On your last day in Switzerland your family was given a parking ticket for parking in the Rämi-Straße in Zürich where parking is not allowed. Write a letter to the Polizeipräsident at the Polizeipräsidium, explaining
– you thought you could park there
– you were in a hurry because the shops were about to close
– you didn't see the 'no parking' sign
– you were only parked there for ten minutes
– you won't do it again.

- **parken** (Germany); **parkieren** (Switzerland, Austria) park
- **die polizeiliche Vorladung** summons; parking ticket
- **das Parkverbot** parking prohibition; 'no parking'

5 a You're in Dresden on a motoring holiday when your suitcase is stolen from your hotel. Once again you're involved with the police, this time with the Volkspolizei, who ask you to make a list of all the things in the suitcase. Use our drawings to help jog your memory, but add whatever you like.

b Because police enquiries are taking so long you find you can't move on to East Berlin to see your friends there until a day later than you expected. Use the form below to send them a telegram saying

 – your suitcase has been stolen
 – there was nothing important in it
 – because of the police enquiries you'll arrive in the afternoon of the 20th instead of the 19th.

Your friends live at Karl-Marx-Allee 199 and are called Förster. When addressing the telegram remember that East Berlin is simply 'Berlin' within the DDR. Write your message using the minimum of words.

deutlich clear
die Druckschrift block capitals

TELEGRAMM form:

```
Leitvermerk:            Deutsche Post        Übermittelt:
                        TELEGRAMM            Tag:    Zeit:
                                             an:    durch:
aus:        Tag:        Aufgabezeit:
Wortzahl:
Dienstvermerk (z. B. tf ...  tlx ...)¹)                    Deutliche Druckschrift!
Empfänger                                                  Vor Aushändigung bitte Rückseite beachten.
Straße/Nr.
Postleitzahl/Ort



                                             Wortgebühr:
                                             Zusatzgebühr:
                                             Telegrammgebühr:
                                             Namenszeichen:
Absender:  (Diese Angaben werden nicht mitbegrafiert)

Bei undeutlicher Schrift, unvollständiger Anschrift oder fehlender Absenderangabe trägt der Absender die Folgen
¹) siehe Rückseite       83 30 38 (C183) VV Spremberg Ag 310/77/DDR/560 1·21·2
```

 • **der Koffer** suitcase
 • **entwendet worden** been stolen
 • **nichts Wichtiges** nothing important

▲ ▶ 6 Your father's German friend is staying with you. It is his first visit to England and he is going to have to make several phone calls from public telephone boxes whilst he is travelling about the country. Your father asks you to note down basic telephoning instructions in German for him:

 – you can put in as many coins as you like of any kind; you do this before you dial
 – you can add further coins at any time
 – at the end of the call you get back any unused coins
 – if you're telephoning Germany you first dial 010 49 (West) or 010 37 (East).

▶ 7 As usual it's you, being the German speaker, who has to do everything for all the family. Make notes in German to help you remember everything you've got to do on this expedition to the bank:

  – change £50 note for your father and find out exactly what the exchange rate is (get receipt)
  – change two £20 notes for your sister. Make sure there is some small change among the German money
  – find out what the D-Mark – Schilling rate of exchange is (your mother wants to know for when you cross the border into Austria)
  – change traveller's cheque for ten pounds for yourself (NB don't forget passport!).

8 a

It was a great mistake to allow your father to try to repair the car himself right at the start of your Swiss holiday. Before taking this pile of clothes to the cleaners, you make notes in German on what is wrong and what needs to be done. There is:

– a man's white pullover with oil on the front
– a jacket with a tear in the right sleeve and a button missing
– a pair of men's trousers with oil on the front and dirt on the back and a tear in the right leg
– a blanket with dirt from the front drive on it (your mother didn't even know he'd borrowed it).

The car still won't start, either, but that's a problem for the next section!

- **das Hosenbein** trouser leg

 ▶ b You're still in Switzerland and you still have the car problem. Make notes on it before telephoning the garage. What seems to be wrong is that:

  – the engine won't start (it's not the battery, that's quite strong)
  – it's losing oil – there's quite a pool underneath it on the drive
  – if it finally does start it stalls at a red light
  – when the engine is hot it sometimes cuts out, even at speed. (The car was serviced three months ago.)

- **will nicht starten** won't start
- **die Batterie** battery
- **die Lache** puddle; pool
- **die Zufahrt** drive
- **aussetzen** stall; cut out

9 On a previous trip to the DDR you were given this list of objects that you were not allowed to take into the country with you. The last item on the list worries you, since you are going on holiday to Weimar and want to take your walkman with you.

Write (in German) to the East German Embassy (Botschaft der Deutschen Demokratischen Republik, Brent House, The Broadway, London NW9) explaining that you are about to visit the country on holiday and asking whether it is forbidden to take your walkman (explain that it's a portable cassette player) and cassettes.

das **Magnettonband** magnetic tape
der **Tonträger** sound recording material

- **einführen** import
- **der Walkman** walkman
- **persönlicher Gebrauch** personal use

- Zeitungen und andere periodisch erscheinende Presseerzeugnisse, soweit sie nicht in der Postzeitungsliste der DDR enthalten sind; Kalender, Almanache, Jahrbücher; Briefmarken und Briefmarkenkataloge, ungültige Zahlungsmittel und Münzen;
- Literatur und sonstige Druckerzeugnisse, deren Inhalt gegen die Erhaltung des Friedens gerichtet ist oder deren Einfuhr in anderer Weise den Interessen des sozialistischen Staates und seiner Bürger widerspricht;
- Schußwaffen, patronierte Munition, Sprengmittel einschließlich pyrotechnische Erzeugnisse, Kartuschen, Schußgeräte (darunter Luftdruckwaffen, Start- und Gaspistolen), Hieb- und Stichwaffen;
- Fernsehgeräte sowie Ersatz- und Zubehörteile dazu;

- Rauschgift, Betäubungsmittel und andere Gifte;
- Kinderspielzeug militaristischen Charakters;
- gebrauchte Gegenstände als Geschenk (ausgenommen davon sind gebrauchte Textilien und Schuhe, wenn diese nach der letzten Benutzung gewaschen oder gereinigt wurden);
- Arzneimittel (ausgenommen davon ist der persönliche Reisebedarf);
- Fotopapier sowie Filme, Fotoplatten (unbelichtete, belichtete und entwickelte) und Diapositive, wenn deren Inhalt bzw. deren Einfuhr den Interessen des sozialistischen Staates und seiner Bürger widerspricht;
- Schallplatten, soweit sie nicht Werke des kulturellen Erbes oder des wirklich kulturellen Gegenwartsschaffens betreffen; Magnettonbänder und andere Tonträger.

10 You were returning from a holiday by train from Frankfurt with a friend and between you you had several bags. When you reached the customs check at the Dutch-German border you realised that one bag, belonging to you, was missing. You're pretty sure that you must have left it on the platform in Frankfurt. Write to the lost property office at Frankfurt Station (Bundesbahnfundbüro, Hauptbahnhof, Frankfurt/Main) to discover if it has been handed in.

- The bag is quite large – about 80 × 50 centimetres.
- It's dark red and has your name and address on it.
- The place you think you left it was platform 7B, the time about 8.30 in the morning, the date August 6th.
- The bag contained mostly personal things, but there was also a camera in it.

- **die Reisetasche** bag
- **und** (*in dimensions*) by

8 EINKAUFEN

In this unit you'll be concerned with shopping at the supermarket, listing souvenirs to take home, having clothes bought for you, complaining about overcharging and about goods that don't work, getting a T-shirt changed, explaining where shops are, buying through small ads and from the Verkehrsamt, and describing a Christmas shopping expedition.

Asking the questions ...

how much is ...? **wieviel kostet ...?**
all together **insgesamt**
what colours have you? **welche Farben haben Sie?**
what is the difference (between)? **was ist der Unterschied (zwischen)?**
have you something cheaper? **haben Sie etwas Billigeres?**

Writing to buy things ...

interested in **interessiert an** (+ *acc.*)
if possible **wenn möglich**
try out **ausprobieren**
enclosed **anbei**
an alternative colour would be ... **eine alternative Farbe wäre ...**
to say thank you **sich bedanken**
in anticipation **im voraus**

Thanking people for buying you things ...

splendid **herrlich**
fabulous **fabelhaft**
fit **passen** (+ *dat.*)
kind of you **nett von dir**
especially pleased with **besonders angetan von**
you've taken a lot of trouble **du hast dir sehr viel Mühe gegeben**
not only beautiful but also useful **nicht nur schön sondern auch nützlich**

Sending things back ...

complain **sich beschweren**
bought from you **bei Ihnen gekauft**
it's stopped working **es funktioniert nicht mehr**
it's broken **es ist kaputt**
it's gone wrong **es ist kaputtgegangen**
I'd like to change it (for) **ich möchte es umtauschen (gegen)**
in a larger size **in einer größeren Größe**

1 Your family, with whom you are on holiday, are clean but forgetful. It's you who does the shopping, so make a list in German:

- your mother wants some soap
- your father wants some disposable razors and some shaving foam
- your sister wants some shampoo (for dry hair)
- your brother wants some toothpaste – if possible with stripes
- you yourself want ...

- **der Einweg-Rasierer** disposable razor
- **der Rasierschaum** shaving cream
- **das Shampoo** shampoo
- **der Streifen** stripe

53

▶ **2 a** You have just received this postcard from your friend in Cologne:

You had forgotten that you had left this German money with Christiane the last time you stayed with her! You desperately need some new clothes. Send her a postcard saying yes please, telling her what article of clothing you would like and in what colour or colours, giving her an alternative and reminding her of your size.

zuschicken mail (*it to you*)

Erinnerst Du Dich noch, daß ich immer noch DM200 von Deinem Geld habe? Soll ich Dir was kaufen und zuschicken? Es wird bald Weihnachten!

Christiane

▶ **b** Christiane has sent you exactly what you asked for, and you really like it. Write her a letter saying:
- it looks fabulous
- it fits perfectly
- it was so good of her to go to all that trouble
- if ever she wants you to buy anything for her in England you'd be glad to get it for her
- thank you very much!

◢ **3 a** You are ill and unable to leave the house where you are staying in Germany. Your host has kindly offered to buy you any souvenirs you may want to take home as presents if you make him a list. Being a generous person, there are at least ten friends and relations for whom you want to take something back. Write your shopping list of presents – in German of course.

Kevin: eine gelbe Plastikbadeente

◢ **b** You have arrived home and distributed the presents your
▶▶ host bought for you. Write to your host and hostess thanking them for being so kind to you, and describing the reactions (positive!) of some of your friends to the presents they were given.

▶ **4** Whilst in Germany you bought a radio alarm which you discovered, when you got home, didn't work properly. The friends you were staying with have offered to try to get it changed for you. You send it back to them enclosing a note saying:

– where you bought it and when (tell them the bill is enclosed)
– when it went wrong (the first time you tried to use it, actually)
– what's wrong with it (only the buzzer works, not the radio, and it buzzes both in the morning and the evening, even though you only set it for the morning).

- **der Radiowecker** radio alarm
- **der Summer** buzzer
- **summen** buzz
- **stellen** set

▶ **5** You bought a T-shirt for your sister from C & A Brenninkmeyer in Hamburg. It is labelled 'mittelgroß'. When you got home you found it was too small for your sister: clearly you should have got one labelled 'groß'. Send it back with an accompanying letter in which you explain

– what is wrong with it (too small)
– when you bought it (beginning of July)
– what you would like to exchange if for (same thing, but 'groß').

You should also ask:

– if the large size is dearer
– what the postage and packing charges are so that you can send them the necessary money and they can then forward the larger size of T-shirt.

- **Anfang ...** at the beginning of ...
- **die Versandspesen** forwarding charges

◣ **6** Your exchange partner is going shopping on her own in your nearest town, for herself and for things to take home as presents. She certainly doesn't seem short of money, since she intends to buy clothes, compact discs, shortbreads, marmalade, tea, books, a videotape and some shoes. She also wants to get some flowers for your mother. Help her by making a note of which shop is best for each item, and where each shop is situated relative to the last one (list the items with their shops in the most convenient order for her to go round town).

- **die CD-Platte** compact disc
- **der Butterkeks** shortbread
- **das Videoband** videotape
- **eine ganze Strecke** quite a way

◣ **7** You are doing a class project on the cities of Germany and you have been given Hamburg to research and write about. Write to the Verkehrsamt there and ask them:

– do they sell posters and slides of the city? If so, do they have a list and what do they cost?
– can they let you have a town plan?
– would they send you any free brochures they publish?
– can they recommend any books on the history of Hamburg?

- **im Begriff sein, etwas zu tun** be in the course of doing something
- **das Projekt** project
- **veröffentlichen** publish
- **über** (+ *acc.*) on (= *about*)

▶ **8** Whilst staying with friends in Germany you notice this small ad. in the local paper.

> **Verkaufe** Telefunken-Tonband, werkstattgeprüft, 2 × 35 W, eingebautes Mischpult, Trick, Echo, 100.-DM. Schnabel, Hermülheim, Luxemburger Str. 971.

das **Tonband** (here, for **Tonbandgerät**) tape recorder
die **Werkstatt** workshop
prüfen test
eingebaut built-in
das **Mischpult** sound mixer

It is *exactly* what you want, and very good value if it's really in good condition. Your friends will lend you the money you need, you're sure you can raise it back in England to repay them, the only problem is that the advertisement has an address rather than a telephone number. So you'll have to write a letter saying:

— you're interested in the recorder and would like to come and see it and, more importantly, try it out
— you're English (Scottish, Welsh, Irish . . .) but that's no problem as you would be able to pay cash
— could they telephone and give a convenient time (you're leaving the country in ten days)?

- **bar zahlen** pay cash
- **eine Zeit, die Ihnen paßt** a convenient time for you

▶▶ **9** Christmas shopping seems to get more exhausting every year. Write to your East German pen-friend describing a Christmas shopping expedition, saying what the shops are like here, and recounting the joys (if any) and difficulties of your trip. Tell your friend that you've bought him/her a Christmas present, you're sending it separately and you hope s/he likes it.

- **die Weihnachtsbeleuchtung** Christmas illuminations

▶▶ **10** Whilst in Germany you stupidly lost your lockable petrol filler cap. At the Araltankstelle in Oldenburg you bought a replacement cap, for which you were charged DM 52.-. On thinking about this back home you decided you had been overcharged and wrote to Ford UK about it.

Ford now write back agreeing with you: they say the appropriate price is DM 22.-. They themselves will contact the garage and they suggest that you write to the garage too. Do so,

— reminding them what they charged you for a new petrol cap, and when (June 13th)
— telling them what Ford UK replied to your letter
— suggesting that they have inadvertently overcharged you and that you are owed DM 30.-.

- **der Tankdeckel** petrol cap
- **angemessen** appropriate
- **aus Versehen** inadvertently
- **einem etwas schulden** owe someone something

9 GESUNDHEIT

In this unit you will be writing about sick people (and the odd sick animal too!), you will be involved in buying medicine and in visits to the doctor, the dentist, and the hospital.

Aches and pains . . .

she's ill/healthy **sie ist krank/gesund**
to suffer from **leiden an**
headache **das Kopfweh**
toothache **das Zahnweh**
pain **der Schmerz**
stomach pains **die Magenschmerzen**
sore throat **die Halsschmerzen**
pain in your back **die Rückenschmerzen**
hay fever **der Heuschnupfen**
indigestion **die Verdauungsstörung**
spot **der Fleck (-e)**
sea/airsick **see-/luftkrank**
to cut your finger **sich in den Finger
 schneiden**
to have a temperature **Temperatur haben**
to be sick (= *vomit*) **sich erbrechen**
accident **der Unfall (¨e)**

How you look and feel . . .

miserable **jämmerlich**
pale **blaß**
not very cheerful **nicht sehr munter**
I'm cold/hot **mir ist kalt/heiß**
completely recovered **völlig erholt**

Curing it . . .

tablet **die Tablette (-n)**
aspirin (=) **die Kopfschmerztablette (-n)**
sticking plaster **das Leukoplast (-e)**
medicine **die Medizin (-en)**
hospital **das Krankenhaus (¨er)**
doctor **der Arzt (¨e)/die Ärztin (-nen)**
dentist **der Zahnarzt (¨e)/die
 Zahnärztin (-nen)**
surgery **das Sprechzimmer (-)**
to treat **behandeln**

1 You're on a family holiday and everyone seems to be ill except you. You offer to go to the chemist's to get some medicines. Make out a 'shopping list' of everyone's ailments:

— your mother has a headache
— your father has an upset stomach
— your sister has a badly cut finger and has now run out of sticking plasters
— your brother has hay fever
— your grandfather . . .
— your grandmother . . .

2

Ostsee: Warnemünde

Ich bin endlich wieder gesund! Ich schreib Dir von meiner Blinddarmoperation, nicht wahr? Jetzt verbringe ich eine Woche hier am Meer und erhole mich so richtig. Wie geht es Euch allen?
Adrian

You receive this card from the Baltic coast from your East German pen-friend who has been ill:

That's all very well, but everyone in *your* family is ill in some way, what with your mother's continual headaches, your father's stomach, your brother's hay fever and now you've got toothache. Send Adrian a return postcard with a really good moan!

der Blinddarm appendix

- **auf irgend eine Weise** in some way or other

3 Everyone is going to be out all day, except your Swiss exchange partner who has work to do for her exams. Unfortunately the dog is ill, and the vet's instructions have to be followed strictly. Write a reminder in German for your exchange partner so she doesn't forget what she has to do.

- 10 a.m.: red tablet
- before food (at about 12): two green tablets and another red one
- in food (can is on worktop): two little packets of white powder, mixed in well
- after food: another red tablet

- **das Futter** (*animal*) food
- **die Arbeitsfläche** work surface; worktop
- **daruntermischen** mix in

4 You are on a group exchange visit to Frankfurt-am-Main. Whilst you are alone in the house where you are staying the teacher accompanying the group telephones to tell you that your sister, who is also with the group and staying in another family, has been taken to the Rotkreuz hospital. It isn't too serious (it appears to be appendicitis) but he's coming to collect you and take you with him to the hospital. Leave a note for your German hosts telling them

- who has telephoned
- what has happened to your sister
- that it isn't very serious
- where you have gone to and with whom
- that you don't know exactly when you'll be back

- **die Austauschgruppe** exchange group
- **die Blinddarmentzündung** appendicitis

▶ 5 Your Austrian friend who is staying with you has sprained his wrist falling off your bicycle and can't write. Write a short note to his parents telling them

- how it happened
- that it isn't serious
- that Klaus is quite cheerful and pleased that you're now having to write his letters for him

- **verrenken** sprain
- **das Handgelenk** wrist

◣ 6 You are staying in the home of your German friend who this morning is not feeling well at all. He/She seems to have a temperature, looks pale, feels sick, has a headache and also has some red spots around the throat. You tell him/her to go to bed, then you make a quick note, in German, of each of the symptoms before ringing his/her mother at work . . .

- **der Hals** throat

7 Your German exchange partner who is staying with you is out, but is coming back for lunch, which you, being the only person at home, are going to prepare.

At 11.45 a.m. you get the most dreadful toothache – it's in a tooth which you had filled only a fortnight ago, and you think there may be problems with the filling. At all events the pain is so excruciating that you ring the dentist, who tells you to come over to the surgery straight away.

Leave your exchange partner a note saying what has happened, where you've gone, when you expect to be back (not until after lunch) and that there's a plate of cold meat and some salad in the fridge.

- **ist gefüllt worden** was filled
- **die Füllung** filling
- **er sagte, ich sollte** he said I was to

▶ 8 Your brother was about to go on an exchange visit to Germany when he caught the measles. He was supposed to leave a week next Monday. Write to the parents of his exchange partner apologizing for the fact that he will be unable to make the trip.

- Explain how disappointed he is and say how sorry you all are that he can't come.
- Say how much you are looking forward to the visit of Dieter (his exchange partner) in the summer.
- Suggest that perhaps next year your brother will be able to go to Germany.

- **er sollte** he was supposed to
- **die Masern** measles
- **sich freuen auf** (+ *acc.*) look forward to . . .

Magdeburg, den 3. Juni

Liebe Jo,

Wie kann man nur so blöde sein? Ich liege hier im Bett mit einem gebrochenen Knöchel und bin selber daran schuld!
Kannst Du Dir das vorstellen, ich bin direkt vorm Krankenhaus von meinem Fahrrad gefallen und konnte nicht wieder aufstehen. Sehr praktisch, wenn so ein Unfall direkt vorm Krankenhaus passiert!
Ich trage einen Gipsverband und muß ihn vielleicht noch vier Wochen anbehalten.
Schreib mir bald!

Dein
Adrian

blöd(e) stupid
der Knöchel ankle
ich bin daran schuld it's my fault
der Gipsverband plaster cast
anbehalten keep on

You're Jo, and today you received the above letter from your East German friend. You too have a plaster cast on your arm! Write back (either a postcard or a letter), explaining the coincidence, telling Adrian how your accident occurred, saying that you too have to wear a cast and telling him for how long.

- **welcher Zufall!** what a coincidence
- **stolpern über** (+ *acc.*) trip over

10 Whilst staying in Germany with your family your small sister, who is only three, was taken ill with very bad stomach pains in the middle of the night. You telephoned a doctor who came straight away, examined your sister, gave her some medicine and tablets and reassured the family.

All your family were pleased with the service they received and have asked you to write and thank the doctor (Frau Dr. Herborn, Fachärztin für Kinderkrankheiten, Diesterweg 3, Mittenwald, Bayern).

— Remind her of the occasion.
— Thank her again.
— Say that your sister is completely recovered.

- **der Facharzt (die Fachärztin)** specialist
- **wegen Magenschmerzen** because of stomach pains
- **beruhigen** reassure
- **die Dienstleistung** service (*rendered*)

10 FREIZEIT UND FREUNDE

In this unit you'll be writing about your own leisure interests, about local leisure facilities, films and cinemas, concerts and sporting events, fishing and photography; you'll be introducing yourself, rejecting proposals, choosing where to go ...

What people like to do ...

interest **das Interesse (-n)**
hobby **das Hobby (-s)**
collect **sammeln**
athletics **die Leichtathletik**
computer games **die Computerspiele**
amateur play **das Laienspiel (-e)**
swimming **das Schwimmen**
singing in a choir **das Chorsingen**
to fish **angeln**
to play football/tabletennis/cricket/rugby/
   chess **Fußball/Tischtennis/Cricket/Rugby/
   Schach spielen**
scout/guide **der Pfadfinder(in) (-/-nen)**
riding **das Reiten**
to listen to records **Schallplatten hören**
lazing about **das Faulenzen**

What you think about it ...

great! **Klasse!**
funny **komisch**
awful **furchtbar**

exciting **spannend**
uninteresting **uninteressant**
boring **langweilig**
it's very unpleasant **es ist sehr unangenehm**
it's great fun **es macht wirklich Spaß**

Inviting someone to do something ...

how about ...? **wie wäre es mit ...?/wie wäre
   es, wenn ...?**
shall we go to the cinema/concert? **wollen wir
   ins Kino/Konzert gehen?**
would you like to ...? **möchtest du ...?**
we could go for a walk **wir könnten
   spazierengehen**

Responding to an invitation ...

yes I'd like that **ja gerne**
with pleasure **mit Vergnügen**
that depends **es kommt darauf an**
I'm afraid it's impossible **es ist leider unmöglich**
I'd prefer to ... **ich würde lieber ...**

1 You've been asked to produce a breakdown of your class's favourite sports and hobbies for your German sister school's magazine. Collect these on the blackboard in two columns (Sportarten; Hobbys) together with the number of pupils claiming each as their favourite.

2 Your German exchange partner is coming to stay with you for the first time. Make a list of at least ten things that you could do together locally, putting them more or less in *your* order of preference.

schwimmen gehen
ins Kino gehen
...

3 A group of teenagers is visiting your town from your German twin town, and your class is to act as hosts. In order to pair off individuals the German group organiser has asked each of you to give a full account of your leisure interests.

die **Beschäftigung im Freien**
  open-air occupation
die **Sendung** broadcast
die **Zeitschrift** magazine
Sonstiges other things
freiwillig voluntary

> Haupthobbys?
> Was für Sport treibst du?
> Andere Beschäftigungen im Freien?
> Was für Musik hörst du gern?
> Spielst du ein Instrument?
> Lieblingsfernseh- und Radiosendungen
> Was für Bücher und Zeitschriften liest du?
> Sonstiges (z.B. Kirche, Pfadfinder, Chorsingen, Laienspiele, freiwillige Sozialarbeit usw.)

4 You're on an exchange in Bremen. Your partner is at school today and you aren't. You promised, before you went out for the day, that you'd phone the local cinemas and choose two or three possible films that the two of you might want to go and see tonight.

der **Spion** spy
die **Hexe** witch
zurückkehren return

Leave him/her a note of your selection (put them in the order you'd actually prefer):

— *Noch ein Spion* at the Rex (starts 9.00). It's a German film and supposed to be funny.
— *Die Hexen* at the Capitol (starts 8.30). It's an American horror film dubbed into German.
— *Der rosarote Panther kehrt zurück* (yet again! – but you like it) at the UFA Palast. Starts 9.00, it's in English with German sub-titles.

- **er soll ... sein** it's supposed to be ...
- **synchronisiert** dubbed
- **mit Untertiteln** with sub-titles

5 Your German pen-friend asks you in a letter if you ever go to concerts. Write to him/her about the last pop (or other) concert you went to. Use this framework to help:

stattfinden take place
etwas Besonderes something special
dauern last

> Wann war es? – Wer spielte? – Wo fand es statt? – Mit wem bist du hingegangen? – Wie gut wurde gespielt? – Wie war das Publikum? – Was war an diesem Konzert Besonderes? – Wie lange hat es gedauert? – Wie war der Abend?

6 German student hostels can be a cheap place to stay in the holidays, but you may find yourself taking messages for other people. Whilst you were in the hostel this morning the phone rang three times. You took down these messages in a mixture of English and German. Put them into comprehensible German so you can leave them for the people they were intended for:

> Peter Spremberg: Mother rang: has extra ticket for Staatstheater, Saturday, 8. Play called "Der Hauptmann von Köpenick"(?). Ring her tonight.
>
> Günter Habicht: Hans rang - "Fußballspiel fällt aus" - can't get a full team together. He'll see you at the club as usual, though.
>
> Ilse Schaum: Karl rang. Please ring back as soon as possible. "Sehr dringend." Not immediately after lunch though, and not between 7 and 8, and if it's later than ten, then ring on 54-78-76.

der Hauptmann captain
ausfallen be cancelled
dringend urgent

7

> Was ich aber am liebsten tue, ist angeln. Das ist ein wunderbarer Sport — man verbringt den Tag im Freien, die Sonne scheint, man hat Zeit genug, ein bißchen nachzudenken. Das ist auch so eine Art Schachspiel zwischen Dir und dem Fisch — und wenn Du gewinnst, da hast Du auch Dein Abendbrot!

- **zusammenbringen** get . . . together

verbringen spend
im Freien in the open air
eine Art a sort of
das Schachspiel game of chess

The above paragraph turns up in a letter to you from your German pen-friend. In a similar paragraph, *either*

- disagree with him and point out all the unpleasantnesses involved in fishing, *or*
- agree with him and say why you yourself like fishing, *or*
- tell him about your own favourite leisure activity and compare it to his.

- **mit dir bin ich völlig/gar nicht einverstanden** I completely agree with you/don't agree with you at all

8 You're writing to your Austrian pen-friend and want to tell him/her about an excellent weekend you spent a fortnight ago. To refresh your memory you turn up your diary for that Friday evening, Saturday and Sunday. Use it to help you write the letter. ➤

▶▶ **9** The photos you took on your last trip to Germany were really not very good (out of focus, badly composed, wrong exposure) and those you took of your German friend were especially bad. You're sending them, as promised, but you have to enclose a note sending your apologies and trying to explain what happened.

- **unscharf** out-of-focus
- **komponiert** composed
- **die Belichtung** exposure
- **. . . ist daran schuld** it's . . .'s fault

▶▶ **10** You're staying with your German exchange partner and have been out a couple of times with a group of friends to the local youth club. Your German exchange partner passes on to you this rather surprising note . . .

The person who wrote the note is one of the less interesting members of the opposite sex that you have met, and certainly your answer would be 'no'; however, you hate hurting people's feelings, so you write back saying:

- you do remember who the writer is
- you enjoyed talking to them
- you don't think it's a good idea to meet as suggested – you have a lot to do with your exchange partner in the evenings
- you're going back home in three or four days
- thanks, though, for the invitation.

- **die Bahn (-en)** *(fairground)* ride
- **das Feuerwerk** firework display

FRIDAY	evening - concert, terrific!
SATURDAY	shopping (new T-shirt, new jeans) - afternoon, evening trip to Alton Towers, great rides!
SUNDAY	walk (with S.!) - sun - picnic - evening with S. at home - records, TV - fireworks!

Ich habe Dich schon zwei- oder dreimal im Jugendklub gesehen und habe gestern abend auch eine Zeitlang mit Dir gesprochen. Vielleicht erinnerst Du Dich noch? Ich finde Dich wirklich interessant, ganz anders als die meisten im Jugendklub, und ich würde Dich gern besser kennenlernen. Könnten wir vielleicht an einem Abend bei MacDonalds einen Hamburger essen und anschließend vielleicht ins Kino gehen? Schreib mir, ob Du daran interessiert bist.

eine Zeitlang for a time
die meisten most of them
kennenlernen get to know
anschließend afterwards

- **es hat mich gefreut**
  I enjoyed it
- **keine so gute Idee** not such a good idea
- **der (die) Austauschpartner(in)**
  exchange partner

Im BRAVO-Treffpunkt könnt Ihr Brieffreunde aus dem In- und Ausland finden. Die Veröffentlichung ist kostenlos.

Wer hat Lust, einem 16jährigen Jungfrau-Girl zu schreiben? Alter ist egal. Hobbys erfahrt Ihr im Antwortbrief. Schreibt an: Beatrice Ksink, R.-Luxemburg-Straße 38, DDR-1240 Fürstenwalde

Wer von Euch hat mal Lust, mir (15) zu schreiben? Hobbys: Schwimmen, Wasserski, Tiere, Madonna. Wenn Ihr Interesse habt, schreibt bitte mit Foto an: Christine Katz, Podbielskiallee 78, 1000 Berlin 33

Aufgepaßt, Mädchen! Seid Ihr bereit, einem hübschen 16jährigen Boy zu schreiben? Hobbys: Disco. Schwimmen, Musik ... Schreibt an Armin Kotsoba, W.-Busch-Straße 10, 8901 Herbertshofen

Hallo, Boys! Ich bin 16 und würde mich freuen, wenn Ihr mir schnell schreibt. Vielleicht lernen wir uns ja mal kennen. Schreibt mit Foto an: Daniela Mundt, Armenische Straße 7, 1000 Berlin 65

Welches hübsche Girl bis 16 hätte Lust, einem 16jährigen Kino- und Musikfreak zu schreiben? Jede Bildzuschrift wird garantiert beantwortet. Bitte schreibt an: Wolfgang Stelzer, Fasanenweg 4, 7099 Adelmannsfelden

Hallo, Boys von 16-20! Habt Ihr Lust, mit mir (16) eine tolle (Brief-)Freundschaft zu beginnen? Wer wie ich auf Tanzen, Natur und auf Disco-Musik steht, der schreibt schnell an: Beate Sander, Bodelshofer Weg 58, 7312 Kirchheim

Welches nette Mädchen zwischen 15 und 18 hat Lust, einem 17jährigen Zwilling zu schreiben? Hobbys: Schwimmen, Fußball, Tennis, Schach ... Schreibt bitte mit Foto an: Frank Wehrse, Kirchstraße 3 a, 3074 Steyerberg

Ich habe lange keinen lieben Brief mehr bekommen. Wer auf Tennis, Reiten, Musik, M. Jackson ... steht, sollte mir möglichst schnell schreiben Ihr solltet zwischen 13 und 16 sein. Schreibt bitte mit Foto an Natalie Tauche, Baunsbergstraße 48, 3507 Baunatal 1

Welcher nette Junge hat Lust, mir (14) zu schreiben? Hobbys: Musik, Tanzen ... Du solltest zwischen 14 und 16 sein. Schreib bitte mit Foto an: Jutta Littig, Greifswalder Straße 5, 6750 Kaiserslautern

Lustiger Stier-Boy sucht Girls von 13-25 zwecks Briefkontakt. Hobbys: Schwimmen, gute Musik ... Schreibt bitte mit Foto an: Sascha Walden, Kopernikusstraße 111, 4100 Duisburg 11

Welches Girl hat Lust, einem 15jährigen Boy zu schreiben? Hobbys: Tanzen. Musik, Faulenzen. Du solltest zwischen 14 und 17 sein. Schreib an Anton Cicak, Nürnberger Straße 103, 8510 Fürth

Welches Mädchen zwischen 14 und? hat Lust, einem netten 16jährigen Jungen zu schreiben? Hobbys: Musik, Tischtennis. Disco und Schwimmen. Wer Interesse hat, schreibt mit Foto an: Marcus Allig, Kienlesweg 3, 7916 Nersingen

---

aus dem In- und Ausland at home and abroad	**bereit** ready
die Veröffentlichung publication	**sich freuen** be pleased
kostenlos free	**kennenlernen** get to know
Lust haben want	**die Bildzuschrift** reply with picture
die Jungfrau virgin; (*here, astrol.*) virgo	**toll** crazy
das Alter age	**stehen auf** be keen on
es ist egal it doesn't matter	**der Zwilling** twin; (*here, astrol.*) gemini
erfahren learn	**lieb** nice
das Tier animal	**lustig** cheerful
aufgepaßt! attention!	**der Stier** bull; (*here, astrol.*) taurus

From the above correspondents choose the one who seems most interesting to you and write a letter saying you've seen his/her photo in 'Bravo' and introducing yourself. Say you're sending a photo, point out that you're English but you speak German and would like to spend some time in Germany, and also say what your own leisure interests are.

Auf einen Blick

BASKETBALL
DBB-Pokal der Frauen, Viertelfinale: Samstag: SG München – BSC Köln, Barmer TV – Bayer Leverkusen (beide 20 Uhr), TSV Weilheim – SG Porz/Hennef (19.30 Uhr), BG Monheim – Agon Düsseldorf (19 Uhr).

BIATHLON
Weltcup-Wettbewerbe in Ruhpolding: Samstag (ab 9.30 Uhr): 10 km Männer, 5 km Frauen, 10 km Junioren. – Sonntag (ab 9 Uhr): 4 × 7,5 km Männer und Junioren, 3 × 5 km Frauen.

EISHOCKEY
Bundesliga, 36. Spieltag: Sonntag: Kaufbeuren – Berlin (15.30 Uhr), Landshut – Köln (18.30 Uhr), Rosenheim – Schwenningen, Frankfurt – Mannheim (beide 19.00 Uhr).

EISSPEEDWAY
WM-Viertelfinale in Inzell: Sa. (19 Uhr) und So. (14 Uhr).

FUSSBALL
Hallen-Finalrunde in Frankfurt mit BW Berlin, Fortuna Düsseldorf, Eintracht Frankfurt, Bayer Uerdingen, VfL Osnabrück und Werder Bremen (Sa.)

HANDBALL
Bundesliga, Männer, 15. Spieltag: Samstag: Hofweier – Milbertshofen (19.30 Uhr). – Sonntag: Schwabing – Kiel (16 Uhr, Rudi-Sedlmayer-Halle), Wallau-Massenheim – Gummersbach (15.30 Uhr), Düsseldorf – Nürnberg (16.30 Uhr), Essen – Göppingen (17 Uhr).
Bundesliga, Frauen, 12. Spieltag.

HOCKEY
Hallen-Europameisterschaft der Männer in Wien (Sa./So.).

LEICHTATHLETIK
Int. Hallensportfest in Stuttgart (Sa. ab 14.30 Uhr).

RADSPORT
Querfeldein-WM in Hägendorf/Schweiz: Samstag: Amateure (14.00 Uhr). Sonntag: Junioren (11.30 Uhr), Profis (14.00 Uhr).

RODELN
Europameisterschaft in Königssee: Samstag: Einsitzer Frauen, Doppelsitzer Männer (ab 9.30 Uhr). – Sonntag: Mannschaftswettbewerbe (ab 10.30 Uhr).

SKI ALPIN
Männer: Weltcup-Riesenslalom in Schladming (Sa.). Frauen: Weltcup-Riesenslalom und Slalom in Kranjska Gora/Jugoslawien (Sa./So.).

TENNIS
Schaukampf in der Frankfurter Festhalle: Becker – Lendl, Becker/Jelen – Kühnen/Steeb (So., ab 13.00 Uhr).

VOLLEYBALL
DVV-Pokal der Frauen, Viertelfinale: Samstag: Türk Gücü München – Rudow Berlin, CJD Feuerbach – USC Münster (beide 19.30 Uhr), Post SV Köln – TG Rüsselsheim (20.00 Uhr). – Sonntag: TV Hörde – VSV Vilsbiburg (16.30 Uhr).
Bundesliga, Männer u. a.: 1860 München – USC Gießen (Sa. 19.00 Uhr, Rudi-Sedlmayer-Halle).

It's January, you're in Munich, and you want to spend Saturday evening at a sporting event. You promised your exchange partner (who has stayed at home) that in the course of the morning whilst you were in town you would buy a paper, look at what was on, and then phone him/her with your choice.

So here you are, sitting over a cup of coffee and a copy of the Süddeutsche Zeitung, putting a ring round any possible event. Since you're in Munich, some of these places are not reachable; in other cases you're not at all sure where the town is. Not all events are on Saturday evening.

Choose two possible events and make a note in German on each, so that you can phone the essential details to your friend and leave the final choice to him/her.

der Pokal cup
der Wettbewerb competition
die Bundesliga West German League
die Meisterschaft championship
das Rodeln tobogganing
der Schaukampf exhibition match

● **die Wahl triffst du** it's your choice

11 SCHULE

In this unit you'll be writing about your school, your classroom, the subjects you study, your school day and year, and about types of school and of examination. You'll be describing the perfect teacher, finding out about German schools, and applying for a place at a language school in Germany.

Buildings ...

entrance hall **die Eingangshalle (-n)**
assembly hall **die Aula**
classroom **das Klassenzimmer (-)**
gymnasium **die Turnhalle (-n)**
laboratory; lab **das Labor (-s)**
playground **der Schulhof (¨e)**
office **das Büro (-s)**
staircase **die Treppe (-n)**
corridor **der Gang (¨e)**
fire door **die Feuertür (-en)**
staff room **das Lehrerzimmer (-)**

Subjects ...

subject **das Fach (¨er)**
chemistry **die Chemie**
physics **die Physik**
biology **die Biologie**
history **die Geschichte**
geography **die Erdkunde**
mathematics; maths **die Mathematik; die Mathe**

French **Französisch**
Spanish **Spanisch**
religious studies **die Religionskunde**
music **die Musik**
art **die Kunst**
computer science **die Computerwissenschaft**
practical subjects **die praktischen Fächer**
technology **die Technologie**
domestic science/home economics
 die Hauswirtschaftslehre
gym **das Turnen**

Study ...

how long have you been learning ...? **wie lange lernst du ...?**
for three years **seit drei Jahren**
timetable **der Stundenplan**
take an exam **eine Prüfung nehmen**
pass **bestehen**
fail **durchfallen** (*sep.*) **in** (+ *dat.*)
a good mark **eine gute Note**
report **das Zeugnis (-se)**
certificate **das Prüfungszeugnis (-se)**

◢ 1

Montag

1 Deutsch – schwer (und die erste Stunde montags bin ich auch immer verschlafen!)
2 Mathematik – ziemlich schwer
3 Englisch – wesentlich einfacher
4 Erdkunde – sehr schwierig, und eine ganz unsympatische Lehrerin
5 Geschichte – beinahe unmöglich!
6 Physik – verhältnismäßig einfach, aber der Lehrer ist so streng!

Your West German friend has just produced this breakdown of a typical Monday's schoolwork to impress you with how much she has to do. Produce a similar one of your typical Monday, showing, if possible, that you have an even worse time of it than she does.

verschlafen sleepy
ziemlich fairly
wesentlich einfacher considerably easier
schwierig difficult
verhältnismäßig relatively
streng strict

Montag

2 Your town has been newly twinned with a town in Germany, and the twinning committee is producing an account of the town, in words and pictures (and in German, naturally) for its new sister town. You have been asked to present an account of your own school in not more than 100 words. Use this framework:

> Wo? – Wie groß? – Wie viele Lehrer/Schüler? – Beschreibe die Bauten und ein typisches Klassenzimmer – der Schultag – Deutsch im Studienprogramm (wer studiert es, ab wann?) – Sports, Klubs, Austausch.

die Bauten buildings
das Studienprogramm curriculum
ab from
der Austausch (*no pl.*) exchange

3 Your German friend is staying with you and is following you to school to join your German class. She/He knows where your school is, but not where the classroom is in the school. Give her/him written directions to get from the school entrance to your German classroom.

4 a Your West German friend writes you a long letter asking about your school and your school life. Here is an extract from it:

> Sind Eure Klassenzimmer wie unsere? Wie sieht Deins aus? In welchem Stockwerk liegt es? Wie ist es möbliert und gestrichen? Wie viele Schüler sind in Deiner Klasse? Sitzt Du vorne oder hinten? Wer sitzt neben Dir? Wie sind diese Leute, nett oder?

das Stockwerk storey
möbliert furnished
gestrichen painted

Describe your classroom for your friend, answering his/her questions as you do so.

b Here's another extract from the same letter with more questions, this time about your school subjects. Try to answer them.

> wir haben gerade angefangen, Computerwissenschaft zu lernen. Ich finde es interessant, aber sehr schwer. Hast Du auch dieses Fach? Ich weiß eigentlich nicht genau, welche Fächer Du hast. Schreib es mir mal, und erzähl mir auch, was nach dem normalen Schultag in deiner Schule los ist, und was Du dann machst.

gerade just
eigentlich in fact
genau exactly
was ist los what happens

c This extract is about school holidays ...

> hier in Westdeutschland haben wir ca. 270 Tage Schule pro Jahr. Früher war das Schuljahr in jedem Land der Bundesrepublik anders, jetzt ist es überall das gleiche. Die längsten Ferien sind die Sommerferien: sechs Wochen. Zu Weihnachten haben wir zwei Wochen frei. Wie ist es bei Euch?

das gleiche the same
zu Weihnachten at Christmas

Answer your West German friend's question by writing back about:

- the length of *your* school year
- how long your summer holidays are
- how long your Christmas and Easter holidays are
- what other holidays you get (half term, bank holidays).

- **die Osterferien** Easter holidays
- **die Halbtrimesterferien** half-term holidays
- **der Bankfeiertag (-e)** bank holiday

d This final extract from your West German friend's letter
is about British examinations. In your reply try to explain
the main points of the British examination system in as
few words as possible, clearing up his/her specific
problems as you go along.

> Du, ich habe neulich hier in der Zeitung über Eure Prüfungen in England gelesen, GSEC oder so etwas. Ich habe wirklich kein Wort davon verstanden. Was ist denn SEGC, oder wie das wohl heißt? Und was ist A-level? Gibt es auch ein B-level? Muß man diese Prüfungen in allen Fächern bestehen, oder kann man wählen? Bitte, versuch mal mir das alles zu erklären.

so etwas something like that
oder wie das wohl heißt or
  whatever it's supposed to be called
wählen choose

- **mit ... Jahren** at age ...
- **die Klassenarbeit** class work

5 Your Austrian pen-friend says that his class is running a competition called 'Der perfekte Lehrer/Die perfekte Lehrerin' – you have to describe in not more than 100 words the teacher who comes closest to your ideal teacher. Your pen-friend thinks you might like to have a go too. You're not allowed to say who the teacher is, of course, though it's possible that some people may be able to guess!

- describe him/her physically (groß/klein, jung/alt, dunkel/blond . . .)
- describe what s/he usually wears (Kleidung, Farbe, chic oder unauffällig? . . .)
- then say what his/her teaching personality is like (streng, freundlich, fröhlich, interessant, lebhaft, anspruchsvoll . . .?).

- **mittelgroß** of medium height
- **steinalt** ancient
- **kahlköpfig** bald

unauffällig inconspicuous
fröhlich cheerful
lebhaft lively
anspruchsvoll demanding; exacting

6 Your East German pen-friend wants you to produce a short article for her class's wall magazine on 'Die Schulen in Großbritannien'. She/He writes:

> Soweit ich das verstanden habe, gibt es verschiedene Arten von Schulen in Großbritannien. Außer Gesamtschulen (was wir hierzulande Polytechnische Oberschulen nennen würden) gibt es auch immer noch in verschiedenen Teilen Eures Landes Gymnasien und Volksschulen – und auch Privatschulen? Stimmt das alles? Gibt es auch noch andere Arten von Schulen bei Euch? Was für eine Schule ist Deine? Erkläre uns das alles!

soweit as far as
verschieden various
die Gesamtschule comprehensive school
hierzulande in this country
der Teil part
das Gymnasium grammar school
die Volksschule secondary modern school
erklären explain

Write the article, explaining what sort of school yours is and what other sorts of secondary school there are.

7 Your school is planning a new exchange with a German school. Part of the time that the British students are in Germany will be spent in the German school in their partners' classes. With an eye to publicizing the exchange in your school, devise a set of questions (at least ten) to send off to your German partners in order to find out as much as possible about their school. If you look back through this unit you will find quite a lot of relevant questions to use or adapt.

8 Consider this advertisement for German language courses for foreigners in Hermülheim. Reply to it, asking for further details of the courses, including whether the spoken or the written word is emphasized. Give a little of your own language background (how long you have been learning German, any visits to Germany, any other languages studied). Choose one of the courses and ask whether it is likely to be too difficult or too easy for you.

die Fremdsprache (-n) foreign language
prüfungsbezogen examination related
die Erläuterung (-en) explanation
der Aufbau construction
die Grundstufe elementary level
erwerben acquire
der Teilnehmer (-) participant
die Kenntnisse (*pl.*) knowledge
das Lehrbuch (¨er) textbook
die Zahl (-en) number

Deutsch als Fremdsprache

Deutsch als Fremdsprache — Prüfungsbezogene Kurse
Erläuterungen zum Aufbau der Kurse
Grundstufe
In diesen Kursen erwerben sich die Teilnehmer gute Grundkenntnisse in der gesprochenen und geschriebenen Sprache. Die Gruppen sind international zusammengesetzt.

Grundstufe I — 1. + 2. Semester

22310
Hermülheim
Montags
14.30–16.00
und
Mittwochs
14.30–16.00
Beginn:
18. 1. 1988

Lehrbuch: Themen 1, Band 1, Lektionen 1 ff.
Agnes Henn
Bürgerhaus, Friedrich-Ebert-Straße 40
(15 × 4) 60 UStd., DM 90,–/45,–
Höchstteilnehmerzahl: 20

Grundstufe I — 3. + 4. Semester

22311
Hermülheim
Montags
17.45–19.15
und
Mittwochs
17.45–19.15
Beginn:
18. 1. 1988

Lehrbuch: Themen Kursbuch und Arbeitsbuch Inland Band 1, Lektionen 5 ff.
Michael Thau
Gymnasium, Bonnstraße 64–66
(15 × 4) 60 UStd., DM 90,–/45,–
Höchstteilnehmerzahl: 20

Grundstufe II — 1. + 2. Semester

22312
Hermülheim
Dienstags
18.30–20.00
und
Donnerstag
18.30–20.00
Beginn:
19. 1. 1988

Lehrbuch: Themen 1, Band 1, Lektionen 10 ff.
Hans Peter Koziol
Bürgerhaus, Friedrich-Ebert-Straße 40
(15 × 4) 60 UStd., DM 90,–/45,–
Höchstteilnehmerzahl: 20

- **der Kursus** (*pl.* **Kurse**) course
- **nähere Einzelheiten** further details
- **wird besonders betont** is especially emphasized

12 ARBEIT

In this unit you will be writing about work you have done and work you might do, here and abroad – including that of grape-picker, postman, au pair, hotel cleaner . . . You'll be writing about part-time work you have done and full-time career possibilities.

Jobs . . .

job (= *profession*) **der Beruf (-e)**
job (= *post*) **die Stelle (-n)**
factory **die Fabrik (-en)**
favourite job **der Lieblingsberuf (-e)**
office **das Büro (-s)**
in the open air **im Freien**
commercial **kaufmännisch**
apprentice **der Lehrling (-e)**
engineer **der Ingenieur (-e)**
factory worker **der Fabrikarbeiter (-)**
hairdresser **der Friseur(-e)/die Friseuse (-n)**
chef **der Koch (¨e)/die Köchin (-nen)**
clerk **der/die Büroangestellte** (*a.n.*)
driver **der/die Fahrer(in) (-/-nen)**
secretary **der/die Sekretär(in) (-e/-nen)**
word-processing **die Textverarbeitung**
postman **der/die Briefträger(in) (-/-nen)**
farmer **der Bauer (-n)**
doctor **der Arzt (¨e)/die Ärztin (-nen)**

vet **der Tierarzt (¨e)/die Tierärztin (-nen)**
nurse **die Krankenschwester (-n)**; male nurse **der Krankenpfleger (-)**
mechanic **der Mechaniker (-)**

No jobs . . .

unemployed **arbeitslos**
unemployed person **der/die Arbeitslose** (*a.n.*)
unemployment **die Arbeitslosigkeit**

Getting a job . . .

apply for **sich bewerben um**
half day/full time **halbtags/ganztags**
temporary **zeitweilig**
permanent post **die Dauerstellung (-en)**
interview **das Interview (-s)**
earn **verdienen**
salary **das Gehalt (¨er)**

1 Your Austrian friend's English class are making a list of possible part-time jobs that they might apply for during future visits to England. Help them by collecting on the blackboard (in German of course!) . . .

   a any part-time jobs that members of the class have done
   b any that older brothers, sisters, friends and acquaintances have done
   c any other jobs that seem possible

2 Your German pen-friend writes that her class are sending out a questionnaire to discover who does most part-time work – German, British or French teenagers. They are asking both their British and French pen-friends to complete it. Here it is:

regelmäßig regularly
gelegentlich occasionally

```
Arbeitest du am Wochenende? ......................    Was machst du? ......................
Arbeitest du auch während der Woche? .............    Wie lange arbeitest du pro Tag? .......
Regelmäßig oder nur gelegentlich?    .............    Wieviel verdienst du? .............
Nur sonnabends oder auch am Sonntag? .............    Was machst du mit dem Geld? ..........
```

3 A German friend writes from Zell an der Mosel that there is a possibility of some casual labour at the wine harvest. Write to the address he has given you, using this skeleton letter:

```
                              ...... , den ...... 19..
Herrn Friedrich Katze,
Weinbau Gütenich,
Zell a.d. Mosel,
Deutschland.


Sehr geehrter Herr Katze,

mein guter Zeller Freund Klaus Schnabel hat mir geschrieben,
daß Sie für die Weinernte Arbeitskräfte brauchen.

Ich möchte mich dafür melden.  Ich bin Engländer
(Waliser/Schotte/Irländer...)(-in), bin ........ alt und
spreche ...... und ...... (und ......).
Ich bin zuverlässig und Fleißig und habe schon letztes/
vorletzes/ früher dieses Jahr in meiner Freizeit gearbeitet,
als .......

Mit vorzüglicher Hochachtung,

.......
```

die Weinernte wine harvest
die Arbeitskräfte (*f.pl.*) labour
brauchen need
zuverlässig reliable
fleißig hard-working
vorletztes Jahr the year before last

4 Many jobs ask you to enclose a curriculum vitae (**der Lebenslauf**), a complete, chronological account of your life so far. Devise one for yourself in German (useful for a holiday job perhaps?), using this pattern:

```
Name........................  Alter...............
Anschrift...................  Geschlecht..........
............................  Familienstand.......
............................  Geboren am..........
Telefonnummer...............

Schulen.......................................................
     .........................................................
     .........................................................

Prüfungen (bestanden und zu bestehen)................
     .........................................................

Fremdsprachen.................................................
Sportarten....................................................

Sonstige Interessen...........................................
     .........................................................
     .........................................................
     .........................................................

Referenzen (a)................................................
          (b)................................................
     .........................................................
```

die Anschrift address
der Familienstand family status
das Geschlecht sex
die Prüfung examination
bestehen take
die Fremdsprache foreign language
sonstig other

5 Write a letter of application (enclosing the curriculum vitae you have just completed) for any of the jobs in these 'situations vacant' small ads from a Cologne newspaper that you think you might be (even remotely!) qualified for. Explain why you want to work in Germany and why you feel yourself particularly qualified for *this* job. Sell yourself!

Stellenangebote

Starten Sie mit uns ins neue Berufsjahr. Kaufmännische Mitarbeiter-innen mit guten Schreibmaschinenkenntnissen für sofort oder später gesucht. Steno, Fremdsprachen und Erfahrung in der Textver-arbeitung wären natürlich ideal. Wir bieten Ihnen einen festen Arbeits-platz mit vielseitigen Aufgaben. Schriftliche Bewerbungen bitte an: Agentur Wolf, Am Kreuzeich 199, 5451 Melsbach.

Bürohilfe als zweite Kraft für Architekturbüro, halbtags, vormittags, gesucht. ZM 3586 KStA, Breite Str. 170, 5000 Köln 1.

Schreibkraft für modernes Büro und selbständige Arbeit, halbe Tage, von 12.00 – 17.00 Uhr. Gute Bezahlung. Frau Monika Zimmermann, Burgstr. 98, 4152 Kempen.

Zehn Warenhausdetektive/innen dringend gesucht! Eine interes-sante und abwechslungsreiche Tätigkeit erwartet Sie. Wir bieten ein gutes Gehalt in feinster Einstellung. Interessenten schreiben bitte zwecks Terminabsprache: Willick, Postfach 10 10 09, 5000 Köln 1.

Friseurinnen als Aushilfen für 2 – 3 Tage wochentlich in Dauerstellung gesucht. Intercoiffeur Dietz-Ganser, Ebertstr. 29, Köln.

Zahnarzthelferin für Behandlung und Abrechnung oder nur Abrech-nung für moderne Praxis gesucht. ZL3585 KStA, Breite Str. 270, 5000 Köln 1.

Jungkoch, Buffetkraft, Küchenhilfe, Putzfrau für neuerrichtete Gaststätte in der Innenstadt gesucht. Wir bieten geregelte Arbeitszeit, Fünftagewoche, gute Sozialleistungen. Postfach 99 01 99, 5000 Köln 1.

Wohnungsverwaltung sucht nebenberuflichen Hausmeister für sofort. Bewerbungen bitte an: Curate GmbH, Aachener Str. 160 – 162, 5000 Köln 1.

Aushilfe (Imbißverkäuferin) für die späten Abendstunden auf der Kölner Messe gesucht. Postfach 01 70 07, 5000 Köln 1.

Weibliche Hilfskraft (Studentin) ganztags nach Sürth ab 4. Januar gesucht. Postfach 11 88 76, 5000 Köln 1.

Schülerbürojob. 5, – Nettostundenlohn zuzüglich Fahrkosten. Postfach 55 52 56, 5000 Köln 1.

der Mitarbeiter member of staff
bieten offer
die Kraft worker; employee
selbständig independent
abwechslungsreich varied
die Tätigkeit work
zwecks with a view to
die Terminabsprache
  arrangement of an interview
die Behandlung treatment
die Abrechnung accounting
neuerrichtet newly built
geregelt regular
die Wohnungsverwaltung
  housing administration
nebenberuflich as an extra
  occupation
der Hausmeister caretaker
der Imbiß snack
der Nettostundenlohn net
  hourly wage
zuzüglich plus

- **schon (ziemlich/sehr) fließend sprechen** already speak (quite/very) fluently
- **besonders gut geeignet** especially suitable

6 Your German friend writes:

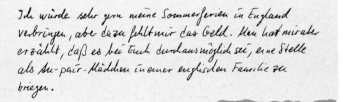

Ich würde sehr gern meine Sommerferien in England verbringen, aber dazu fehlt mir das Geld. Man hat mir aber erzählt, daß es bei Euch durchaus möglich sei, eine Stelle als Au-pair-Mädchen in einer englischen Familie zu kriegen.

fehlen be lacking
erzählen tell
durchaus entirely; very
kriegen get

Write back to your German friend saying that yes, such jobs are available, and pointing out the advantages and disadvantages of this sort of work.

7 These are some examples of 'jobs wanted' ads from the same newspaper. Invent a similar advertisement, seeking any temporary job anywhere in Germany during the month of August. Give your age, sex, nationality and say what languages you speak. Make the advertisement as short as possible whilst getting in all the necessary information. Give your home phone number or address.

- **Halbtags- oder Ganztagsarbeit** half-time or full-time work
- **egal wo** it doesn't matter where

8 You are working in the beautiful town of Rothenburg ob der Tauber in a temporary job in what is, from your point of view, a less than beautiful hotel. You clean out rooms and bathrooms, peel potatoes and other vegetables, wash pans, sweep floors. And when you get this letter from your German friend you don't have time to send him more than a postcard in return. Still, in the space that that gives you, you try to disillusion him a little by telling him exactly what you *are* doing.

- **zwar schön, aber ...** admittedly beautiful but ...
- **erschöpft** exhausted

9 Your twinned class in a German Gesamtschule are conducting an enquiry into career intentions. They have asked you to find out what members of your class intend to do.

- Find out what the career intentions of each member of the class are (this should be done communally and results put up in German on the blackboard, including 'don't knows').
- Copy out and complete this table in German to convey these results.

weiterstudieren continue to study
sofort immediately
unter among
anschließend subsequently
wünschen wish for

---

7 **Stellengesuche**

Junger Mann, 35, zuverlässig, sucht als Pförtner o.ä. Beschäftigung. Wechseldienst angenehm. Führerschein Kl. III vorhanden. Köln 7 90 15 74.
Chefsekretärin, 49, perfekt. ab sofort frei. ✉ u. HL 12 442 Zweigst. KSTA, Kalker Hauptstr. 161, 5000 Köln 91.
Kellner / Büfettier zur Aushilfe frei, auch für Tagdienst. 02 21 / 39 12 20.
Suche Stelle als Haushaltshilfe (Babysitter etc.) Köln 7 60 12 16.

der Pförtner doorkeeper; caretaker
der Wechseldienst shift work
angenehm acceptable
der Führerschein driving licence
die Zweigstelle branch
der Büfettier barman

ich wette, Du liegst den ganzen Tag auf der Terrasse oder neben dem Schwimmbad, oder Du sitzt in der Bar. Sicher ißt Du und trinkst Du reichlich und umsonst. Arbeitest Du ab und zu auch ein bißchen?

wetten bet   **umsonst** free; for nothing
reichlich plenty   **ab und zu** now and then

```
Weiterstudieren:                         ..........%

Sofort Arbeit suchen:                    ..........%

Unter denen, die sofort Arbeit
suchen wollen:

  Prozent, die noch nicht wissen,
  was sie tun wollen:                    ..........%
  Liste von Stellen, die gesucht
  werden                                 ............
                                         ............
                                         ............

Unter denen, die weiterstudieren
wollen:

  Prozent die noch nicht wissen,
  was sie anschließend tun wollen        ..........%
  Liste von Stellen, die nach dem
  Studium gewünscht werden               ............
                                         ............
                                         ............
```

► **10** Your German pen-friend has written to you 'Jetzt weiß ich, was ich mit meinem Leben mache: ich werde Raumfahrer(in) werden', a career decision you don't take too seriously. But you do write seriously back to him/her about your own career intentions and prospects. Use the answers to the following set of questions to give you a framework:

> Wie viele Jahre gehst du noch zur Schule? – Wenn du nach GCSE dort bleibst, worauf möchtest du dich spezialisieren? – Hast du vor, anderswo weiter zu studieren? wo? wie lange? – Möchtest du Lehrling werden? – Was hoffst du zu machen, wenn du zu arbeiten anfängst? – Fürchtest du dich vor der Arbeitslosigkeit? – Wo würdest du am liebsten arbeiten?

der Raumfahrer spaceman
anderswo somewhere else
hoffen hope
anfangen begin
sich fürchten vor be afraid of

► **11** You're alone in the house of your exchange partner, Rainer, in Germany when the phone rings with a message for him. He has applied to the local supermarket for a part-time job on Saturday mornings. It is the supermarket ringing, and these are the notes you take of the telephone conversation:

- not holding interviews
- Rainer to come along with other applicants this Saturday at 8.30.
- if he's successful, job will start there and then: 9.30 on Saturday morning.

Write them out in comprehensible German so that Rainer will have a written record as well as your oral account when he comes home.

- **der Bewerber** applicant
- **auf der Stelle** there and then

◢ **12** Your Swiss friend has sent you a competition from a magazine in which you have to put ten jobs into the order you think preferable and complete a tie-breaker. Order the jobs and (in case you win!) do the tie-breaker as well.

WAS WÄREN SIE AM LIEBSTEN?

Ordnen Sie folgende Berufe nach Ihrer eigenen Vorliebe und Wahl:

RAUMFAHRER(IN)	PREMIERMINISTER	FINANZIER
PILOT	INGENIEUR	KÖNIG(IN)
ARZT (ÄRZTIN)	LEHRER(IN)	JOURNALIST(IN)
SCHIFFSKAPITÄN	DICHTER(IN)	TENNISSPIELER(IN)

Vollenden Sie dann folgende Sätze:

1 ..... ist der interessanteste Job, weil .....
2 ..... finde ich am uninteressantesten, weil .....

Und der Preis? Sie verbringen zwei Tage bei jemandem, der Ihren Lieblingsberuf ausübt!

wären Sie would you be
die Vorliebe preference
die Wahl choice
der Dichter poet
der König king
vollenden complete
verbringen spend
jemand someone
ausüben practice

English-German vocabulary

Where a word has two or more meanings we have always tried to explain the difference between these: if you are still at all unsure though, you should look the word up in a German-English dictionary.

An asterisk (*) after a verb means the verb is strong or irregular. There is a list of these with their past tense and past participles on page 96.

Some verb prefixes (like **be-**) are always inseparable; some (like **auf-**) are always separable; but some (like **über-**) can be either separable or inseparable. With this last kind of verb we have always indicated whether the prefix is separable or not.

Noun plurals are given in brackets. Masculine nouns ending **-er** (names of the jobs people do, etc.) have a feminine form ending **-erin** (pl. **-erinnen**).

The following abbreviations are used:

acc. accusative
adj. adjective
adv. adverb
a.n. adjectival noun (takes adjective endings)
colloq. colloquial
conj. conjunction
dat. dative
esp. especially
gen. genitive
insep. prefix inseparable
interj. interjection
intrans. intransitive (having no direct object)
invar. invariable
n. noun
pl. plural
prep. preposition
sep. prefix separates
sing. singular
trans. transitive (having direct object)
v. verb

A-level (=) das Abitur
about (= *approximately*) ungefähr; etwa; (+ *time*) gegen; be about to (*do something*) im Begriff sein* (etwas zu tun)
abroad im Ausland (das Ausland)
absolutely unbedingt
accept annehmen*
accident der Unfall (¨e); **have an accident** verunglücken
accommodation die Unterkunft
accompany begleiten
account (*bank*) das Konto (-ten)
acquaintance der Bekannte (a.n.)
actor der Schauspieler (-)
actually eigentlich
address die Adresse (-n); die Anschrift (-en)
admire bewundern
admittedly zwar
adult der Erwachsene (a.n.)
advance: in advance im voraus
advantage der Vorteil (-e)
advertisement die Reklame (-n); **small/classified ad(vertisement)** die Kleinanzeige (-n)
advise raten* (+ *dat.*)
afraid: be afraid of Angst haben* vor
after that danach
afternoon der Nachmittag (-e) **in the afternoon** nachmittags
afterwards nachher
again wieder
against: I've nothing against it ich habe nichts dagegen
age das Alter
ago vor . . .
agree (to) einverstanden sein* (mit)
aid die Hilfe; **first aid** erste Hilfe

air die Luft (¨e)
  air bed die Luftmatratze (-n)
  air hostess die Stewardeß (-ssen)
  aircraft das Flugzeug (-e)
  airmail (*n.*) die Luftpost; (*v.*) per Luftpost schicken
  airport der Flughafen (¨)
alarm der Wecker (-)
all all-; **all the best!** alles Gute!
allow erlauben
almost fast
alone allein
along: along the street die Straße entlang; **bring along** mitbringen*
already schon
also auch
although obwohl; obgleich
altogether insgesamt
amazing erstaunlich
ambulance der Krankenwagen (-)
America (das) Amerika
American (*adj.*) amerikanisch; (*n.*) der Amerikaner (-)
amount: any amount of jede Menge von
angry böse
animal das Tier (-e)
announcer der Ansager (-)
annoy ärgern; **be annoyed** sich ärgern
annual jährlich
anorak der Anorak (-s)
answer (*v.*) antworten auf (+ *acc.*); beantworten; (*n.*) die Antwort (-en)
antique antik
apologize sich entschuldigen
apparently anscheinend
appear (= *seem*) scheinen*; (= *put in an appearance*) erscheinen*
apple der Apfel (¨); **apple juice** der Apfelsaft
appointment die Verabredung (-en)
apprentice der Lehrling (-e)
approximately etwa; ungefähr
April der April
area (= *region*) das Gebiet (-e); (= *neighbourhood*) die Gegend (-en)

arm der Arm (-e)
armchair der Lehnstuhl (¨e); der Sessel (-)
arranged abgemacht
arrival die Ankunft
arrive ankommen*
art die Kunst (¨e)
article der Artikel (-)
ashtray der Aschenbecher (-)
as (= *since*) da; denn
ask (*ask for*) bitten* (um); (= *to question*) fragen; **ask a question** eine Frage stellen
asleep: fall asleep einschlafen*
assure (*someone of something*) (einem etwas) versichern
athletics die Leichtathletik (*sing.*)
attempt versuchen
attention: pay attention to aufpassen auf (+ *acc.*)
attractive reizvoll; (*person*) reizend
audience die Zuschauer (*pl.*)
August der August
aunt die Tante (-n)
Austria (das) Österreich
Austrian (*adj.*) österreichisch; (*n.*) der Österreicher (-)
autumn der Herbst (-e)
awake (*v.*) erwachen (*intrans.*); wecken (*trans.*); (*adj.*) wach; **stay awake** wach bleiben*
awful grauenhaft

baby das Baby (-s)
back der Rücken (-)
  at the back hinten
  backwards rückwärts
bad schlecht; (= *dreadful*) schlimm; **bad-tempered** schlecht gelaunt
badminton das Badminton; der Federball
bag der Sack (¨e); (*paper*) die Tüte (-n)
bake backen
baker der Bäcker (-)
baker's die Bäckerei (-en)
balcony der Balkon (-e)
ball der Ball (¨e); **ball-point** der Kugelschreiber (-)
Baltic die Ostsee

banana die Banane (-n)
bandage der Verband (¨e)
bank die Bank (-en); (*of river*) das Ufer (-)
bar die Bar (-s); die Schenke (-n); (*of chocolate*) die Tafel (-n)
bark bellen
basement das Untergeschoß (-osse)
basket der Korb (¨e)
bat (*sports*) der Schläger (-)
bath das Bad (¨er); (= *bathtub*) die Badewanne (-n); **bath soap** die Badeseife
bathe baden
bathroom das Badezimmer (-)
battery die Batterie (-n)
beach der Strand (¨e)
bean die Bohne (-n)
beard der Bart (¨e)
beautiful schön
because weil; **because of** wegen (+ *gen.*)
become werden*
bed das Bett (-en)
  bedroom das Schlafzimmer (-)
  bedside table der Nachttisch (-e)
  go to bed ins Bett gehen*
  make the bed das Bett machen
beef das Rindfleisch
beer das Bier (-e)
begin anfangen*; beginnen*
beginning der Anfang (¨e); der Beginn; **at the beginning of March** Anfang März
behind (*prep.*) hinter (+ *acc./dat.*); (*adv.*) hinten; **from behind** hinter (+ *dat*) ... hervor
Belgian (*adj.*) belgisch; (*n.*) der Belgier (-)
Belgium (das) Belgien
believe glauben
belong (*to*) gehören (+ *dat.*)
belt der Gürtel (-)
bench die Bank (¨e)
best best-; **all the best!** alles Gute!
better besser; **get better** (= *recover*) sich erholen
bible die Bibel
bicycle das Fahrrad (¨er)

big groß

bill die Rechnung (-en); (= *sales slip*) der Kassenzettel (-)

biology die Biologie

bird der Vogel (̈)

birthday der Geburtstag (-e)

biscuit der Keks (-e)

bit: a bit ein bißchen

bite beißen*

black schwarz

blanket die Wolldecke (-n); die Bettdecke (-n)

bleed bluten

blind blind

block der Block (̈e)

blond blond

blood das Blut

blouse die Bluse (-n)

blue blau

board (*blackboard*) die Tafel
  full board (*hotel*) Vollpension
  on board an Bord

boat das Boot (-e)

body der Körper (-)

boil (*intrans.*) kochen; (*trans.*) kochen lassen*

book (*v.*) buchen; (*a room*) reservieren; (*n.*) das Buch (̈er)

bookcase das Bücherregal (-e)

bookshop die Buchhandlung (-en)

boot der Stiefel (-); (*car*) der Kofferraum (̈e)

border die Grenze (-n)

boring langweilig

born geboren

borrow leihen*

both beide

bottle die Flasche (-n)

bottom: at the bottom unten

bowl (*v.*) (*game*) kegeln; (*n.*) (*dish*) die Schüssel (-n)

box die Schachtel (-n)

box-office die Kasse (-n)

Boxing Day der zweite Weihnachtstag

boy der Junge (-n)

bracelet das Armband (̈er)

brake (*v.*) bremsen; (*n.*) die Bremse (-n)

bread das Brot (-e); **black** (*rye*) **bread** das Schwarzbrot

break (*v.*) brechen*; (*n.*) die Pause (-n); **break down**

versagen; **breakdown** die Panne (-n)

breakfast (*v.*) frühstücken; (*n.*) das Frühstück (-e)

breathless atemlos

bridge die Brücke (-n)

briefcase die Mappe (-n)

bright hell

bring bringen*; **bring along** mitbringen*

British britisch

broad breit

broadcast (*v.*) senden; (*n.*) die Sendung (-en)

brochure die Broschüre (-n); der Prospekt (-e)

broken kaputt

brother der Bruder (̈)
  brother(s) and sister(s) die Geschwister (*pl.*)
  brother-in-law der Schwager (̈)

brown braun

brush (*v.*) bürsten; (*n.*) die Bürste (-n)

bucket der Eimer (-)

budgerigar der Wellensittich (-e)

build bauen

building das Gebäude (-);
  building site die Baustelle (-n)

built-in eingebaut

bulb (*for light*) die Birne (-n)

bungalow der Bungalow (-s)

bureau de change die Wechselstube (-n)

burn (*intrans.*) brennen*; (*trans.*) verbrennen*

bus der Bus (-se); **bus station** der Busbahnhof (̈e); **bus stop** die Bushaltestelle (-n)

business (= *firm*) der Betrieb (-e); (= *matter*) die Sache (-n)

businessman der Geschäftsmann (*pl.* Geschäftsleute)

butcher der Fleischer (-); (*esp. S. Germany*) der Metzger (-)

butcher's die Fleischerei (-en); die Metzgerei (-en)

butter die Butter

button der Knopf (̈e)

buy kaufen; (*ticket*) lösen

by (*with time*) bis

cabin die Kabine (-n)

cable railway die Seilbahn (-en)

café das Café (-s); die Konditorei (-en)

cage der Käfig (-e)

cake der Kuchen (-)

cake-shop die Konditorei (-en)

calculate rechnen; **calculator** (*pocket*) der (Taschen)rechner (-)

call rufen; **be called** heißen*

calm ruhig

camera der Fotoapparat (-e)

camp zelten; **camping stove** der Campingkocher (-); **campsite** der Campingplatz (̈e)

can die Dose (-n); **can opener** die Dosenöffner (-)

cancelled: be cancelled ausfallen*

candle die Kerze (-n)

cap die Mütze (-n)

capital die Hauptstadt (̈e)

car der Wagen (-); das Auto (-s)
  car ferry die Autofähre (-n)
  car park der Parkplatz (̈e); (*multi-storey*) das Parkhaus (̈er)
  car wash die Autowäsche

caravan der Wohnwagen (-)

card die Karte (-n)

care: take care of besorgen

caretaker der Hausmeister (-)

carol das Weihnachtslied (-er)

carpet der Teppich (-e)

carry tragen*

carving knife das Tranchiermesser (-)

case: in any case sowieso; **in case** (*conj.*) falls

cassette die Kassette (-n); **cassette recorder** der Kassettenrecorder (-)

castle das Schloß (-össer); (*fortified*) die Burg (-en)

cat die Katze (-n)

catch fangen; (*an illness*) sich (*dat.*) (eine Krankheit) holen

cathedral der Dom (-e); die Kathedrale (-n)

Catholic katholisch

cauliflower der Blumenkohl (-e)

ceiling die Decke (-n)

celler der Keller (-)

centigrade Celsius; **25 degrees**

centigrade 25 Grad Celsius

centimetre der Zentimeter (-)

central heating die Zentralheizung; **gas/coal/oil central heating** die Gas-/ Kohlen-/Ölheizung

centre die Mitte (-n)

century das Jahrhundert (-e)

certain (= *some and not others*) bestimmt; gewiß; (= *sure*) gewiß; sicher

chain die Kette (-n)

chair der Stuhl (⁻e)

chalk die Kreide (-n)

championship die Meisterschaft (-en)

change (*v.*) wechseln (*also money, tyres*); (*trains*) umsteigen* (*sep.*); (*clothes*) sich umziehen* (*sep.*); (*goods*) umtauschen (*sep.*); (*n.*) der Wechsel (-); (*money*) das Kleingeld

channel der Kanal (⁻e) (*also = English Channel*)

chapel die Kapelle (-n)

charge (*n.*) die Gebühr (-en); (*v.*) berechnen; **you're charging me too much for it** sie berechnen mir dafür zuviel

charming reizend

chat plaudern

cheap billig

cheat mogeln (*colloq.*)

check (*v.*) kontrollieren; (*n*) (*bank*) der Scheck (-s)

cheerful heiter; lustig

cheerio tschüs

cheers! zum Wohl!

cheese der Käse

chemist der Apotheker (-); der Drogist (-en)

chemistry die Chemie

chemist's die Apotheke (-n); (*without prescription drugs*) die Drogerie (-n)

cherry die Kirsche (-n)

chess das Schach

chest die Brust

chest of drawers die Kommode (-n)

chew kauen; **chewing gum** der Kaugummi

chicken das Huhn (⁻er); (*spring chicken*) das Hähnchen (-);

chicken broth die Hühnerbrühe

child das Kind (-er)

chips die Pommes frites

chocolate die Schokolade; (= *a chocolate*) die Praline (-n); **block of chocolate** die Tafel Schokolade

choice (*decision*) die Wahl (-en); (*selection offered*) die Auswahl

choose wählen

chop das Kotelett (-s)

Christmas (*n.*) (das) Weihnachten (*plural in greetings:* fröhliche Weihnachten); (*adj.*) Weihnachts- **at Christmas** zu Weihnachten

Christmas cake der Weihnachtskuchen (-)

Christmas Day der Weihnachtstag

Christmas Eve der Heilige Abend

Christmas pudding der Weihnachtspudding (-e)

Merry Christmas! fröhliche Weihnachten!

church die Kirche (-n)

cigarette die Zigarette (-n)

cigar die Zigarre (-n)

cinema das Kino (-s)

circle der Kreis (-e); (*in cinema etc.*) der Rang (⁻e)

city die Großstadt (⁻e)

class Klasse (-n); **classmate** der/die Klassenkamerad(in) (-en/-nen); **classroom** das Klassenzimmer (-); **travel second class** zweiter Klasse fahren*

classic(al) klassisch

clean (*adj.*) sauber; (*v.*) putzen; reinigen; **clean up** saubermachen; **keep clean** sauberhalten*

clear (*adj.*) klar; (*v.*) (= *clear away*) abräumen; **clear the table** abdecken

clever klug

climate das Klima

climb steigen*; (*more difficult; as sport*) klettern

clinic die Klinik (-en)

clock die Uhr (-en)

close (*v.*) schließen*; zumachen; (*adj.*) (*weather*) schwül; **closed** (*adj.*) zu; geschlossen; (*road*) gesperrt

cloth der Stoff (-e)

clothes die Kleidung (*sing.*)

cloud die Wolke (-n); **cloudy** wolkig

club der Klub (-s); der Verein (-e)

coal die Kohle (-n)

coast die Küste (-n)

coat der Mantel (⁻)

cocoa der Kakao

code (*dialling*) die Vorwahl

coffee der Kaffee; **coffee pot** die Kaffeekanne (-n)

coin die Münze (-n)

coincidence der Zufall (⁻e)

cola die Cola

colander das Sieb (-e)

cold (*adj.*) kalt; (*n.*) (*temperature*) die Kälte; (*disease*) die Erkältung (-en); (= *head cold*) der Schnupfen; **catch a cold** einen Schnupfen bekommen; **have a cold** erkältet sein; **I'm cold** mich friert

colleague der Kollege (-n)/die Kollegin (-nen)

collect sammeln

collection die Sammlung (-en)

collision der Zusammenstoß (⁻sse)

colour die Farbe (-n); **colour blind** farbenblind; **colour film** der Farbfilm (-e)

colourful bunt

comb (*v.*) kämmen; (*n.*) der Kamm (⁻e); **comb one's hair** sich kämmen

come kommen*; **come from** (*a country/town*) stammen aus; **come with** (*us*) mitkommen*

comfortable bequem

compact disc die CD-Platte (-n)

comparison der Vergleich (-e); **in comparison to; compared with** im Vergleich zu

complain (*about*) sich beklagen (über + *acc.*); sich beschweren (über + *acc.*)

complete vollkommen; total;
  completely völlig
complicated kompliziert
comprehensive school die
  Gesamtschule (-n)
compulsory Pflicht-;
  compulsory subject (school)
  das Pflichtfach (¨er)
computer der Computer (-)
concert das Konzert (-e)
conductor (bus)
  der Schaffner (-)
congratulate gratulieren
congratulations die
  Glückwünsche (pl.)
  congratulations! herzlichen
  Glückwunsch!
connect verbinden*;
  connection die Verbindung
  (-en)
consider in Betracht ziehen*
consist (of) bestehen* (aus)
contain enthalten*
content zufrieden
continually andauernd
convenient praktisch
conversation das Gespräch (-e)
cook kochen
cooker das Herd (-e); der
  Kocher (-) (also camping)
cool kühl
copy (out; down) abschreiben*
corner die Ecke (-n)
correct korrigieren; (an error)
  verbessern
corridor der Gang (¨e)
cost kosten; **costs** die Unkosten
  (pl.)
cosy gemütlich
cotton die Baumwolle
cough husten
counter die Theke (-n); (in
  bank, post-office etc.) der Schalter
  (-)
country das Land (¨er); **in the
  country** auf dem Lande
countryside die Landschaft
course (policy; line) der Kurs
  (-e); (education) der Kursus (pl.
  Kurse); **of course** natürlich
court der Hof (¨e); (law) das
  Gericht (-e)
cousin der Vetter (-n); die
  Cousine (also die Kusine) (-n)

cover decken
cow die Kuh (¨e)
crash (vehicles) der
  Zusammenstoß (¨e)
cream die Sahne; **whipped
  cream** die Schlagsahne
crime novel/film der Krimi (-s)
crisp der Chip (-s)
cross (street; border) überqueren
  (insep.)
crossing (sea) die Überfahrt
  (-en)
crossroad(s) die Querstraße
  (-n)
crowd die Menge (-n)
cry schreien; (= weep) weinen
cup die Tasse (-n); (sports) der
  Pokal (-e)
cupboard der Schrank (¨e)
curious (about) neugierig (auf
  + acc.)
current der Strom (¨e)
curry der Curry
curtain die Gardine (-n); (also
  theatre) der Vorhang (¨e)
cushion das Kissen (-)
customs der Zoll; **customs
  inspection** die Zollkontrolle
cut schneiden*
cycle (v.) radfahren*; (n.) das
  Rad (¨er)
cyclist der Radfahrer (-)

dad der Vati (-s)
daily täglich
dairy die Molkerei (-en)
damaged beschädigt
damp feucht
dance tanzen
danger die Gefahr (-en)
dangerous gefährlich
Danube die Donau
dark dunkel; **dark red**
  dunkelrot
date das Datum (pl. Daten);
  (= appointment) die
  Verabredung (-en); **date of
  birth** das Geburtsdatum
daughter die Tochter (¨);
  daughter-in-law die
  Schwiegertocher (¨)
day der Tag (-e); **day off** der
  Ruhetag (-e); **good day** guten
  Tag

dead tot
deaf taub
dear teuer; (starting letter) lieb-
death der Tod
December der Dezember
decide beschließen*
decorate (Christmas tree etc.)
  schmücken; putzen
deep tief
definite(ly) bestimmt
degree der Grad (-e)
delicious (= tasty) lecker
deliver liefern; (newspapers)
  austragen*
dentist der Zahnarzt (¨e)
depart abfahren*; (plane)
  abfliegen*
department die Abteilung
  (-en); **department store** das
  Kaufhaus (¨er); das Warenhaus
  (¨er)
departure die Abfahrt; (plane)
  der Abflug; **departure lounge**
  das Warteraum (¨e)
depend on ankommen* auf
  (+ acc.); **it depends** es kommt
  darauf an; **it depends on him**
  es kommt auf ihn an
describe beschreiben*
description die Beschreibung (-en)
desire die Lust (¨e)
desk der Schreibtisch (-e);
  (school) das Pult (-e)
dessert der Nachtisch; die
  Nachspeise (-n)
destination das Ziel (-e)
detached house das
  Einzelhaus (¨er)
detective story der Krimi (-s)
detergent das Spülmittel (-)
dial (phone number) wählen;
die sterben*
difference der Unterschied
  (-e); **different** ander-;
  differently anders; **different
  from** anders als
difficult schwierig; schwer
difficulty die Schwierigkeit
  (-en)
dining room das Eßzimmer (-)
dinner (= evening meal) das
  Abendessen; (= midday meal)
  das Mittagessen; **have dinner**
  zu Abend/Mittag essen

direct(ly) direkt
direction die Richtung (-en)
director der Direktor (-en)
dirt der Schmutz
dirty schmutzig; (*more colloq.*) dreckig
disadvantage der Nachteil (-e)
disappear verschwinden*
disappointed enttäuscht
disco die Diskothek (-en)
discount der Rabatt (-e)
discover entdecken
discuss besprechen*
dishes das Geschirr
dishwasher die Spülmaschine (-n)
display die Aufstellung (en)
distance der Abstand (⁻e); **long distance call** das Ferngespräch (-e)
dive tauchen
diversion die Umleitung (-en)
divorced geschieden
dizzy schwindlig
do tun*; machen; **that won't do** das geht* nicht
doctor der Arzt (⁻e)/die Ärztin (-nen)
dog der Hund (-e)
doll die Puppe (-n)
door die Tür (-en)
double room das Doppelzimmer (-)
doubt der Zweifel
downstairs unten
draught der Luftzug (⁻e); **it's draughty** es zieht*
draw zeichnen
drawer die Schublade (-n)
drawn (*sports*) unentschieden
dreadful furchtbar; schrecklich
dream (*v.*) träumen; (*n.*) der Traum (⁻e)
dress (*v.*) (= *get dressed*) sich anziehen*; (*n.*) das Kleid (-er)
dressing table der Frisiertisch (-e)
drink (*v.*) trinken*; (*n.*) das Getränk (-e)
drive (*v.*) fahren*; (*n.*) (*of a house*) die Zufahrt (-en)
driver der Fahrer (-)
driving licence der Führerschein (-e)

drop (*v.*) fallen lassen*; (*n.*) der Tropfen (-)
drums das Schlagzeug (*sing.*)
drunk betrunken
dry (*adj.*) trocken; (*v.*) trocknen; (*dishes*) abtrocknen; **dry cleaning/dry cleaner's** die Reinigung
duck die Ente (-n)
dull (*weather*) trüb
dumb stumm
during während (+ *gen.*)
duster der Lappen (-)
Dutch holländisch
Dutchman der Holländer (-)
duty (*excise*) der Zoll (⁻e); **duty-free** zollfrei; **pay duty on** verzollen
duvet das Federbett (-en)

e.g. z.B. (zum Beispiel)
ear das Ohr (-en)
early früh
earn verdienen
earth die Erde
east (*adj.*) östlich; Ost-; (*n.*) der Osten
Easter (das) Ostern (*plural in greetings:* fröhliche Ostern)
easy leicht
eat (*of people*) essen*; (*of animals*) fressen*
effect (on) (= *impression*) der Eindruck (⁻e) (auf + *acc.*)
egg das Ei (-er); **fried egg** das Spiegelei (-er); **scrambled egg** das Rührei (-er)
elderly älter-
elect wählen
election die Wahl (-en)
electric elektrisch; Elecktro-
electricity die Elektrizität
elephant der Elefant (-en)
emergency Not-; **emergency exit** der Notausgang (⁻e)
employ anstellen
employed (= *in work*) berufstätig
employee der/die Angestellte (-n); der Arbeitnehmer (-)
employer der Arbeitgeber (-)
empty (*adj.*) leer; (*v.*) leeren
enclose (*in letter*) beilegen; **enclosed** anbei

end das Ende (-n)
energetic energisch
engaged verlobt
England (das) England
English englisch
Englishman/woman der/die Engländer(in) (-/-innen)
engine der Motor (-en)
engineer der Ingenieur (-e)
enjoy: I enjoyed it es hat mich gefreut
enormous riesig
enough genug; **be enough** genügen; **enough room** Platz genug
enquire about sich erkundigen nach
entertainment die Unterhaltung (-en)
enthusiastic begeistert
entrance der Eingang (⁻e) (*on foot*); die Einfahrt (-en) (*in vehicle*)
envelope der (Brief)umschlag (⁻e)
escalator die Rolltreppe (-n)
especially besonders
etc. usw.
Europe (das) Europa
even selbst; sogar; **even if** wenn auch; **not even** nicht mal
evening der Abend (-e); **evening meal** das Abendbrot; das Abendessen; **in the evening** abends; **good evening** guten Abend
ever immer; (*in questions*) je; **if ever** wenn . . . je
everyday life das Alltagsleben
everything alles
everywhere überall
exact(ly) genau
examine (*customs, doctor*) untersuchen (*insep.*); (= *test*) prüfen; **examination** die Prüfung (-en)
example das Beispiel (-e); **for example** zum Beispiel
excellent ausgezeichnet
except außer (+ *dat.*)
exchange (*v.*) (*goods, money*) umtauschen (*sep.*); (*n.*) der Umtausch; (*scholastic*) der Austausch

exciting spannend
excursion der Ausflug (¨e)
excuse entschuldigen; verzeihen*
exercise die Übung (-en); **exercise book** das Heft (-e)
exit (*theatre etc.*) der Ausgang (¨e); (*motorway*) die Ausfahrt (-en)
expect erwarten
expensive kostspielig; (= *valuable*) kostbar
explain erklären
express der D-Zug (¨e)
extra zusätzlich; **an extra ...** noch ein ...
extremely äußerst
eye das Auge (-n)

fabulous fabelhaft
face das Gesicht (-er)
fact die Tatsache (-n); **in fact** eigentlich
factory die Fabrik (-en)
fail (in) durchfallen (*sep.*) (bei)
fair das Jahrmarkt (¨e)
fairly ziemlich
faithfully: yours faithfully hochachtungsvoll
fall fallen*; **fall off** abfallen* von
family die Familie (-n)
famous berühmt
fan (*sport etc.*) der Fan (-s)
fanatic der Fanatiker (-)
far weit
fare der Fahrpreis (-e)
farm der Bauernhof (¨e)
farmer der Bauer (-n)
fashion die Mode (-n)
fat dick
father der Vater (¨); **Father Christmas** der Weihnachtsmann (¨er); **father-in-law** der Schwiegervater (¨)
faulty mangelhaft
favourable günstig
favourite Lieblings-; **favourite subject** das Lieblingsfach (¨er)
fear die Angst (¨e)
February der Februar
Federal Republic (*W. Germany*) die Bundesrepublik

feed (*people*) zu essen geben*; (*animals*) füttern
feel sich fühlen; **feel like (doing)** Lust haben* (etwas zu tun); **feeling** das Gefühl (-e)
female, feminine weiblich
fence der Zaun (¨e)
ferry die Fähre (-n)
fetch holen
fever das Fieber; **have a fever** Fieber haben*
few wenige; **a few** ein paar; einige
fiancé(e) der/die Verlobte (*a.n.*)
field das Feld (-er)
fill füllen; **fill in** (*form etc.*) ausfüllen; **fill (up)** (*car*) tanken
film der Film (-e)
final (*sport*) das Endspiel (-e)
finally (*after so long*) endlich; (*in the end*) schließlich
find finden*
fine die Geldstrafe (-n)
finger der Finger (-)
finished fertig
fire das Feuer (-)
fire-brigade die Feuerwehr (-en)
firm die Firma (*pl.* Firmen)
first erst-; **firstly** (*counting*) erstens; (= *at first*) zuerst; **for the first time** zum erstenmal
fish (*v.*) angeln; (*n.*) der Fisch (-e)
fishing rod die Angelrute (-n)
fit (*adj.*) (*healthy*) fit; (*v.*) passen (+ *dat.*); **keep fit** sich trimmen
fix reparieren
fizzy drink der Sprudel (-)
flat (*adj.*) flach; (*n.*) die Wohnung (-en)
flight der Flug (¨e)
floor der (Fuß)boden (¨); (*of block of flats*) die Etage (-n); der Stock (-); **on the third floor** im dritten Stock
flour das Mehl
flower die Blume (-n); **flower shop** das Blumengeschäft (-e)
flu die Grippe
fluent fließend
flute die Flöte (-n)
fly (*v.*) fliegen*; (*n.*) die Fliege (-n)
fog der Nebel (-)
foggy neblig

folding klappbar; **folding chair** der Klappstuhl (¨e)
follow folgen (+ *dat.*)
food (*for people*) das Essen; (*for animals*) das Futter
foot der Fuß (¨e); **on foot** zu Fuß
football der Fußball
forbidden verboten; **I am forbidden** mir ist verboten
foreign fremd; **foreign language** die Fremdsprache (-n)
foreigner der Ausländer (-)
forget vergessen*
fork die Gabel (-n)
form das Formular (-e)
forward: look forward to sich freuen auf (+ *acc.*); **forwards** vorwärts
France (das) Frankreich
frankfurter (*sausage*) die Bockwurst (¨e)
free frei; (= *gratis*) kostenlos; umsonst; **free time** die Freizeit
freeze frieren*; **freezer** die Tiefkühltruhe (-n)
French französisch
Frenchman der Franzose (-n)
Frenchwoman die Französin (-nen)
fresh frisch
Friday (der) Freitag
fridge der Kühlschrank (¨e)
friend der/die Freund(in) (-e/-nen)
friendly freundlich
front die Vorderseite (-n); **in front; at the front** vorne; **go in front** vorgehen*
frontier die Grenze (-n)
fruit das Obst (*no pl.*)
fry braten*; **frying pan** die Bratpfanne (-n)
full voll; (*with food*) satt; (= *complete*) ganz
fun das Vergnügen; **be fun** Spaß machen
funny komisch
furious entsetzt
furniture die Möbel (*pl.*)
furnished möbliert
further weiter
future die Zukunft

gale der Sturmwind (-e)

game das Spiel (-e); **play games** Sport treiben*

garage die Garage (-n)

garden der Garten (-); (*public*) die Anlage (-n) (*usually pl.*)

gas das Gas (-e)

gate das Tor (-e)

gateau die Torte (-n)

generosity die Großzügigkeit

generous großzügig

gentle leise

gentleman der Herr (-en)

genuine echt

geography die Erdkunde; die Geographie

German (*adj.*) deutsch; (*n.*) der Deutsche (*a.n.*); **German Democratic Republic** (*East Germany*) die Deutsche Demokratische Republik

Germany (das) Deutschland

get bekommen*; (*more colloquial*) kriegen; **get back** (= *have returned*) zurückbekommen*; **get in; get on** (*vehicle*) einsteigen*; **get out; get off** (*vehicle*) ausstiegen*; **get up** aufstehen*

girl das Mädchen (-)

give geben*; (*as a present*) schenken; **give up** aufgeben*

glad froh; **be glad (about)** sich freuen (über + *acc.*)

gladly gern

glass das Glas (-er); **glasses** (= *spectacles*) die Brille (-n)

glove der Handschuh (-e)

go (*on foot*) gehen*; (*in vehicle*) fahren*; **go back** zurückfahren*; **go out** ausgehen*

god der Gott (-er)

gold (*n.*) das Gold; (*adj.*) golden

goldfish der Goldfisch (-e)

gone (= *finished*) alle

good gut; **good-tempered** gut gelaunt

goods die Waren (*sing.* die Ware)

goodbye! auf Wiedersehen!; **say goodbye** sich verabschieden

gossip plaudern

grab zupacken

gradually allmählich

gram das Gramm (-)

grammar school das Gymnasium (-sien)

grandad der Opa (-s)

granddaughter die Enkelin (-nen)

grandfather der Großvater (-)

grandma die Oma (-s)

grandmother die Großmutter (-)

grandparents die Großeltern

grandson der Enkel (-)

grape die Traube (-n)

grass das Gras (-er)

grateful dankbar

gravy die Soße

great (*colloq.*) toll; prima (*invar.*)

green grün

greengrocer's die Gemüsehandlung (-en)

greeting der Gruß (-e)

grey grau

grill grillen

groceries die Lebensmittel (*pl.*)

grocer's das Lebensmittelgeschäft (-e)

ground die Erde; (*sports*) der (Sport)platz (-e); **ground floor** das Erdgeschoß

group die Gruppe (-n)

grow wachsen*

guest der Gast (-e); **guest house** die Pension (-en)

guide (= *girl guide*) die Pfadfinderin (-nen)

guitar die Gitarre (-n)

gym(nastics) das Turnen; **do gymnastics** turnen

gymnasium die Turnhalle (-n)

hail (*v.*) hageln; (*n.*) der Hagel

hair das Haar (-e) (*pl.* often used for 'hair'); **colour of one's hair** die Haarfarbe (-n)

hairbrush die Haarbürste (-n)

hairdresser der Friseur (-e); die Friseuse (-n)

half (*adj.*) halb; (*n.*) die Hälfte (-n); **half board** die Halbpension

hall (*school*) die Aula (*pl.* Aulen); (*house*) der Flur (-e); (*concert, etc.*) der Saal (*pl.* Säle)

hamburger der Hamburger (-)

hamster der Hamster (-)

hand die Hand (-e); **hand in** einreichen

handbag die Handtasche (-n)

handicapped körperbehindert

handkerchief das Taschentuch (-er)

handwriting die Schrift

hangover der Kater (-)

happen geschehen*; passieren

happy froh; glücklich

harbour der Hafen (-)

hard hart; (*difficult*) schwer; (*as work*) anstrengend

hardly kaum

hardworking fleißig

hat der Hut (-e)

have haben*; **have to** müssen*; **I had to do it** ich habe es tun müssen

head der Kopf (-e); **headache** das Kopfweh; **headlight** der Scheinwerfer (-)

healthy gesund

hear hören

heart das Herz (-en)

heat die Hitze

heating die Heizung

heaven der Himmel

heavy schwer; (*weather*) schwül

hedge die Hecke (-n)

helicopter der Hubschrauber (-)

hello! hallo!; **say hello to** grüßen

help (*v.*) helfen* (+ *dat.*); (*n.*) die Hilfe; **help oneself** sich bedienen; **helpful** hilfreich

hen das Huhn (-er)

here hier

hide verbergen*

hifi die HiFi-Anlage (-n)

high hoch; **high jump** der Hochsprung

hike (*v.*) wandern; (*n.*) die Wanderung (-en)

hill der Hügel (-)

hips die Hüften (*pl.*)

hire mieten; **hire out** vermieten

history die Geschichte (-n)

hit (*v.*) schlagen*; (*a target*) treffen*; (*n.*) (*song*) der Schlager (-); **hit parade** die Hitparade

hitch(-hike) trampen; per Anhalter fahren*; **hitch-hiker** der/die Anhalter(in) (-/-nen)

hobby das Hobby (-s)

hold halten*; **get hold of** (= *obtain*) besorgen; **hold up** (= *detain*) festhalten*

hole das Loch (¨er)

holiday (*one day*) der Feiertag (-e); (= *holidays*) die Ferien (*pl.*); **on holiday** auf/in Urlaub

Holland (das) Holland

home (*adv.*) nach House; **at home** zu Hause

homeland das Heimatland; die Heimat

homesick: be homesick Heimweh haben*

homework (*one piece of homework*) die Hausaufgabe (-n)

honest ehrlich

honey der Honig

hope hoffen; **it is to be hoped that** hoffentlich

horror film der Horrorfilm (-e)

hors-d'œuvre die Vorspeise (-n)

horse das Pferd (-e)

hospital das Krankenhaus (¨er)

host der Gastgeber (-)

hot heiß; **I'm hot** mir ist heiß

hotel das Hotel (-s)

hour die Stunde (-n)

house das Haus (¨er)

  household der Haushalt (-e)
  housewife die Hausfrau (-en)
  housework die Hausarbeit

how wie

human being der Mensch (-en)

hunger der Hunger

hungry hungrig; **I'm hungry** ich habe Hunger

hurry sich beeilen; **be in a hurry** es eilig haben*

hurt (*adj.*) verletzt; (*v.*) weh tun* (+ *dat.*); schmerzen (+ *acc.*)

husband der (Ehe)mann (¨er)

hut die Hütte (-n)

i.e. d.h. (das heißt)

ice das Eis (-)

idea die Idee (-n); die Ahnung (-en) (*esp. in* keine Ahnung, *no idea*)

ideal ideal

identity card der Ausweis (-e)

ill krank; **I feel ill** mir ist übel

imagine sich (*dat.*) vorstellen

immediately (so)gleich; sofort

impatient ungeduldig

important wichtig

imposition (*school*) die Strafarbeit (-en)

impossible unmöglich

impressed by beeindruckt von

impression (*on*) der Eindruck (¨e) (auf + *acc.*)

improve verbessern

included inbegriffen

including einschließlich; inklusive

independent unabhängig; (= *self-supporting*) selbständig

indicate angeben*

industry die Industrie (-n)

industrial town die Industriestadt (¨e)

inform (*someone*) Bescheid sagen (+ *dat.*)

information die Auskunft

inhabitant der Einwohner (-)

injection die Spritze (-n)

injured verwundet

inquisitive neugierig

insect das Insekt (-en)

insist (on) bestehen* (auf + *dat.*)

instead of statt (+ *gen.*)

instrument das Instrument (-e)

insurance die Versicherung (-en)

intelligent intelligent

intend vorhaben*

interest (*v.*) interessieren; (*n.*) das Interesse; **be interested in** sich interessieren für; **interested in** interessiert an (+ *acc.*); **interesting** interessant

introduce (to) bekannt machen (mit); **introduce oneself** sich vorstellen

invite einladen*

invitation die Einladung (-en)

involved (in) verwickelt (in + *acc.*); (= *concerned with*) beteiligt (an + *dat.*)

Ireland (das) Irland

Irish irisch

Irishman der Ire (-n)

Irishwoman die Irin (-nen)

iron bügeln

island die Insel (-n)

Italy (das) Italien

Italian (*adj.*) italienisch; (*n.*) der Italiener (-)

jacket die Jacke (-n)

jam die Marmelade (-n)

January der Januar

jeans die Jeans (*pl.*)

jewellery der Schmuck

job (= *task*) die Aufgabe (-n); (= *position*) der Job (-s); die Stelle (-n); (= *profession*) der Beruf (-e); **job centre** das Arbeitsamt; **what's her job?** was ist sie von Beruf?

jog joggen

jogging das Jogging

journey die Fahrt (-en); die Reise (-n)

jug der Krug (¨e)

juice der Saft (¨e)

July der Juli

jump springen*

junction (*roads*) die Kreuzung (-en)

June der Juni

just gerade; **just after** kurz nach; **just as** (= *equally*) genauso; **not just** nicht bloß

keep behalten*

key der Schlüssel (-); (*on keyboard*) die Taste (-n)

kilo das Kilo (-)

kilometre der Kilometer (-)

kind (*n.*) die Sorte (-n); die Art (-en); (*adj.*) freundlich; **of all kinds** jeder Art

kiosk der Kiosk (-e)

kitchen die Küche (-n)

knee das Knie (-)

knife das Messer (-)

knit stricken

knock klopfen; **knock down** (*accident*) überfahren* (*insep.*)

know (*a person, a place*) kennen*; (*a fact*) wissen*; **get to know** kennenlernen

laboratory das Labor (-s)
lady die Dame (-n)
lake der See (-n)
lamp die Lampe (-n)
land landen
landscape die Landschaft (-en)
language die Sprache (-n)
large groß
last (*adj.*) letzt; (*previous*) vorige; (*v.*) dauern
late (*time*) spät; (*person, vehicle*) verspätet; **be late** Verspätung haben*
Latin (das) Latein
laugh lachen
lawn der Rasen (-)
lay legen; (*table*) decken
lazy faul
lead führen
leaf das Blatt (ˇer)
leaflet die Broschüre (-n)
lean mager
learn lernen; (= *come to hear of*) erfahren*
least: at least mindestens
leather das Leder
leave (*trans.*) lassen*; (= *quit*) verlassen*; (*something in error*) liegen lassen*; (*intrans.*) gehen*; (*of vehicle*) abfahren*; **leave on** (*light; clothing*) anlassen*
left link-; (*left over*) übrig; **on the left** links; **to the left of** links von
left-luggage office die Gepäckaufbewahrung
leg das Bein (-e)
leisure die Freizeit; **leisure occupation** die Freizeitsbeschäftigung (-en)
lemon die Zitrone (-n)
lend leihen*
length die Länge (-n)
less weniger
let lassen*; (*house*) vermieten
letter der Brief (-e); **letter box** der Briefkasten (ˇ)
lettuce der (Kopf)salat
library die Bibliothek (-en)
lie liegen*; **lie down** sich hinlegen
life das Leben (-)
lift der Aufzug (ˇe);

der Fahrstuhl (ˇe) (*people only*); (*esp. skiing*) die Lift (-s)
light (*v.*) anzünden; (*n.*) das Licht (-er); (*adj.*) (*of colours*) hell; **red light** das Rotlicht (-er)
lighten (*weather*) blitzen
lighter das Feuerzeug (-e)
lightning der Blitz (-e)
like:
  I don't like that das mag ich nicht
  I like him ich habe ihn gern
  I like chocolate ich esse gern Schokolade
  I like dancing ich tanze gern
  I should like ich hätte gern; ich möchte
line die Linie (-n)
lion der Löwe (-n)
list die Liste (-n)
listen zuhören; **listen to** hören (auf + *acc.*)
little (= *not much*) wenig; (= *not big*) klein; **a little** ein wenig
litre der Liter (-)
live leben; (*in a particular place*) wohnen; **living room** das Wohnzimmer (-)
local Orts-; **local call** das Ortsgespräch (-e); **local train** der Personenzug (ˇe)
lock (*v.*) verschließen*; (*n.*) das Schloß (ˇsser); **lock (up)** abschließen*
locker das Schließfach (ˇer)
loft der Dachboden (ˇ)
long lang; **for a long time** lange; **no longer** nicht mehr
look (*v.*) sehen*; (*with care*) schauen; (= *appear*) aussehen*; (*n.*) der Blick (-e)
  have a look gucken
  look (like) aussehen* (wie)
  look at ansehen*; sehen* auf (+ *acc.*)
  look for suchen;
  look forward to sich freuen auf (+ *acc.*)
  look up (*in dictionary etc.*) nachsehen*
loose locker
lorry der Lastkraftwagen (-) (*often abbreviated*: der Lkw)

lose verlieren*
  get lost sich verirren; (*driving*) sich verfahren*
  lost property office das Fundbüro (-s)
lot: a lot eine Menge (*colloq.*)
loud laut; **loudspeaker** der Lautsprecher (-)
love lieben
low niedrig
lucky glücklich; **be lucky/ unlucky** Glück/Pech haben*; **bad luck!** Pech!
luggage das Gepäck
lunch das Mittagessen; **have lunch** zu Mittag essen*; **lunch hour** die Mittagspause (-n)

machine die Maschine (-n)
mad toll; **mad about** begiestert von
magazine die Zeitschrift (-en); (*illustrated*) die Illustrierte (-n)
main Haupt-; **main-line station** der Hauptbahnhof (ˇe); **main road** die Hauptstraße (-n)
make machen; **make it easily** es leicht schaffen
male männlich
man der Mann (ˇer); (= *human being*) der Mensch (-en); **man's/men's** Männer-
many viele; **as many as you like** soviel Sie wollen*
map die (Land)karte (-n)
March der März
margarine die Margarine
mark (*in school*) die Note (-n)
market der Markt (ˇe); **market place** der Marktplatz (ˇe)
marmalade die Orangenmarmelade
marry (*intrans.*) heiraten; (*trans.*) heiraten; sich verheiraten mit; (*as priest*) verheiraten; **married** verheiratet
marvellous herrlich
masculine männlich
mass (*religion*) die Messe (-n); **midnight mass** die Mitternachtsmesse

match (*v.*) passen zu; (*n.*) das Streichholz (¨er)

material der Stoff (-e)

mathematics die Mathematik (*sing.*); **maths** die Mathe

matter (= *business*) die Sache (-n); **it doesn't matter** es macht nichts (aus); **what's the matter?** was ist los?

May der Mai

may mögen*; (= *be allowed*) dürfen*; **may I ...?** darf ich ...?; **that may be** das mag sein

meadow die Wiese (-n)

meal die Mahlzeit (-en)

mean (*have as meaning*) bedeuten; (*hold opinion*) meinen; **what do you mean?** wieso?

meat das Fleisch; **cold meat(s)** der Aufschnitt

mechanic der Mechaniker (-)

medicine die Medizin (*also the science*); die Arznei (-en)

Mediterranean das Mittelmeer

medium(-sized) mittelgroß

meet (*by appointment*) treffen*; (*one another*) sich treffen*; (*accidentally*) begegnen (+ *dat.*); (= *collect*) abholen; **meeting place** der Treffpunkt (-e)

member das Mitglied (-er)

mention: don't mention it nichts zu danken

menu die (Speise)karte (-n)

mess das Durcheinander

metre der Meter (-)

microwave cooker der Mikrowellenherd (-e)

middle die Mitte (-n); **in the middle of** mitten in

midnight (die) Mitternacht

mild mild

mile die Meile (-n)

milk (*n.*) die Milch; (*v.*) melken*

mince pie die Mincepastete (-n)

mind: change one's mind about something sich (*dat.*) etwas anders überlegen (*insep.*); **she doesn't mind** ihr macht es nichts aus

mineral water das Mineralwasser

minute die Minute (-n)

mirror der Spiegel (-)

Miss Frau; (*very young*) Fräulein

miss (*e.g. train*) verpassen; **be missing** fehlen

mistake der Fehler (-)

misunderstanding das Mißverständnis (-se)

mix mischen

modern modern

moment der Moment (-e); der Augenblick (-e); **at the moment** zur Zeit

Monday (der) Montag

monkey der Affe (-n)

month der Monat (-e); **monthly** monatlich

moon der Mond (-e)

more mehr; (= *some more*) noch etwas

morning der Morgen; der Vormittag; **good morning** guten Morgen; **in the morning** morgens; vormittags

Moselle die Mosel

mosque die Moschee (-n)

most meist-; **at the most** höchstens; **mostly** vorwiegend; (= *most frequently*) meistens

mother die Mutter (¨); (*familiar*) (die) Mutti; **mother-in-law** die Schwiegermutter (¨)

motion die Bewegung; **in motion** in Bewegung

motorcycle das Motorrad (¨er)

motorcyclist der Motorradfahrer (-)

motorway die Autobahn (-en)

mouse die Maus (¨e)

moustache der Schnurrbart (¨e)

mouth der Mund (¨er)

mountain der Berg (-e) **mountain walk** die Bergwanderung (-en) **mountains** (= *mountain region*) das Gebirge

mountaineering das Bergsteigen

mountainous bergig

move (*trans.*) bewegen; (*intrans.*) sich bewegen

Mrs; Ms Frau

much viel; **how much** wieviel

muesli das Müsli

multistorey building das Hochhaus (¨er)

museum das Museum (*pl.* Museen)

mushroom der Champignon (-s)

music die Musik; (= *sheet music*) die Noten (*pl.*)

must müssen*; **I must have done it** ich muß es getan haben

mustard der Senf (-e)

name (*v.*) nennen*; (*n.*) der Name (-n)

narrow (*as e.g. face*) schmal; (= *constricted*) eng

nationality die Staatsangehörigkeit (-en)

naturally natürlich

nature die Natur

near in der Nähe von; **near by** in der Nähe; **nearest** (*adj.*) nächst

necessary nötig

neck der Hals (¨e)

need brauchen

needle die Nadel (-n)

neighbour der Nachbar (-n)

neighbourhood die Gegend (-en)

neither ... nor weder ... noch

nephew der Neffe (-n)

nervous nervös

net das Netz (-e)

never nie

new neu; **New Year** das Neujahr; **New Year's Eve** (das) Silvester

news die Nachrichten (*pl.*); **piece of news** die Nachricht (-en)

newspaper die Zeitung (-en)

next nächst; **next door** nebenan; **people next door** die Nachbarn (*pl.*)

nice nett; schön; niedlich

niece die Nichte (-n)

night die Nacht (¨e); **at night** nachts; **good night** gute Nacht;

spend the night übernachten (*insep.*)

nil (*in scores*) null

nobody niemand

noise der Lärm

none the less trotzdem

non-smoker der Nichtraucher (-)

noon der Mittag

normal normal; **normally** normalerweise

north (*adj.*) nördlich; Nord-; (*n.*) der Norden; **North Sea** die Nordsee

nose die Nase (-n)

note die Note (-n); (*banknote*) der Schein (-e); **notebook** das Heft (-e)

nothing nichts; **nothing but** nichts als

notice bemerken

novel der Roman (-e)

November der November

now jetzt; nun

number die Nummer (-n)

nurse die Krankenschwester (-n)

nut die Nuß (¨sse)

obtain besorgen

occupation der Beruf (-e)

occupied besetzt

October der Oktober

offer bieten*; anbieten*

office das Büro (-s)

official der Beamte (*a.n.*)

often oft

oil das Öl (-e)

O.K. in Ordnung

old alt

omelette das Omelett (-s)

once einmal; **once again** noch einmal

one and a half anderthalb

one-way street die Einbahnstraße (-n)

onion die Zwiebel (-n)

only (*adj.*) einzig; (*adv.*) nur; (*with time*) erst; (*conj.*) allein; **not only ... but also** nich nur ... sondern auch

open (*v.*) öffnen; aufmachen; (*adj.*) offen; geöffnet; **in the open air** im Freien; **opening times** die Öffnungszeiten (*pl.*)

opinion die Meinung (-en)

opposite (*prep.*) gegenüber; (*n.*) das Gegenteil

oral mündlich

orange die Orange (-n); die Apfelsine (-n); **orange juice** der Orangensaft

orchester das Orchester (-)

order (*v.*) bestellen; (*n.*) die Ordnung (-en); **in order** in Ordnung; **out of order** außer Betrieb

organize organisieren

other ander-

otherwise sonst

ought: you oughtn't to have done that das hättest du nicht tun sollen

outside draußen

oval oval

oven der Ofen (¨)

over there drüben

overcast bewölkt

overcharge überfordern (*insep.*); (einem) zuviel berechnen

overtake überholen (*insep.*)

overturn umwerfen* (*sep.*)

own (*v.*) besitzen*; (*adj.*) eigen

pack (up) einpacken

packet das Päckchen (-); (*larger*) das Paket (-e)

page die Seite (-n)

paint streichen*; (*as artist*) malen

pair das Paar (-e)

pale blaß

pan (*saucepan*) der (Koch)topf (¨e); (*frying pan*) die Bratpfanne (-n)

paper das Papier (-e); **paperback** das Taschenbuch (¨er); **paper handkerchief** das Papiertaschentuch (¨er); **slip of paper** der Zettel (-)

parcel das Paket (-e)

pardon? wie bitte?

parents die Eltern

park (*v.*) parken; (*n.*) der Park (-s); **parking meter** die Parkuhr (-en)

part der Teil (-e)

party die Party (-s); **go to a party** auf eine Party gehen*

pass vorbeigehen* an (+ *dat.*); (*pass something over*) reichen; (*exam etc.*) bestehen* in (+ *dat.*)

passenger der Fahrgast (¨e); der Passagier (-e)

passport der Paß (¨sse)

past an (+ *dat.*) ... vorbei

path der Weg (-e)

patient (*adj.*) geduldig; (*n.*) der/die Patient(in) (-e/-nen)

pause die Pause (-n)

pavement der Bürgersteig (-e)

pay (*v.*) (*intrans.*) zahlen; (*trans.*) bezahlen; (*n.*) das Gehalt (¨er)

pea die Erbse (-n)

peach der Pfirsich (-e)

pear die Birne (-n)

pedestrian der Fußgänger (-); **pedestrian zone** die Fußgängerzone (-n)

peel (*v.*) schälen; (*n.*) die Schale

pencil der Bleistift (-e)

pen-friend der/die Brieffreund(in) (-e/-nen)

pensioner der Rentner (-)

people die Leute (*pl.*)

pepper der Pfeffer

per pro

perfect(ly) vollkommen

performance die Leistung (-en); (*theatre etc.*) die Vorstellung (-en)

perhaps vielleicht

person die Person (-en)

personal persönlich

pet (*animal*) das Haustier (-e)

petrol das Benzin; **petrol station** die Tankstelle (-n)

phone (*v.*) anrufen*; telefonieren; (*n.*) das Telefon (-e)

photo(graph) (*v.*) fotografieren; (*n.*) das Foto (-s); die Aufnahme (-n); **take a photo** eine Aufnahme machen

physics die Physik (*sing.*)

piano das Klavier (-e)

pickpocket der Taschendieb (-e)

picnic das Picknick (-s)

picture das Bild (-er); **picture postcard** die Ansichtskarte (-n)

piece das Stück (-e)

pig das Schwein (-e)

pill die Pille (-n)

pillow das (Kopf)kissen (-)
pink rosa (*invar.*); rosarot
pitch (*tent*) aufbauen
pity: what a pity! wie schade!
place der Ort (-e); (*smaller*) der
Platz (¨e); **place of birth** der
Geburtsort; **take place**
stattfinden*
plan (*v.*) planen; (*be planning*)
vorhaben*; (*n.*) der Plan (¨e)
plane das Flugzeug (-e)
plant die Pflanze (-n)
plaster das Pflaster (-)
plastic (*n.*) der Kunststoff (-e);
das Plastik (-s); (*adj.*) Plastik-
plate der Teller (-)
platform der Bahnsteig (-e)
play (*v.*) spielen; (*n.*) das
Schauspiel (-e); das Stück (-e);
play games Sport treiben*
playground der (Schul)hof (¨e)
pleasant angenehm
please bitte; (*v.*) gefallen* (+ *dat.*)
pleased froh; erfreut;
(= *content*) zufrieden; **I'm
pleased (that)** es freut mich
(, daß)
pleasure das Vergnügen
plug (*electrical*) der Stecker (-)
plum die Pflaume (-n)
pocket die Tasche (-n); **pocket
money** das Taschengeld
poem das Gedicht (-e)
point der Punkt (-e); **pointed**
spitz
police (*n.*) die Polizei; (*adj.*)
polizeilich; **police station** die
Polizeiwache (-n); **policeman**
der Polizist (-en)
polite höflich
Polytechnic (=) Technische
Hochschule (-n)
poor arm
pop (*music*) die Popmusik
popular beliebt
pork das Schweinefleisch
port der Hafen (¨)
portable tragbar
portion die Portion (-en)
position die Stelle (-n)
possess besitzen*
possible möglich; **possibility**
die Möglichkeit (-en)
post (*v.*) aufgeben*; (*n.*) die Post

post office das Postamt (¨er)
postcard die Postkarte (-n)
postcode die Postleitzahl (-en)
postman der Briefträger (-)
poster das Poster (-s)
postpone verschieben*
pot der Topf (¨e); (*of jam*) das
Glas (¨er)
potato die Kartoffel (-n)
boiled potatoes die
Salzkartoffeln; **mashed
potatoes** der Kartoffelbrei
potato salad der Kartoffelsalat
pound das Pfund
pour out einschenken
powder das Pulver (-)
practical praktisch
practise üben
praise loben
pram der Kinderwagen (-)
prefer vorziehen*; (*something*)
etwas am liebsten haben*; (*to do
something*) am liebsten tun*
preparation die Vorbereitung (-en)
prepare vorbereiten; **be
prepared** (*to do something*)
bereit sein* (etwas zu tun)
prescription (*medical*) das
Rezept (-e)
present (*n.*) das Geschenk (-e);
(*adj.*) jetzig
press drücken
pretty hübsch
price der Preis (-e)
primary school die
Grundschule (-n)
priority (*right-of-way*) die
Vorfahrt
private privat
prize der Preis (-e)
probable, probably
wahrscheinlich
problem das Problem (-e)
production (*theatre*) die
Aufführung (-en)
profession der Beruf (-e); **she
is ... by profession** sie is ...
von Beruf
programme das Programm (-e)
promise versprechen*
pronounce aussprechen*
protect schützen
Protestant evangelisch;
protestantisch

proud of stolz auf (+ *acc.*)
pub das Gasthaus (¨er); das
Wirtshaus (¨er); die Gaststätte
(-n); (*more colloq.*) die Kneipe
(-n)
public öffentlich
pudding der Nachtisch; die
Nachspeise (-n)
pull ziehen*
pullover der Pullover (-); (*more
colloq.*) der Pulli (-s)
punctual pünktlich
puncture die Reifenpanne (-n)
punish bestrafen;
punishment die Strafe (-n)
pupil der Schüler (-)
purse das Portemonnaie (-s);
die Geldtasche (-n)
push schieben*
put (*in a lying position*) legen; (*in
a standing position*) stellen; (*put
into*) stecken
put down abstellen
put in (*money in machine*)
einwerfen*
put on anziehen*
put out (*light*) ausmachen;
(*fire*) löschen
put up aufbauen

quality die Qualität (-en)
quarter das Viertel (-); **quarter
of an hour** die Viertelstunde
queue (*v.*) anstehen*; (*n.*) die
Schlange (-n)
quick schnell
quiet (*adj.*) ruhig; still; (*n.*) die
Ruhe
quilt die Steppdecke (-n)
quite ganz

rabbit das Kaninchen (-)
radiator der Heizkörper (-)
radio das Radio (-s);
(= *broadcasting*) der Rundfunk
rain (*v.*) regnen; (*n.*) der Regen;
raincoat der Regenmantel (¨)
rainy regnerisch
raspberry die Himbeere (-n)
rather ziemlich
razor der Rasierapparat (-e);
der Raisierer (-)
reach erreichen
read lesen*

ready fertig
real echt
really wirklich
realize begreifen*
receipt die Quittung (-en)
receive erhalten*; bekommen*
receiver (*phone*) der Hörer
recently neulich
reception der Empfang; (*desk*) die Anmeldung
recipe das Rezept (-e)
reckon rechnen
recognize erkennen*
recommend empfehlen*
record die (Schall)platte (-n); **long-playing record** die Langspielplatte (-n); **record player** der Plattenspieler (-)
recorder (*instrument*) die Blockflöte (-n)
recording die Aufnahme (-n)
recover sich erholen
red rot; **red wine** der Rotwein (-e)
reduction die Ermäßigung (-en)
refreshment die Erfrischung (-en)
refrigerator der Kühlschrank (-e)
refuse ablehnen
region das Gebiet (-e)
register sich anmelden
relation der/die Verwandte (*a.n.*)
reliable zuverlässig
religion die Religion (-en)
remain bleiben*
remember sich erinnern an (+ *acc.*)
renew erneuern
rent mieten
repair (*v.*) reparieren; (*n.*) die Reparatur (-en)
repeat wiederholen (*insep.*)
replace ersetzen
reply (*to*) antworten (auf + *acc.*)
report (*v.*) melden; (*n.*) die Meldung (-en); (*school*) das Zeugnis (-se)
reservation (*train*) die Platzkarte (-n)
reserve reservieren

rest (*v.*) sich ausruhen; (*n.*) die Ruhe; (= *a rest*) die (Ruhe)pause (-n); (= *what's left*) der Rest (-e)
restaurant das Restaurant (-s); die Gaststätte (-n); **restaurant car** der Spiesewagen (-)
result das Ergebnis (-se)
return die Rückkehr (*a person*); die Rückgabe (*of a thing*); (*ticket*) die Rückfahrkarte (-n)
Rhine der Rhein
rice der Reis
rich reich
ride (*horse*) reiten*
right richtig; **be right** Recht haben*; **on the right** rechts; **that's right** das stimmt; **to the right of** rechts von
ring (*v.*) (*bell*) läuten; (*electric bell; phone*) klingeln; (= *ring up*) anrufen*; (*n.*) der Ring (-e); **ring back** zurückrufen
river der Fluß (-sse)
road die Straße (-n); **road sign** das Verkehrsschild (-er)
roast braten*; **roast potatoes** die Bratkartoffeln
roll (*bread*) das Brötchen (-)
roller skate der Rollschuh (-e)
roof das Dach (-er)
room das Zimmer; (= *space*) der Platz
rough roh; (*sea*) stürmisch
round rund
row die Reihe (-n); (*in cinema etc.*) der Rang (-e)
row (*v.*) rudern; **rowboat** das Ruderboot (-e)
rub reiben*
rubber das Gummi; (= *eraser*) das Radiergummi (-s)
rubbish der Abfall (-e) (*usually pl.*); (*interj.*) Quatsch!; **rubbish bin** der Mülleimer (-)
rucksack der Rucksack (-e)
rude unhöflich
rule die Regel (-n)
ruler das Lineal (-e)
run laufen*; (*faster*) rennen*; (*train*) verkehren; (*road*) verlaufen*; **run over** (*accident*) überfahren* (*insep.*)

runner der Läufer (-)
rush stürzen

sad traurig
safety belt der Sicherheitsgurt (-e)
sail segeln; **sailing boat** das Segelboot (-e)
salad der Salat (-e)
sale der Ausverkauf
salesman der Verkäufer (-)
salt das Salz (-e)
same gleich; **it's all the same to me** es ist mir egal; **the same to you** gleichfalls (*not rude!*)
sand der Sand
sandal der Sandale (-n)
sandwich das belegte Brot (-e)
satchel die Schultasche (-n)
satisfied (*by food*) satt
Saturday (*N. Germany*) (der) Sonnabend; (*elsewhere*) (der) Samstag
sauce die Soße (-n)
saucer die Untertasse (-n)
sausage die Wurst (-e)
save (*money*) sparen; (= *rescue*) retten; (= *keep free*) freihalten*; **savings bank** die Sparkasse (-n)
say sagen; **say 'du' to** duzen; **say 'Sie' to** siezen
scarf der Schal (-s)
school die Schule (-n)
scooter der Roller (-)
Scot der Schotte (-n); die Schottin (-nen)
Scotland (das) Schottland
Scottish schottisch
scout der Pfadfinder (-)
sea das Meer (-e); die See; **seasick** seekrank
season die Jahreszeit (-en)
seat der Platz (-e); **take a seat** Platz nehmen*
second (*n.*) die Sekunde (-n)
secretary der/die Sekretär(in) (-e/-nen)
see sehen*; **see again** wiedersehen* (*sep.*); **thing worth seeing** die Sehenswürdigkeit (-en); **worth seeing** sehenswert
seem scheinen*
seldom selten
self-service die Selbstbedienung

sell verkaufen

semi(-detached house) das Doppelhaus (¨er)

send schicken*; (*letters etc.,* = *dispatch*) senden; **send on** nachschicken; **sender** (*of e.g. letter*) der Absender (-)

separate getrennt; **separately** (*post*) mit getrennter Post

September der September

serious ernst

serve dienen (+ *dat.*); bedienen

service (*military etc.*) der Dienst (-e); (*in restaurant*) die Bedienung; (*church*) der Gottesdienst (-e); **service area** (*motorway etc.*) die Raststätte (-n); **service station** die Reparaturwerkstatt (¨en)

set (*TV etc.*) das Gerät (-e)

set off abfahren*

several mehrere; **several times** mehrmals

sew nähen

sex das Geschlecht (-er)

shadow der Schatten (-)

shame: what a shame! wie schade!

shampoo das Shampoo

share das Teil (-e)

sharp scharf

shave sich rasieren

sheep das Schaf (-e)

sheet das Bettuch (¨er)

shell (*eggs; nuts*) die Schale (-n)

shine scheinen*

ship das Schiff (-e)

shirt das Hemd (-en)

shoe der Schuh (-e)

shoot schießen*

shop (*v.*) einkaufen; (*n.*) der Laden (¨); das Geschäft (-e); die Handlung (-en); **shop window** das Schaufenster (-)

shopping die Einkäufe (*pl.*); **shopping basket** der Einkaufskorb (¨e); **shopping expedition** der Einkaufsbummel (-); **shopping trolley** der Einkaufswagen (-)

short kurz

shoulder die Schulter (-n)

show zeigen

shower (*v.*) sich duschen; (*n.*) die Dusche (-n); (*of rain*) der Schauer (-)

shut (*v.*) schließen*; zumachen; (*adj.*) geschlossen; zu

sick krank; **I feel sick** (= *queasy*) mir ist übel; **be sick** (= *vomit*) sich übergeben* (*insep.*)

side die Seite (-n); **side street/ road** die Seitenstraße (-n)

sights (*of a town etc.*) die Sehenswürdigkeiten (*f. pl.*)

sign (*v.*) unterschreiben* (*insep.*); (*n.*) (= *signboard*) das Schild (-er) (*also road sign*); **signature** die Unterschrift (-en)

signpost der Wegweiser (-)

silent still; (*without words*) stumm

silk die Seide

silly blöd(e); (= *daft*) doof

silver (*n.*) das Silber; (*adj.*) silbern

similar ähnlich

since (*time*) seit (*prep.*); seitdem (*conj.*); (*because*) da; denn

sing singen*; **singer** der Sänger (-)

single (*adj.*) einzeln; (= *unmarried*) ledig; (*n.*) (*record*) die Single (-s); **single bed** das Einzelbett (-en); **single room** das Einzelzimmer (-)

sink das Spülbecken (-)

simple einfach

sister die Schwester (-n); **sister-in-law** die Schwägerin (-nen)

sit (= *be sitting*) sitzen*; **sit down** sich (hin)setzen

situated gelegen; **be situated** sich befinden*; **nicely situated** schön gelegen

situation die Lage (-n)

size die Größe (-n)

skate (*n.*) der Schlittschuh (-e); (*v.*) Schlittschuh laufen*

ski (*v.*) skifahren*; skilaufen*; (*n.*) der Ski (-er)

skirt der Rock (¨e)

sky der Himmel

sleep schlafen*; **sleeper**

(*railway*) der Schlafwagen (-); **sleeping bag** der Schlafsack (¨e)

sleeve der Ärmel (-)

slice die Scheibe (-n)

slide (= *transparency*) das Dia (-s)

slim schlank

slipper der Pantoffel (-n)

slow langsam; **the clock is slow** die Uhr geht* nach

small klein

smell (of) riechen (nach)

smile lächeln

smoke rauchen; **smoker** der Raucher (-); **smoking** das Rauchen

snack der Imbiß (-sse); **snack bar** die Imbißstube (-n)

snake die Schlange (-n)

snap (*photo*) knipsen

sneeze niesen

snow (*v.*) schneien; (*n.*) der Schnee

so (= *as a result of that*) also

soap die Seife (-n)

sock die Socke (-n)

socket (*electrical*) die Steckdose (-n)

sofa das Sofa (-s)

soft (*sound*) leise; (*texture*) weich; **soft drink** die Limonade (-n)

sold out ausverkauft

solve lösen

some einige

someone jemand

something etwas

sometimes manchmal

somewhere irgendwo; **somewhere else** anderswo

son der Sohn (¨e); **son-in-law** der Schwiegersohn (¨e)

soon bald; **as soon as** sobald; **as soon as possible** sobald wie möglich

sorry! entschuldige(n Sie)!; Verzeihung!; **I'm sorry** es tut* mir leid; **I'm really very sorry** ich bitte* um Entschuldigung

sort die Art (-en); **what sort of** was für

sound (*v.*) klingen; (*n.*) das Geräusch (-e)

soup die Suppe (-n)

sour sauer

south (*adj.*) südlich; Süd-; (*n.*) der Süden

souvenir das (Reise)andenken (-)

spa der Kurort (-e)

space der Raum (⁻e) (*also = outer space*)

Spain (das) Spanien

Spaniard der Spanier (-)

Spanish spanisch

spare Ersatz-; **spare tyre** der Ersatzreifen (-)

speak sprechen*; **speaking** (*on phone*) am Apparat

special besondere; Sonder- **special offer** das Sonderangebot (-e) **specially** besonders

spectacles die Brille (-n)

spectator der Zuschauer (-)

speed die Geschwindigkeit (-en)

spell buchstabieren

spend (*money*) ausgeben*; (*time*) verbringen*

in spite of trotz (+ *gen.*); **in spite of that** trotzdem

sponge der Schwamm (⁻e)

spoon der Löffel (-)

sport, sports der Sport (*always sing.; pl.* Sportarten = *types of sport*); **sports club** der Sportverein (-e); **sports ground** der Sportplatz (⁻e)

spring der Frühling (-e)

sprouts der Rosenkohl (*sing.*)

spy der/die Spion(in) (-e/-nen)

square (*in town*) der Platz (⁻e)

stable der Stall (⁻e)

stadium das Stadion (-dien)

staff room (*in school*) das Lehrerzimmer (-)

stage die Bühne (-n)

stairs die Treppe (-n) (*sing.*)

stalls (*theatre*) das Parkett

stamp die Briefmarke (-n); (*officialese*) das Postwertzeichen (-)

stand stehen* **I can't stand him** ich kann ihn nicht leiden* **stand up** aufstehen*

standard lamp die Stehlampe (-n)

star der Stern (-e)

start (*v.*) anfangen*; beginnen*; (*race, engine*) starten; (*n.*) der Anfang (⁻e); der Beginn

starter (*meal*) die Vorspeise (-n)

state der Staat (-en)

station der Bahnhof (⁻e)

stationery die Schreibwaren (*pl.*); **stationer's** die Schreibwarenhandlung

stay (*v.*) bleiben*; (*n.*) der Aufenthalt (-e)

steak das Steak (-s)

steal stehlen*

steamer der Dampfer (-)

steel der Stahl (⁻e)

steep steil

step on betreten*

stereo (*system*) die Stereoanlage (-n)

stern streng

stick (*v.*) kleben; (*n.*) der Stock (⁻e); **sticking plaster** das Leukoplast (-e)

still (immer) noch

stocking der Strumpf (⁻e)

stomach (*visible protuberance*) der Bauch (⁻e); (*internal organ*) der Magen (⁻)

stone der Stein (-e)

stop (*v.*) (*intrans.*) aufhören; (*vehicle, regular stop*) halten*; (*vehicle, temporary halt*) anhalten*; (*n.*) (*for bus etc.*) die Haltestelle (-n); **I've stopped smoking** ich habe das Rauchen aufgegeben

store das Warenhaus (⁻er)

storm (= *gale*) der Sturm (⁻e); (= *thunderstorm*) das Gewitter (-)

stormy stürmisch

story die Geschichte (-n)

stove (*cooking*) der Herd (-e); (*heating*) der Ofen (⁻)

straight gerade; **straight away** gleich; **straight on** geradeaus

strange fremd

stranger: he's a stranger to me er ist mir fremd

straw der Strohhalm (-e)

strawberry die Erdbeere (-n)

stream der Bach (⁻e)

street die Straße (-n)

stretch die Strecke (-n)

strict streng

stroll bummeln

strong stark

student der Student (-en)

study studieren

stuffing die Farce

stupid dumm

subject (*in school etc.*) das Fach (⁻er); **optional subject** das Wahlfach (⁻er)

suburb der Vorort (-e)

successful erfolgreich

such solch

suddenly plötzlich

suede das Wildleder

suffer (*intrans.*) leiden*; (*trans.*) erleiden*

sugar der Zucker

suggest vorschlagen*

suit (*n.*) der Anzug (⁻e); (*woman's*) das Kostüm (-e); (*v.*) passen (+ *dat.*)

suitcase das Koffer (-)

sultry schwül

summer der Sommer (-)

summit der Gipfel (-)

sun die Sonne (-n) **sunburn** der Sonnenbrand **sunglasses** die Sonnenbrille (-n) **sunny** sonnig **sunshine** der Sonnenschein **suntan** die Sonnenbräune **suntan cream** die Sonnencreme

Sunday (der) Sonntag

supermarket der Supermarkt (⁻e)

supposed: be supposed to sollen*

surcharge der Zuschlag (⁻e)

surgery das Sprechzimmer (-); **surgery hours** die Sprechstunden (*pl.*)

surname der Familienname (-n); der Nachname (-n)

surprise (*v.*) überraschen (*insep.*); (*n.*) die Überraschung (-en)

surroundings die Umgebung (*sing.*)

swallow schlucken

sweat schwitzen

sweep fegen

sweet (*adj.*) süß; (*n.*) der Bonbon (-s)

swim schwimmen*;
   swimming pool das
   Schwimmbad (¨er); (*open air*)
   das Freibad (¨er); (*indoor*) das
   Hallenbad (¨er)
swimming trunks die
   Badehose (-n)
swimsuit der Badeanzug (¨e)
Swiss (*adj.*) schweizerisch; (*n*)
   der/die Schweizer(in) (-/-nen);
   Swiss German (*language*) (das)
   Schweizerdeutsch
switch (*n.*) der Schalter (-);
   switch on anschalten;
   einschalten; anmachen;
   switch off ausschalten;
   ausmachen
Switzerland die Schweiz
sympathetic mitfühlend
synagogue die Synagoge (-n)

T-shirt das T-shirt (-s)
table der Tisch (-e); **table
   tennis** das Tischtennis
tablet die Tablette (-n)
tail der Schwanz (¨e)
take (*into your hand*) nehmen*;
   (*away somewhere*) bringen*
take away wegnehmen*
take-away (*adj.*) zum Mitnehmen
take down (= *dismantle*) abbauen
take off (*plane*) (*v.*) abfliegen*;
   (*n.*) der Abflug
take on anstellen;
take with you mitnehmen*
talk reden
tap der Wasserhahn (¨e)
tape recorder das
   Tonbandgerät (-e)
task die Aufgabe (-n)
taste (*good*) schmecken; (= *take
   a taste of*) kosten; **did it taste
   good?** hat es geschmeckt?
taxi das Taxi (-s)
tea der Tee; **teapot** die
   Teekanne (-n)
teach lehren; **teacher** der
   Lehrer (-); **teaching** der
   Unterricht
team die Mannschaft (-en)
tear (*v.*) reißen*; (*by mistake*)
   zerreißen*; (*n.*) der Riß (-sse)
technical school die
   Berufsschule (-n)

telegram das Telegramm (-e)
telephone (*v.*) anrufen*;
   telefonieren; (*n.*) das Telefon
   (-e); der Fernsprecher (-) (*more
   formal*); **telephone kiosk** die
   Telefonzelle (-n); **telephone
   number** die Telefonnummer
   (-n)
television das Fernsehen;
   television set der Fernseher
   (-); der Fernsehapparat (-e);
   watch television fernsehen*
tell sagen (+ *dat.*); (*a story*)
   erzählen
temperature die Temperatur
   (-en); **have a temperature**
   Fieber haben*; Temperatur
   haben*
**tempered: good/bad
   tempered** gut/schlecht
   gelaunt
temporary Hilfs-
tennis das Tennis
tent das Zelt (-e)
term (*English: 3 a year*) das
   Trimester (-); (*German: 2 a year*)
   das Semester (-)
terminus die Endstation (-en)
terrace die Terrasse (-n);
   terrace house das Reihenhaus
   (¨er)
terrible schrecklich
terrific herrlich; großartig;
   (*more colloq.*) Klasse!
test prüfen
thank danken (+ *dat.*);
   bedanken
thanks! danke (schön/sehr)!;
   say thanks (for) sich bedanken
   (für)
theatre das Theater (-)
then (= *next*) dann; (= *in that
   case*) denn; (= *in those days*)
   damals
there da; (*more specific*) dort
thermometer das
   Thermometer (-)
thief der Dieb (-e)
thin dünn; mager
thing (*concrete*) das Ding (-e);
   (*figurative*) die Sache (-n)
think denken*; (= *hold an
   opinion*) meinen
thirst der Durst

thirsty durstig; **be thirsty**
   Durst haben*
throat der Hals (¨e); **sore
   throat** die Halsschmerzen (*pl.*)
throw werfen*; **throw away**
   wegwerfen*
thumb der Daumen (-)
thunder (*v.*) donnern; (*n.*) der
   Donner (-)
Thursday (der) Donnerstag
ticket die Karte (-n); (*cinema
   etc.*) die Eintrittskarte (-n);
   (*railway*) die Fahrkarte (-n);
   (*bus, tram*) der Fahrschein (-e)
tidy Ordnung machen; **tidy
   (up)** aufräumen; in Ordnung
   bringen*
tie (*v.*) binden*; (*n.*) der Schlips
   (-e); die Krawatte (-n)
tiger der Tiger (-)
tights (*pair*) die Strumpfhose
   (-n)
till die Kasse (-n)
time die Zeit (-en); (*by the clock*)
   die Uhrzeit; (= *occasion*) das Mal
   (-e)
   at any time zu jeder Zeit
   at the same time zur gleichen
   Zeit
   have a good time sich
   amüsieren
   high time höchste Zeit
   on time pünktlich
timetable (*bus etc.*) der
   Fahrplan (¨e); (*school*) der
   Stundenplan (¨e)
tin die Dose (-n); **tin opener**
   die Dosenöffner
tipsy beschwipst
tired müde
toast der Toast (-e)
tobacco der Tabak (-e)
today heute
toe die Zehe (-n)
together zusammen
toilet die Toilette (-n)
tomato die Tomate (-n)
tomorrow morgen; **the day
   after tomorrow** übermorgen
tongue die Zunge (-n)
too auch
tooth der Zahn (¨e);
   toothbrush die Zahnbürste
   (-n); **toothpaste** die Zahnpasta

top (*n.*) der Gipfel (-); (*adj.*) Höchst-; **at the top** oben; **top speed** die Höchstgeschwindigkeit

torn zerrissen*

tortoise die Schildkröte (-n)

tough zäh

tour (*v.*) besichtigen; (*n.*) die Besichtigung (-en); (*of town*) die Rundfahrt (-en)

tourist der Tourist (-en) **tourist office** das Verkehrsbüro (-s); das Verkehrsamt (¨er)

towards auf (+ *acc.*) zu

towel das Handtuch (¨er)

tower der Turm (¨e)

town die Stadt (¨e); **town centre** die Stadtmitte; das Stadtzentrum; **town hall** das Rathaus (¨er); **town plan** der Stadtplan (¨e)

toy das Spielzeug (-e)

track suit der Trainingsanzug (¨e)

tractor der Traktor (-en)

traffic der Verkehr; **traffic jam** die Verkehrsstauung (-en); **traffic light** die Ampel (-n)

train (*n.*) der Zug (¨e); (*v.*) trainieren; **express train** der Schnellzug (¨e); der D-Zug (¨e); **stopping train** der Personenzug (¨e)

tram die (Straßen)bahn (-en)

transfer (*person*) versetzen; (*money*) überweisen* (*insep.*)

transistor der Transistor (-en)

translate übersetzen (*insep.*)

travel (*v.*) (= *be moving*) fahren*; (= *go distances*) reisen; (*adj.*) Reise-; **travel agency** das Reisebüro (-s); **travel guide** (*person*) der Reiseleiter (-); (*book*) der Reiseführer (-); **travel information** die Reiseauskunft (¨e)

traveller der Reisende (*a.n.*); **traveller's cheque** der Reisescheck (-s)

tray das Tablett (-s)

treat behandeln

tree der Baum (¨e)

trip (*excursion*) der Ausflug (¨e); (*journey*) die Fahrt (-en); (= *holiday trip*) die Ferienreise (-n); **have a good trip!** gute Fahrt!

trousers (*pair*) die Hose (-n)

trout die Forelle (-n)

true wahr

trumpet die Trompete (-n)

try versuchen; (= *sample*) probieren; **try on** anprobieren

Tuesday (der) Dienstag

tune stimmen

turkey der Truthahn (¨e)

turn: it's my turn ich bin dran; ich bin an der Reihe; **turn back** umkehren; **turn off** (*road*) abbiegen*; (*TV, etc.*) abschalten; **turn left/right** links/rechts abbiegen*

twin-bedded room das Zweibettzimmer (-)

type tippen; **typewriter** die Schreibmaschine (-n)

typical typisch

tyre der Reifen (-); **tyre pressure** der Reifendruck

ugly häßlich

unbelievable unglaublich

umbrella der Regenschirm (-e)

uncle der Onkel (-)

underground (*railway*) die U-Bahn (-en)

understand verstehen*; (*more colloq.*) kapieren

underwear die Unterwäsche

undress sich ausziehen*

unemployed arbeitslos

unexpected unerwartet

unfortunately leider

unharmed unverletzt

unimportant unwichtig

United States die Vereinigten Staaten

university die Universität (-en); (*colloq.*) die Uni (-s)

unkind unfreundlich

unlock aufschließen*

unlucky: be unlucky Pech haben*

unmarried ledig

unpack auspacken

until bis; **not until** (*prep.*) erst um; (*conj.*) erst als; **not until after** erst nach

unused unbenutzt

up hinauf; **up the stairs** die Treppe hinauf

upper Ober-; **upper school** die Oberstufe

upstairs (*place*) oben; (*motion*) nach oben

urgent dringend

usual(ly) gewöhnlich; **as usual** wie immer

use benutzen; gebrauchen; **be used to** gewöhnt sein* (an + *acc.*)

vacuum cleaner der Staubsauger (-)

vain: in vain umsonst

valid gültig

valley das Tal (¨er)

value der Wert; **good value** preiswert; **value added tax (VAT)** die Mehrwertsteuer

van der Lieferwagen (-)

various verschieden

veal das Kalbfleisch

vegetable das Gemüse (-) (*sing. often used for 'vegetables'*)

vehicle das Fahrzeug (-e)

very sehr

via über

videorecorder das Videogerät (-e); der Videorecorder (-)

view (*v.*) besichtigen; (*n.*) die Aussicht

village das Dorf (¨er)

vinegar der Essig

visa das Visum (*pl.* Visa *or* Visen)

visit (*v.*) besuchen; (*n.*) der Besuch (-e)

visitor der Besucher (-); **we have visitors** wir haben Besuch

voice die Stimme (-n)

wages der Lohn (¨e)

waist die Taille (-n)

wait (*for*) warten (auf + *acc.*)

waiter der Kellner (-); (*politer*) der Ober (-)

waiting room der Wartesaal (-säle)

wake wecken; **wake up** aufwachen; erwachen

Wales (das) Wales

walk (v.) gehen*; (colloq.) laufen*; (opposed to ride) zu Fuß gehen*; (n.) der Spaziergang (¨e); (longer) die Wanderung (-en) **go for a walk** spazierengehen* **go walking** wandern **walk on** (something) betreten*

wall (external) die Mauer (-n); (internal) die Wand (¨e); **wallpaper** die Tapete (-n)

wallet die Brieftasche (-n)

want wollen*; (politer) mögen*

ward (hospital) die Station (-en)

warden (youth hostel) der Herbergsvater/die Herbergsmutter

wardrobe der Kleiderschrank (¨e)

warm warm

warning die Warnung (-en)

wash (sich) waschen*; **wash basin** das Waschbecken (-); **washing** die Wäsche; **washing machine** die Waschmaschine (-n); **washing powder** das Waschpulver (-)

wash up (ab)spülen; abwaschen*

washing up (= dishes) das Geschirr; (= the job) das Geschirrspülen; **washing-up brush** die Spülbürste (-n)

water das Wasser

watch out! Achtung!; Vorsicht!

way der Weg (-e); **by the way** übrigens

weak schwach

wear tragen*; (= be wearing) anhaben*

weather das Wetter; **in bad weather** bei schlechtem Wetter; **weather report** der Wetterbericht (-e); **weather forecast** die Wettervorhersage (-n)

Wednesday (der) Mittwoch

week die Woche (-n); **on weekdays** werktags; wochentags; **weekend** das Wochenende (-n); **weekly** wöchentlich

weep weinen

weigh wiegen*

welcome (v.) begrüßen; (n.) der Empfang; (adj.) willkommen

well gesund; **feel well** sich wohl fühlen; **get well soon!** gute Besserung!

Welsh walisisch

Welshman/woman der/die Waliser(in) (-/-nen)

west (adj.) westlich; West-; (n.) der Westen

wet naß

wheel das Rad (¨er)

where wo; (= where to) wohin; **where from** woher

while während; **a while** eine Weile

whistle (v.) pfeifen*; (n.) die Pfeife (-n)

white weiß; **white wine** der Weißwein (-e)

Whitsun(tide) (das) Pfingsten

wicked böse

wide breit

widow die Witwe (-n)

wife die (Ehe)frau (-en)

wild wild

win gewinnen*

wind der Wind (-e); **windy** windig; **windscreen** die Windschutzscheibe (-n)

window das Fenster (-); **windowpane** die (Fenster)scheibe (-n); **go window-shopping** einen Schaufensterbummel machen

wine der Wein (-e); **wine list** die Weinkarte (-n)

winter der Winter

wish wünschen; **best wishes** es grüßt herzlich

witness der Zeuge (-n)

woman die Frau (-en); **woman's/women's** Frauen-

wonderful wunderbar

wood der Wald (¨er); (material) das Holz (¨er)

wool die Wolle

word des Wort (pl. -e, connected words, ¨er, unconnected words)

work (v.) arbeiten; (of a machine) funktionieren; (n.) die Arbeit; **worker** der Arbeiter (-); **working** (of machine) in Betrieb; **not working** außer Betrieb; **workshop** die Werkstatt (¨en)

world die Welt (-en)

worried aufgeregt; (anxious) ängstlich

worse schlimmer; **he's worse** (= health) es geht* ihm schlechter

worth ... ... wert

wound die Wunde (-n)

wristwatch die Armbanduhr (-en)

write schreiben*; **writing paper** das Schreibpapier; **written** schriftlich

wrong falsch; (= wrong way round) verkehrt; **be in the wrong** im Unrecht sein; **be wrong** unrecht haben*; **what's wrong with you?** was fehlt dir?

yard der Hof (¨e)

year das Jahr (-e)

yearly jährlich

yellow gelb

yesterday gestern; **day before yesterday** vorgestern

yet: not yet noch nicht

yoghurt der Joghurt

young jung; **young person** der/die Jugendliche (a.n.)

youth die Jugend; **youth club** der Jugendclub (-s); **youth hostel** die Jugendherberge (-n)

zero null

zoo der Zoo (-s)

Strong and irregular verbs

We give you the vowel changes in the past and the past participle; we also show where **ß** becomes **ss**. Any other irregularities are spelled out in full.

If the present tense is irregular we give it you in brackets. Where we only give you one form of the present, this is the **er**-form: the **du**-form always makes the same changes. **Ich**-forms are regular unless given.

Verbs with prefixes make the same changes as the simple verb.

beginnen, a, o
beißen, i, iss
biegen, o, o
bieten, o, o
binden, a, u
bitten, bat, gebeten
bleiben, ie, ie
braten (brät), ie, a
brechen (bricht), a, o
brennen, brannte, gebrannt
bringen, brachte, gebracht
denken, dachte, gedacht
dürfen (ich, er darf), durfte,
   dürfen
empfehlen (empfiehlt), a, o
essen (ißt), aß, gegessen
fahren (fährt), u, a
fallen (fällt), fiel, gefallen
fangen (fängt), i, a
finden, a, u
fliegen, o, o
fließen, o, oss
fressen (frißt), fraß, gefressen
frieren, o, o
geben (gibt), a, e
gehen, ging, gegangen
genießen, o, oss
geschehen (geschieht), a, e
gewinnen, a, o
gießen, o, oss
haben (du hast, er hat), hatte,
   gehabt
halten (hält), ie, a
heben, o, o
heißen, ie, ei
helfen (hilft), a, o
kennen, kannte, gekannt

klingen, a, u
kommen, kam, o
können (ich, er kann), konnte,
   können
laden (lädt), u, a
lassen (läßt), ie, a
laufen (läuft), ie, au
leiden, litt, gelitten
leihen, ie, ie
lesen (liest), a, e
liegen, a, e
melken, melkte, gemolken
mögen (ich, er mag), mochte,
   mögen
müssen (ich, er muß), mußte,
   müssen
nehmen (nimmt), nahm,
   genommen
nennen, nannte, genannt
pfeifen, pfiff, gepfiffen
raten (rät), ie, a
reiben, ie, ie
reißen, i, iss
reiten, ritt, geritten
rennen, rannte, gerannt
riechen, o, o
rufen, ie, u
scheinen, ie, ie
schieben, o, o
schießen, o, oss
schlafen (schläft), ie, a
schlagen (schlägt), u, a
schließen, o, oss
schneiden, schnitt, geschnitten
schreiben, ie, ie
schreien, schrie, geschrien
schreiten, schritt, geschritten

schwimmen, a, o
sehen (sieht), a, e
sein (bin/bist/ist/sind/seid), war,
   gewesen
senden, sandte, gesandt
singen, a, u
sitzen, saß, gesessen
sollen (ich, er soll), sollte, sollen
sprechen (spricht), a, o
springen, a, u
stehen, stand, gestanden
stehlen (stiehlt), a, o
steigen, ie, ie
sterben (stirbt), a, o
stoßen (stößt), ie, o
tragen (trägt), u, a
treffen (trifft), traf, getroffen
treiben, ie, ie
treten (tritt), a, e
trinken, a, u
tun (tue/tust/tut/tun/tut), tat,
   getan
verbergen (verbirgt), a, o
vergessen (vergißt), a, e
verlieren, o, o
verschwinden, a, u
verzeihen, ie, ie
wachsen (wächst), u, a
waschen (wäscht), u, a
werden (du wirst, er wird), wurde,
   geworden
werfen (wirft), a, o
wiegen, o, o
wissen (ich, er weiß), wußte,
   gewußt
wollen (ich, er will), wollte, wollen
ziehen, zog, gezogen

Leadership, Management & Team Working in Nursing

2nd Edition

Leadership, Management & Team Working in Nursing

Peter Ellis & Shirley Bach

Los Angeles | London | New Delhi
Singapore | Washington DC | Boston

Learning Matters
An imprint of SAGE Publications Ltd
1 Oliver's Yard
55 City Road
London EC1Y 1SP

SAGE Publications Inc.
2455 Teller Road
Thousand Oaks, California 91320

SAGE Publications India Pvt Ltd
B 1/I 1 Mohan Cooperative Industrial Area
Mathura Road
New Delhi 110 044

SAGE Publications Asia-Pacific Pte Ltd
3 Church Street
#10–04 Samsung Hub
Singapore 049483

Editor: Alex Clabburn
Development editor: Richenda Milton-Daws
Production controller: Chris Marke
Project management: Swales & Willis Ltd,
Exeter, Devon
Marketing manager: Camille Richmond
Cover design: Wendy Scott
Typeset by: C&M Digitals (P) Ltd, Chennai, India
Printed in Great Britain by Henry Ling Limited at
The Dorset Press, Dorchester, DT1 1HD

Library of Congress Control Number: 2015932450

British Library Cataloguing in Publication data

A catalogue record for this book is available from
the British Library

ISBN 978-1-4739-1883-2
ISBN 978-1-4739-1884-9 (pbk)

At SAGE we take sustainability seriously. Most of our products are printed in the UK using FSC papers and boards.
When we print overseas we ensure sustainable papers are used as measured by the Egmont grading system.
We undertake an annual audit to monitor our sustainability.

Contents

TRANSFORMING NURSING PRACTICE TNP

Transforming Nursing Practice is a series tailor-made for pre-registration student nurses. Each book in the series is:

○ Affordable
○ Mapped to the NMC Standards and Essential Skills Clusters
○ Full of active learning features
○ Focused on applying theory to practice

Each book addresses a core topic and they have been carefully developed to be simple to use, quick to read and written in clear language.

> " An invaluable series of books that explicitly relates to the NMC standards. Each book cover a different topic that students need to explore in order to develop into a qualified nurse... I would recommend this series to all Pre-Registration nursing students whatever their field or year of study
>
> **Linda Robson**
> **Senior Lecturer, Edge Hill University**
>
> The set of books is an excellent resource for students. The series is small, easily portable and valuable. I use the whole set on a regular basis.
>
> **Fiona Davies**
> **Senior Nurse Lecturer, University of Derby**
>
> I recommend the SAGE/Learning Matters series to all my students as they are relevant and concise. Please keep up the good work.
>
> **Thomas Beary**
> **Senior Lecturer in Mental Health Nursing, University of Hertfordshire** "

About the authors

Peter Ellis is Nursing Director at Hospice in the Weald, Pembury, Kent, where he is responsible for all aspects of nursing practice. Prior to this he was Senior Lecturer in Nursing at Canterbury Christ Church University, where he taught on pre-registration, post-registration and Master's level courses. Peter has taught as both a full-time and visiting lecturer at various universities since 1998 and has particular expertise in research design, evidence-based nursing, renal nursing, leadership and ethics. Peter has been publishing in nursing journals since 1990 and has three other books in the *Transforming Nursing Practice* series.

Shirley Bach is Professor of Nursing Education and Head of the School of Health Sciences at the University of Brighton and also the Series Editor for *Transforming Nursing Practice*. In the past, she has designed curricula for nurses that integrated interpersonal relationship skills with communication studies, before specialising in health psychology and the application of psychology to health and illness settings. She has written a study guide in psychology for nurses, and researched and developed a model for psychological care. Shirley has also led programmes that promote the professional practice of nursing and midwifery, especially in the area of advanced nursing practice, and has co-authored another text in the *Transforming Nursing Practice* series. More recently, she has developed an interest in new learning technologies and has drawn upon her understanding both of communication and of pedagogic theories to publish in this area.

Acknowledgements

PE would like to acknowledge colleagues and students past and present who challenge, inspire, motivate and occasionally frustrate but from whom I have learned to understand people and leadership.

Introduction

This introduction discusses who should read this book, what the book is about, how and why it might be important to you, its structure, and how the book relates to the Nursing and Midwifery Council (NMC) Standards and Essential Skills Clusters (ESCs) for pre-registration nursing.

Who should read the book?

This book is written for anyone working in health and social care who has some element of leadership and management in their role. Most specifically, the book is aimed at student nurses who are trying to make sense of the leadership and management which happen in the places in which they work. New leaders and managers will find the book useful in providing a framework within which to structure their thinking about what they do and why.

What is it about?

This book focuses on the attitudes, values and practices which serve to make for good leadership and management. Throughout the book the focus is on challenging the reader to adopt an approach to leadership and management which is focused on the human elements of the role. Readers are prompted to think about the ideal which brought them into nursing practice in the first place and consider how these might apply to what they do as potential and actual leaders or managers of people.

Why is it important?

Leadership is an integral feature of the work of every nurse. This applies as much to student nurses developing their leadership skills within the ward or clinic team as it does to the ward manager or matron. It is important to engage with and develop leadership skills early on within your nursing career, as the dispositions, attitudes and skills of leadership do not suddenly appear overnight following promotion. Clearly the values student nurses bring to their training and their interactions with patients and clients are the same, perhaps better-defined, values which apply to the effective and ethical management of fellow professionals.

How is it structured?

The format of the book reflects the way in which we see the need for students to think about what it means to be led, to work in a team and to lead and manage developing. The individual chapters can be read and understood on their own merits, but read together they help form a coherent picture of what we believe good leadership and management practice looks like.

Chapter 1, *Experience of management and leadership*, highlights the importance of remembering and understanding what it means to be led and what this might mean for the way in which you subsequently choose to lead.

Chapter 2, *Teams and team work*, identifies what teams are, why they exist and how they can work better towards their common goals. The following chapter, *Working with individuals in teams*, introduces the roles and responsibilities of individuals within teams and issues such as recruitment and delegation. In Chapter 4, *Conflict management and negotiation skills*, the different personality types that may operate within teams are described, and ways of managing conflict within the team and other settings are explored.

Chapter 5, *Coaching, mentoring and clinical supervision*, investigates the role of the leader or manager in supporting team members. This is followed by a chapter on *Frameworks for management and leadership*, which identifies and examines some theories of leadership and management and their interconnectedness.

Chapter 7, *Improving care, change management and entrepreneurial skills*, presents theories which may underpin leadership practice in relationship to the instigation and management of change, while Chapter 8, *Creating a learning environment*, considers the value of understanding the culture within which teams work and the impact this may have on the successful working of the team.

In Chapter 9, *Developing confidence as a manager and leader*, some of the tasks and roles undertaken by the leader or manager are laid bare. The chapter goes on to look at how these might be used to develop certainty in what they do for the developing leader.

NMC *Standards for Pre-registration Nursing Education* and Essential Skills Clusters

The NMC Standards of competence provide guidance on the abilities and dispositions nursing student need to develop in order to meet the requirements for registration. As well as the standards of competence, the NMC identifies skills nursing students need to develop during their training; these ESCs are necessary for students to enter registered practice as capable practitioners.

This book identifies some of the competencies and essential skills which relate to leadership and management which student nurses need in order to attain NMC registration. These competencies and ESCs are presented at the start of each chapter so that readers can focus on how the content of each chapter contributes to their own competence and skill development. All of the competencies and ESCs in this book relate to the *generic standards* that all nursing students must achieve prior to registration. This book includes the latest information taken from the *Standards for Pre-registration Nursing Education* (NMC, 2010).

Activities

The activities contained within each chapter form an integral part of the learning and development strategy for each chapter. Readers will get the most benefit from each chapter if they engage fully with the activities and in the order they are presented. The activities are designed to help illustrate the nature and reality of some of the theory presented and to bring to life some of the situations, scenarios and associated skills and competencies described. Some of the activities require readers to seek out new information and new experiences; engagement with this process adds not only to the development of understanding but also potentially to confidence.

Reflection on the chapter content and on the activities is an important and integral part of the process of the student nurse's development as a leader of people. Some activities require readers to come to a decision or understanding for themselves, while others have suggested answers presented at the end of the chapter. Readers are encouraged to consider each activity for themselves before reading the suggested answers so that they come to an understanding of their own level of comprehension of the content of the chapter as well as their own personal and professional development.

Other features

The text also includes case studies and scenarios, research summaries and the necessary theory. There is also a glossary of terms at the end of the book. Glossary entries will be in bold type the first time they appear.

Chapter 1
Experience of management and leadership

Chapter aims

After reading this chapter, you will be able to:

- identify some of the values which underpin nurse leadership and management;
- understand how the experience of being led affects the ways in which we choose to lead and manage in nursing;
- comment on why leadership and management in nursing are important;
- begin to create a coherent picture of what leadership and management structures in nursing look like.

Introduction

The purpose of this chapter is to increase your awareness of the personal and professional values that influence the ways in which managers and leaders should behave. The chapter will both challenge and reinforce some of the assumptions you hold about the ways in which leaders and managers function.

Our **values** and assumptions about leadership and management are to a great extent derived from our experiences of leading and managing, and of being led and managed. This means they will reflect our personal interpretation of what happened during the process. It is important that, at the start of any quest to understand leadership and management, we should first understand ourselves and our motivations. Only in this way can we hope to understand the context of leadership and management and the behaviours and motivations of those we seek to lead.

As well as exploring the context of values in relation to leadership and management, this chapter will explore some of the characteristics of leaders and managers. These descriptions will reflect the characteristics leadership and management theorists believe good managers and leaders should portray, including their personality traits. After examining these characteristics, you will be encouraged to formulate a picture of how you believe good leaders or managers should behave, and the essential qualities you believe they should exhibit within the nursing context.

(For more detailed discussion of theories and frameworks for leadership and management, and how they can be adopted and adapted by you to help meet the challenges of nurse leadership in the twenty-first century, see Chapter 6.)

A further important theme of this chapter is why leadership and management are important in nursing practice now and in the future, as well as how an understanding of them can contribute to your personal and professional development. We will examine this issue at least in part by discussing the some of the findings of the Francis report (2013), which examined serious failures in care.

Towards the end of the chapter, some of the reasons for the existence of different leadership and management roles in nursing are introduced and discussed. You are invited to collect some data on the nursing structures where you work and how these impact on the work you and your colleagues do.

Understanding context and values

Our ideas and opinions about good leadership and management are coloured to a great extent by our personal experiences of leadership and management, whether we are managers, leaders or team members. The assumptions we have about management and leadership styles and behaviours are also affected by our understanding of what is going on and the motivations behind the management and leadership styles we adopt or see adopted. The inability to understand why a certain approach to management or leadership has been adopted can lead to misconceptions and misunderstandings; this is something an understanding of the context of nurse leadership and management allows us to see beyond. Sometimes this context is better developed as we gain more experience as nurses and reflect thoughtfully on what these experiences actually mean.

Activity 1.1   *Reflection*

When you first came into nursing and went into practice for the first time, how did you feel about the efforts made by the staff to get frail, elderly patients to engage in self-care, for example, encouraging elderly patients to get out of bed in the morning and to get washed and dressed? Now you understand a bit more about the purpose and nature of nursing, have you changed your view? Why?

There are some possible answers and thoughts at the end of the chapter.

Understanding why something is done in a particular way in a given situation allows us to understand the context of an action in the clinical setting. As shown in Activity 1.1, a developing understanding of the nature of nursing and what it means to nurse helps us to make sense of the world of work and the roles in which we find ourselves. The same is true of leadership and management, where actions taken out of context may appear to be wrong.

One of the enduring difficulties for student nurses can be to understand the provision of care beyond the individual. Often the context of nursing management and leadership is about achieving the best outcomes on a regular, recurring and equitable basis for the many. The need to achieve good outcomes for the many rather than the few may help us to understand the context of a management or leadership style we see before us. This view is one which can only develop if we are willing and able to question the leadership and management practices we see around us and are then willing and able to reflect on the answers we find.

Case study: The newly qualified nurse

Julius is a newly qualified staff nurse working on a busy cardiology ward. Julius is irritated by the apparent inactivity of the ward sister Deirdre, who spends vast amounts of time in the office doing what to him appears to be endless and pointless paperwork instead of providing patient care. Julius confronts Deirdre about the lack of time she spends on the ward and suggests much of the time she is doing nothing of value while she is 'hiding away' in her office.

Deirdre understands the point Julius is making and is wise enough to appreciate that his frustrations arise not out of malice towards her but as a result of his inexperience and lack of understanding of what it takes to keep a busy ward functioning smoothly. Deirdre takes Julius into her office and shows him some of the tasks she has to perform on a regular basis, which include writing the duty roster, completing staff appraisals, entering patient dependency scores on to a monitoring database, ordering stock and overseeing staff development planning.

Deirdre explains to Julius she too is frustrated by the lack of time she has to provide care on a daily basis: that, she explains, is after all why she came into nursing. But she also understands her role now is less about providing care and more about facilitating the delivery of care. Deirdre explains she achieves this through supporting the staff on the ward to improve, using appraisals and accessing appropriate education and development; rostering to allow for a good work–life balance; and managing the budget while ensuring the hospital administrators know what the needs of the ward are by recording the level of dependency of the patients and the stock requirements. She explains she sees her role as supporting the staff to care for the patients, and if she did not do the necessary tasks then there would be chaos.

Julius concedes he had not looked at things in this way and he needed to understand the wider context before criticising.

From this example we can see that leadership and management often involve the need to see the bigger picture – which may not always be evident to members of the team. In order to understand the challenges and benefits that accrue from good leadership, it is necessary to understand something of the context of nursing leadership and management.

Clearly, from this example we can see that one of the necessary qualities of a good manager or leader is the ability to see the bigger picture and anticipate and plan what the team will be doing and how they will do it. Leadership and management are therefore as much a forward-looking activity as about managing what is happening in the here and now. One of the characteristics of good managers or leaders is understanding what it is they want to achieve and being able to communicate this, and perhaps effectively delegating associated tasks, to the team.

What we should remember at this stage is that one of the most important things that motivates us as nurses to achieve the goals we do is our values. Before we explore some more about the context of nursing leadership and management, we should stop for a moment to reflect on the values we have as humans, nurses, leaders or managers and see what impact they might have on leadership and management in nursing.

It is not at all easy to state exactly what values are. A cursory search on the internet for values of caring throws up scores of words, all of which may have relevance to nursing, but none of which explain what they are. Various descriptions include reference to best interests, moral duties, likes and preferences.

Concept summary: Human values

One of the widest-cited definitions of values, and one which has resonance with nurse leadership, is the definition by Schwartz (1994, page 20), who says that a value is *a belief pertaining to desirable end states or modes of conduct that transcends specific situations; guides selection or evaluation of behavior, people, and events; and is ordered by the importance relative to other values to form a system of value priorities.*

The notable elements of the definition by Schwartz are that values relate to:

- achieving a good outcome;
- something more important than individual situations;
- how we ought to behave;
- what we ought to look for in the behaviour of others;
- how events ought to be managed;
- ways in which we might prioritise how we use our time and effort.

In essence the suggestion here is that our values should be at the centre of everything we do, both as a guide to how we act as well as what it is we act upon. The additional issue for leaders and managers is of course that they need to role model these values to those they lead.

Evidently, within the case study above, Deirdre had not forgotten the values that took her into nursing in the first place. What had changed then for Deirdre as she moved from a clinical role to a more managerial post was simply the way in which these values were allowed to express themselves. In order to develop continually as nurses, leaders and managers, it is important not only that we question our values from time to time, but that we are also able to express what these values are and refine them in discussion with our colleagues.

Activity 1.2   *Decision making*

Take some time to think about the values you have as a nurse. Now think about how these values show themselves in the ways in which you act when in the clinical setting. Next time you are in practice, ask your team leader or ward manager what values s/he holds and how s/he thinks s/he expresses them in practice. Now compare the lists, looking for areas of overlap and areas of difference. What do you notice about the similarities and differences between your list of values and corresponding actions and the leader's values and actions?

There are some possible answers and thoughts at the end of the chapter.

What is clear about the values of practising nurses, ward managers and more senior nursing staff is they should, and to a great extent do, share similar values and goals. The role of the leader or manager should be to facilitate the team in the achievement of these goals. Evidently, where there are differences in the values and goals of the team and the team leader, then difficulties will arise. When nurses or nurse leaders forget what their values are, then they will lose sight of what it is they are trying to achieve.

Sometimes it is hard to know what exactly our values are or the limits to which they can be stretched. One method for understanding our values as potential leaders or managers is to ask ourselves hypothetical questions, the answers to which can be searching and difficult for us. The answers to these difficult questions enable us, however, to understand what sort of person we are and what motivates us as humans, nurses and managers. Understanding our own values and underlying motivations will then tell us something about what is likely to motivate and guide the actions of those that may be called upon to lead.

Scenario 1.1: Doing the right thing

Imagine you are working in a nursing home on nights. You are tired, having already worked six shifts in a row. One of the residents, Jane, who is in her late 80s, has been in the home for some time as a result of having had a stroke. Jane needs to be turned 2-hourly to avoid her developing pressure sores, but you and the nurse you are working with decide to turn her just occasionally. You justify this to yourselves by saying this avoids disturbing her sleep and it also protects your backs. At the end of the shift you turn her and record in her notes that you have done so 2-hourly throughout the night. She has not developed a pressure sore, so what is the harm?

Now consider this: you turn her at the end of the night and discover that a small area has broken down on her left hip. Is this your fault? If the matron asks if you have turned her 2-hourly, as stated in the care plan, what will you say? You could say you turned her 2-hourly – this would not change anything for Jane, but would make your life easier.

Alternatively you go to turn her at the end of the night shift only to discover that she has died some time during the night. She has been dead for a while judging from how cold she is and the blood that is pooling on the side she was lying on. You know you can just claim that you found her earlier in the night and prepare her body quickly before the day staff come in to work. Surely this will not change anything; no one will be hurt, will they?

Which, if any, of these scenarios are acceptable? Does the blame attached to any of them change because of the outcome? What does your choice of actions say about you? What values are being displayed here? How do they compare with the values you expressed in Activity 1.2?

There are some possible answers and thoughts at the end of the chapter.

Examining examples such as this enable us to see the bigger picture. They are also helpful for us in developing an increasing awareness of our own values as they relate to being led and managed and then, conversely, to us leading or managing. In part our values will be mirrored in the sort of person we are and how we see the world in general, but they will also shape the way in which the world sees us. Of course it might be equally bad if a nurse were to follow policy and procedure blindly, with no thought about the consequences. In this scenario, as in many leadership and management situations, deviating from what we know to be right (i.e. ignoring our values) can have dire consequences for those we care for.

Scenario 1.2: Being clear

You are working on a medical admissions unit and have asked a colleague, Emma, to go round and do the observations. She takes the temperature, pulse and blood pressure of every patient on the unit, as asked. About an hour later you ask if all the observations were OK. Emma replies that the woman in the first bed had a temperature of 39°C. You ask why she had not informed you of this immediately. She replies that it was her job to do all of the observations as you asked, and that is what she has done.

What does this scenario tell you about managing and leading people in the clinical setting? What does this tell you about the need to understand what we do and why? Is there a place for understanding values of care in this scenario?

There are some possible answers and thoughts at the end of the chapter.

By now you should have developed a fairly clear picture of the values that you believe underpin what you do as a student nurse or nurse. You may well also have some insight into the values of those around you and the impact that working among other nurses has on the development of your own value set. It is important to understand that, for leaders or managers to be effective, there is a requirement for there to be some degree of overlap between their values and the values of their team, and the team must be aware of this (Grivas and Puccio, 2012).

What happens when values are forgotten?

Hospitals, care homes, clinics and community teams are made up of collections of people working together to achieve a common task. This common task requires that the values of the individuals involved in the care align to some extent; otherwise they would be working in opposition to, rather than with, each other. One of the challenges of modern healthcare is that our values can get lost in amongst all of the tasks we have to undertake and our attention may be drawn to achieving goals and targets, rather than remembering the values which bring us into nursing in the first place.

When nurses, or indeed any care staff, forget the values that should be driving their work, this has an impact on the culture they work in and this culture ultimately impacts on the care they give.

The following extract is taken from the Francis *Report of the Mid Staffordshire NHS Foundation Trust Public Inquiry* (2013):

> *The negative aspects of culture in the system were identified as including:*
>
> - *a lack of openness to criticism;*
> - *a lack of consideration for patients;*
> - *defensiveness;*
> - *looking inwards, not outwards;*
> - *secrecy;*
> - *misplaced assumptions about the judgements and actions of others;*
> - *an acceptance of poor standards;*
> - *a failure to put the patient first in everything that is done.*
>
> *It cannot be suggested that all these characteristics are present everywhere in the system all of the time, far from it, but their existence anywhere means that there is an insufficiently shared positive culture.*
>
> (Francis, 2013, page 65)

What Francis (2013) is identifying here is not a list of issues with the organisation, but a list of issues which arise as a result of the collective values of the people in the organisation becoming secondary to other issues. If we take each of the bullet points in turn, we can see each one represents a *value* which is not being exercised:

- competence;
- compassion;
- thankfulness;
- mindfulness;
- openness;
- trust;
- principles;
- care.

Francis goes on to say that:

> *To change that, there needs to be a relentless focus on the patient's interests and the obligation to keep patients safe and protected from substandard care. This means that the patient must be first in everything that is done: there must be no tolerance of substandard care; frontline staff must be empowered with responsibility and freedom to act in this way under strong and stable leadership in stable organisations.*

To achieve this does not require radical reorganisation but re-emphasis of what is truly important:

- *Emphasis on and commitment to common values throughout the system by all within it.*

(Francis, 2013, page 66)

The Francis report has had a major impact on the way in which care is delivered in the UK, not because what happened at Mid Staffordshire was unique, because it probably isn't, but because it reminded care professionals and politicians alike that, once managers impose the wrong sorts of *values* and *targets* on care professionals, then values of care can easily be forgotten.

It is probably fair to say that, in order to become an effective leader or manager of people, we first must know ourselves and our values as well as having some insight into how others see us and how they interpret the way in which we display our values. Part of leadership or management is presentation of self to others and encouraging others to follow our lead by behaving in ways and displaying values that others admire and can identify with – creating a situation where others wish to follow. When you think about it, a leader without followers is just a person working alone!

How we see ourselves and others see us

To understand how we see ourselves and how this compares to how others see us, it is worth looking at the work of Joseph Luft and Harry Ingham, whose Johari window illustrates the point about what we know about ourselves and what others know about us.

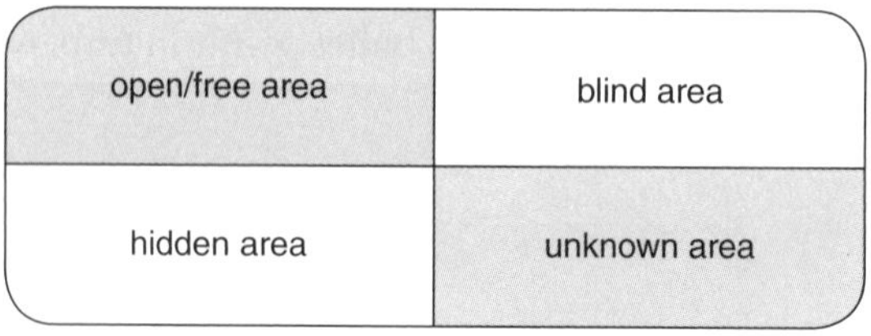

open/free area	blind area
hidden area	unknown area

Figure 1.1: The Johari window

Source: Adapted from Luft and Ingham (1955), page 10.

What the Johari window allows us to see is how much of the perceptions and knowledge we have about ourselves is also seen and shared by others:

- The open/free area refers to what we know about ourselves and what is also known by other people – it is our public face.
- The blind area is the area of our personality we are blind to but which others can see – our blind spot.
- The hidden area is what we know about ourselves but we keep hidden from others, sometimes called the 'avoided self' or 'facade'.
- The unknown area refers to what is unknown both to ourselves and to others (which can be regarded as an area for potential development and self-exploration).

What is interesting about this model is it shows us there is great potential for us as individuals to lack understanding of ourselves as much as there is potential for other people not to understand us. To some extent we can manage the view others have of us as individuals by allowing them to see what we want them to see and by managing our behaviours at work and in our private lives. On the other hand, people are often aware of issues with our values and personality that we are sometimes aware of and sometimes not.

Being able to adapt who we are and how we behave at work is part of the process of socialising to be both a nurse and a member of society at large. By being aware of our values and acting upon them we allow ourselves the ability to become someone we want to become and potentially to develop the traits that will help us to develop as a person, a nurse and over time as a manager or leader.

Activity 1.3 — *Communication*

In order to get some idea of how your view of yourself is similar to, or differs from, that of other people, undertake the following exercise which may tell you something about how you communicate with and are perceived by other people: Choose five words to describe what sort of person you believe yourself to be and write these down. Ask a number of people who you know to choose five words which describe what sort of person you are and write these down. Include fellow students, lecturers, mentors and other people you work with. Examine the lists for similarities and differences and assign the responses to the various boxes of the Johari window and consider what this says about how your perception of self concurs or contrasts with the views of others.

Since this is based on your own thoughts and reflections, there is no specimen answer at the end of the chapter.

Activity 1.3 will help you to see that sometimes people see good and sometimes bad things about us which we may or may not see for ourselves. The lesson for the would-be leader is to learn to change the negatives that we can change and to manage the areas of our personality that we cannot. You should also be prepared to take on board positive insights and use these to continue to improve your relationships with others.

What are the characteristics of a good leader or manager?

What makes a good leader or manager has been explored by many theorists and academics over the years. Some of the early theorists identified characteristics such as physical size, strength and 'presence' (Wright, 1996). Other characteristics and traits that have been favoured include intelligence, personality type such as extroversion, and **charisma** and other interpersonal skills.

Certainly it is true that being **charismatic** and intelligent helps with the processing of ideas and when communicating with others can help a leader. But, as we have seen above, there must be more to being a good nurse, good leader or good manager than these superficial qualities alone. Sometimes extreme examples allow us to see things that are perhaps not clear to us in the day-to-day process of being managed or led.

Activity 1.4   *Reflection*

Reflect on some of the well-known and successful leaders you know from history, perhaps Winston Churchill, Nelson Mandela, Martin Luther King or Florence Nightingale. What characteristics do they share that makes them great leaders? Why are they thought of as great individuals as well as successful leaders?

Next think about some of the other successful leaders from history, like Adolf Hitler, Napoleon Bonaparte, Joseph Stalin or Saddam Hussein. What characteristics made them successful leaders? Why are they thought of as immoral leaders?

There are some possible answers and thoughts at the end of the chapter.

Interestingly, from the examples of good leaders given above, none of them was particularly impressive physically, so their ability to lead and inspire has to be explained in some other way. Certainly this observation calls into question some of the early physical appearance theories of what makes a good leader. Clearly there may be issues relating to their charisma and intellect that attracted other people to them.

What we can see about the leaders in Activity 1.4, and what perhaps others know about some of them that they do not see for themselves, is the leaders we admire have a vision of something better for the people they lead. In the case of Mandela and Luther King, this was freedom from oppression and the achievement of equality of status and human rights. The pursuit of these values and the veracity with which they pursued them give us a clue as to one other quality we might admire in a leader: integrity (Frankel, 2008). In this sense integrity may be understood as acting in a manner that reflects the values, ethics and morals that an individual believes to be important.

Integrity alone is not enough, however. Hitler, Stalin and Saddam Hussein all perhaps believed in what they were doing; in that sense they had integrity. What is interesting about what they believed and what they set out to achieve was that it was often more about achieving power for themselves than it was about achieving what was right or something that benefits others.

What is missing therefore is an understanding about what this integrity and leadership should be aimed at achieving. Leaders and managers are the figureheads of teams and teams exist to get a job done (Ward, 2003). In nursing this job is about providing care for others in a manner that reflects the positive values we hold as humans and as nurses. For a nurse leader or manager, therefore, integrity of action means leading and managing in a manner that reflects the values of care which are part of what being a nurse is about and which you have identified for yourself in Activity 1.2.

Activity 1.5 — Reflection

It is perhaps worth reflecting on the answers you gave to Activity 1.2 and comparing them to what you have learnt so far in this chapter. You should be able to see some commonalities between the ideas and therefore have some ideas of what being a good nurse leader or manager is all about.

Since this is based on your own observations there is no specimen answer at the end of the chapter.

So far in this chapter we have seen that being a good leader or manager in nursing is about the expression of the same values of care that being a good nurse requires. What changes when one moves from being a nurse to a nurse leader or manager is the way in which these values are expressed through what we do and how we behave towards others. The consistency of the values between nursing and nurse leadership/management demonstrates integrity. It is perhaps a sad fact that those nurse leaders and managers who we see losing sight of their values are the ones we least admire. The report into the failings at the Mid Staffordshire Hospital identified poor leadership coupled with clinical staff *accepting standards of care … that should not have been tolerated* (Clews, 2010). The collective failing here was that clinically trained managers did not support their staff as well as they might have and the managers and leaders, as well as their staff, allowed the standards of care to slip below a level reflective of the true *values* of nursing.

One of the challenges of this book is for you to recognise and acknowledge the values that you have as a nursing student and to think about how you will continue to exercise these values throughout your nursing career.

Structures of nurse leadership

What we have not discussed so far are the structures that relate to the exercise of leadership and management. Clearly a manager occupies a formal role. The role of the manager is conferred upon the individual by an organisation and its staff are responsible to the manager by virtue of their contract of employment with the organisation – often called **legitimate power** (first identified by French and Raven in 1960). How these lines of responsibility are created and what they mean in practice should be clearer after the next activity.

Activity 1.6 — *Reflection*

To understand the lines of responsibility that form part of a contract, look at the programme handbook for the programme you are on. There will be clear guidelines about some things you can and cannot do as a university student. There will be identified individuals to whom you would have to answer if you break these rules. This forms part of your contract with the university and ultimately with the Nursing and Midwifery Council (NMC) in relation to the fitness to practise criteria.

Alternatively, if you have a contract of employment you may notice it identifies the person to whom you are answerable, usually a line manager.

As this is based on your own observations there is no specimen answer at the end of the chapter.

Managerial power and responsibility, as you can see from Activity 1.6, are therefore formalised within the contract of employment or training. They are validated by the fact that we choose to submit to these contracts of our own free will, usually because they will confer some benefit on us (in the case of a job, through being paid and in the case of being a student nurse, in gaining a qualification). Similarly, as nurses we agree to be bound by *The Code* and other regulations pertaining to nursing (NMC, 2015).

Within most organisations there are a number of managers at different levels who have different responsibilities for different organisational activities. These managers report to a more senior manager who in turn reports to more senior management. Such structures are formalised and are usually created in order to allow for the overseeing of the functions of the organisation. Each tier within the system of management should be aware of their responsibilities and the limits of their powers in fulfilling the tasks associated with these roles. It is often helpful for novice nurses to have some idea of what the structure of the organisation they work in looks like.

In Chapter 8 we discuss a little about cultures of care and you may find it useful to look up Charles Handy's work (1994) on cultures in order to inform your thinking about the formal and informal management structures which can exist in health and social care.

Activity 1.7 — *Evidence-based practice and research*

Try to find out something about the management structure in the hospital in which you are placed. There may be a diagram that shows the relative management positions (sometimes called an organogram); then try to find out what the main responsibilities are of the people in the various roles you have identified. You might also like to do something similar for a ward or other practice area you work in so you can get an overview of who is responsible for what.

As this is based on your own observation there is no specimen answer at the end of the chapter.

So we can see that being a manager is a formalised position that is conferred by position within an organisation. Being a leader, on the other hand, may or may not be the result of position within a team or organisation. How can this be?

As we will see elsewhere in the book, leadership is in many instances one of the roles of a manager; think about the ward managers in the areas where you have worked who as well as managing the ward also lead the team. Think also about the areas where you have worked where individuals who occupy a junior role in a team exercise leadership. Sometimes then the leadership function is one of the roles of the manager, while on other occasions something else is at work.

How then do some non-managers function as leaders? Essentially there are three answers to this question. First, some leaders, such as team leaders at the ward level, are designated leaders because they are more experienced than the other staff or they hold a higher, non-management grade. They exercise the power of leadership also through virtue of the formal position they hold and the delegation of certain duties from their line manager. In this respect the power they exercise comes from the person who has delegated it to them – this is sometimes referred to as legitimate power. Legitimate power, within society and organisations, arises out of the fact that people vote for their leaders (in the societal sense) or they enter into contracts of work whereby they agree to be subject to the power of others within an organisation. The leadership roles within such arrangement are therefore legitimised by virtue of the fact that they represent a choice on the part of the people who are led by these elected, or contractual, leaders.

Second, other leaders exercise leadership in relation to specific projects or responsibilities within the team. For example, in many clinical areas there are link nurses with responsibility for areas such as diabetes care, wound management or infection control. Again their power to act as leaders is in part conferred by the position they are asked to play in the team and is delegated from the team manager. The other reason they are a leader in their particular area is because they have specialist knowledge of the practice, procedures and guidelines that relate to whatever it is they are responsible for. In this situation a good leader will share the information the team needs to know to get the job done – a bad leader will not! Clearly, then, one of the characteristics of a leader is information management and good communication.

Third, there are those people who lead by virtue of their character. These charismatic individuals are the sort of people others like and respond to. They are able to motivate others and to get the team to follow them by virtue of who they are. They have a compelling vision of what should be done and how, and have a conviction and surety about them which encourage others to follow their lead (Mahoney, 2001). They may not be in positions of formal power, but perhaps they have knowledge or good communication skills that single them out as people others like to follow.

Case study: The new nursing sister

Eileen is a newly appointed sister on the dialysis unit of a busy general hospital. Eileen is liked by all of the staff, but has rapidly built up a reputation for being quite disorganised. When she is in charge of the shift, things go wrong. She gets sidetracked by small details and disappears for long periods of time to sort out seemingly minor issues.

continued . . . .

> *Karen is a healthcare assistant who has worked in the dialysis unit for many years. Karen is familiar with the routine and is able to cope with most situations that arise. Karen often takes charge of the unit, even when Eileen is there. She co-ordinates the workload, makes telephone calls and arranges transport. Karen uses her connections and the relationships she has built up over the years to get things done.*

What we can see in this case study is that, even within an essentially quite hierarchical structure, leadership can be found at all levels of the team. In this example there is a real danger that Eileen will lose control of the unit and Karen might overstep her own competence, role and responsibilities. Clearly one of the issues that arises out of this scenario is accountability. Eileen as a registered nurse is accountable for what she does as well as the actions of her team, especially the untrained members. Karen as a care assistant is not accountable for her actions in the same way, but is responsible to her employer (actually, Eileen) for what she does.

In this scenario the power which Karen exercises is not strictly speaking legitimate. As with all members of the team, she has roles and responsibilities for which she may need to exercise the power given to her by virtue of her position. It may be that Karen has the power to order stores and perhaps organise transport, but these are subject to the need to recognise the roles and responsibilities of other members of the team, who may need support in developing the skills necessary for them to operate effectively within their identified role.

It may be argued therefore that the leadership that Karen exercises is in this instance a bad thing. Karen is perhaps motivated to get the immediate job done, but perhaps misses some of the bigger-picture issues, such as the quality of the dialysis, that she is not trained in and not in a position to understand. Because Karen takes over the day-to-day running of the unit, she is also both undermining Eileen and preventing her from developing into her new role. While in the short term this might appear to work, it is not a long-term solution.

Activity 1.8 *Reflection*

Take some time to think about the implications of this case study. What might this mean for the quality of nursing practice in the dialysis unit? What implications might this have for Eileen and for Karen in the long term? How are the other staff likely to feel about this situation?

There are some possible answers and thoughts at the end of the chapter.

So we have seen that leadership and management within nursing can be broken down into many levels, from the most senior member of the nursing team right through to the most junior, and the qualities that make a good leader can be present at all levels. We have also seen that some managers fail to lead and that some leaders do not really have the formal position or power to do so.

Leading and managing: the policy context

Nursing is not undertaken in a vacuum. What we do as nurses and what nurse managers and leaders do occurs within a healthcare context and is subject to policy, procedure and guidelines. If leadership or management is about leading or managing a team to achieve certain outcomes, and within healthcare these outcomes are derived from policy and guidelines, then there is a need for nurse leaders and managers not only to be aware of what the guidelines are but also to act on them and ensure their team acts on them too.

Historically the caring professions had a great deal of autonomy over the ways in which they worked. In the past they set the standards by which their work was to be measured and audited and decided on clinical and non-clinical priorities. More recently, most notably following the policies of the Thatcher government and subsequently New Labour, clinical priority setting and the standards for care have been determined more centrally through government policy via agencies such as the National Institute for Health and Care Excellence (NICE) or via nationally drawn-up structures for care, such as the National Service Frameworks. So part of the role of nurse leaders or managers will be having the ability to lead or manage their team through the change process to achieve the outcomes of care determined from outside the team (see Chapter 8).

As well as general policy and guidelines in the area of health, as nurses we are subject to policy and guidance from our professional body, the NMC. In order to understand the context of leadership and management in nursing from the point of view of the NMC, it is worth familiarising yourself with the standards of proficiency and Essential Skills Clusters identified at the start of each chapter and asking yourself how these apply within the context of each chapter. You may also wish to look at and reflect on how these ideas reflect the issues identified within other NMC documentation, including *The Code* (NMC, 2015). Most especially, this chapter has highlighted the need for nurse leaders to *be self-aware and recognise how their own values, principles and assumptions may affect their practice* (NMC, 2010), as expressed in Competency 4 of the 'Leadership, management and team working' domain of the competency framework, identified at the start of this chapter.

For example, in this chapter we have discussed some of the values that underpin nursing practice, as well as leadership and management characteristics of the nurse leader/manager which may contribute to our development as good leaders and managers. These characteristics translate well from both the code of professional conduct and the standards of proficiency identified at the start of the chapter. What they validate is perhaps the most important message of the chapter: in order to become a good leader or manager of nurses it is important to remain grounded in the values, beliefs and behaviours that guide professional nursing practice.

Chapter summary

Rather than launch straight into a discussion about the nature of leadership and management in nursing, this chapter has sought to identify some of the values, beliefs and behaviours that might be associated with becoming a good nurse leader or manager. These

continued . . . .

characteristics have been compared and contrasted with some of the values that underpin being a good nurse. There is an explicit challenge within this chapter for you to identify and confront the values you have as a nurse, a nursing student, a team member and a leader.

In some part this challenge has been posed by reference to some of the shortcomings identified in the Francis report. While the failings at Mid-Staffordshire NHS Trust are useful as a benchmark of what can go wrong, they are exactly that, a benchmark. They should not be considered as merely a footnote in history, but should be seen as a salutary lesson in what could quite easily happen anywhere when nurses and other care professionals neglect their values.

An understanding of the context of care and of ourselves is an important first step on the road to becoming a competent leader of nurses; failure to understand what motivates us as individuals lays us open to external criticism. Furthermore, some of the skills and values we develop as nurses in clinical practice will translate well into leadership and management roles. It is never too soon for student nurses to think about what type of leader/manager they want to be and to look around them for suitable role models to guide their development.

Activities: brief outline answers

Activity 1.1 Reflection

This reflection is not about understanding the rehabilitation of the elderly as such; it is about understanding context. As a new nurse you may consider asking people to undertake their own care as lazy nursing, because you consider nursing as a caring profession that does things for people. As you understand the nature of care better, you will see the same scenario in a different light, or context, as you understand that encouraging self-care is about helping people address their care deficits and achieve the activities of daily living for themselves.

Activity 1.2 Decision making

What you will notice is that the basic values of caring, moral behaviour, putting others before self, protection of rights, autonomy and dignity are common to both lists. What will be different is that the leader will attempt to achieve these aims through the way in which s/he leads. This will include acting as a role model and promoting the welfare of the team who in turn are expected to support these values one to one with patients and clients (Bondas, 2006). If you are still struggling to think about what your values are, try some of the words above or choose some from this list: accountability, accuracy, calm, committed, decisive, fair, honesty, integrity, justice, open, reliable, team worker or truthfulness.

Scenario 1.1 Doing the right thing

We hope you found none of these scenarios acceptable. On each occasion, regardless of the outcome, the choice being made was to avoid your duty to Jane to protect her from potential further physical harm. The values displayed here are self-regarding and not other-regarding and are against everything that is to be found in the nursing code of conduct. At best, the scenario demonstrates lies being told and at worst a dereliction of the duty of care, leading to harm to the patient. Some people might argue that, as no harm ensued, the first scenario might be all right, but the consequences that *could* accrue (as seen later in the scenario) show this to be wrong, regardless of any arguments about duty and outcomes.

Scenario 1.2 Being clear

This scenario suggests that as a manager or leader it is important not only to have team members who do what they are asked, but also that they understand the purpose of what they are doing. There is a clear need here for the nurse to understand that doing observations is not enough in itself; it is acting on what is found that is important. The values which should drive the undertaking of such tasks is **person-centred** care, which requires that nurses not only undertake a task, but that they think about what it means for the patient or client.

Activity 1.4 Reflection

Clearly one of the characteristics of good leaders is that people want to follow them. In many of the cases mentioned as potential positive role models, people choose to follow the leader because they believe in what the person is doing. This is also the case for some of the examples of negative leadership role models given, so what is the difference? Some people would not choose to follow the likes of Hitler or Hussein, and although many did, many more were forced to do so. Other people follow bad leaders because they generate a sense of belonging and solidarity, perhaps at a time when there is uncertainty in the world. The integrity and ethicality of the examples of bad leaders are questionable at best and evil at worst. So perhaps integrity and morality are two of the things that we admire in good leaders?

Activity 1.8 Reflection

While Karen does a good day-to-day job in making the dialysis unit function, there may be longer-term considerations to take into account. As we saw earlier in the chapter, one of the roles of a leader is operating within the bigger picture. This also resonates with the role of the trained nurse, who has to account not only for the day-to-day running of the dialysis unit but also for the long-term health of the patients. So while it may be all right for the leader to allow someone else to take charge of some of the activities of the team, it is better if s/he is selective about who takes over what tasks and what they do. The staff in a scenario where it is uncertain who the real leader is will be confused, and may even be slightly angry as they see someone without genuine authority taking control.

Further reading

Aldgate, J and Dimmock, B (2003) Managing to Care, in Henderson, J and Atkinson, D (eds) *Managing Care in Context*. London: Routledge.

This chapter explores the values of care as well as social inclusion.

Handy, C (1994) *Understanding Organisations* (4th edition). London: Penguin.

This is the classic text on organisational culture.

Scott, J, Gill, A and Crowhurst, K (2008) *Effective Management in Long-Term Care Organisations.* Exeter: Reflect Press.

See especially Chapter 4 on Leadership.

Useful websites

www.businessballs.com
An interesting and quirky leadership and management resources website.

www.kingsfund.org.uk/topics/leadership_and_management/index.html
Perhaps the leading UK healthcare think tank.

www.midstaffspublicinquiry.com/report
The Francis report: *Report of the Mid Staffordshire NHS Foundation Trust Public Inquiry.*

Chapter 2
Teams and team work

Introduction

In this chapter we will begin by looking at your experiences of working in a team and progress to how you will develop skills to manage and lead a team. Nurses are educated to make autonomous and independent professional decisions to manage patient care. At the same time, in healthcare environments, there will be an expectation for nurses to:

- work within teams of similar professionals (e.g. in wards or units);
- work with interdisciplinary teams (e.g. specialist teams, stroke management);
- manage and direct teams with specific tasks to be achieved (e.g. infection control);
- lead teams to introduce new ways of working or maintain high standards of care (e.g. implement initiatives to ensure care is dignified).

The chapter will examine how teams work and how to evaluate the effectiveness of teams working together. The different roles that team members assume in teams are covered next and skills for dealing with improving team working, difficulties with team members and communication are explored. In this section we also explore some of the theoretical positions that have helped to explain team members' behaviour based upon social psychology. The practicalities of leading team meetings are described and finally the role of interdisciplinary team working is discussed.

How teams work

Understanding group dynamics is the starting point for recognising how to work best within and with teams. Group dynamics is the study of how people come together and then work together in teams or groups to share a common goal and purpose. It may seem that some groups can work well together as if by magic, but it often needs a deeper understanding of the nature of groups and the individuals within them to ensure they work together.

Activity 2.1   *Reflection*

Think of the last team or group in which you worked with others. Think about what went on in that team or group and jot down those activities. Would you describe the experience as one where individuals came together for personally focused but unifying relationships, such as found in families, religious groups, political affiliations or students studying the same module? Or did the experience involve a number of persons associated together in specific work, activity or task?

If it was the former, this would be described as a group activity. If it was the latter, it would be described as a team. A team has:

- defined objectives;
- positive relationships operating in a supportive environment;
- a spirit of co-operation and collaboration that is focused on accomplishing something specific;
- specific outcomes that require the members to be effective.

There is no right or wrong answer to this activity. The aim is to help you differentiate between a team and a group.

In summary, a team is a number of people organised to function co-operatively as a unit. By contrast, a group is deemed to be a number of people sharing something in common, such as an interest, belief or political aim. In common with wider organisations, teams exist to get a job of work done and again, like organisations, the purpose of teams is to get the job done efficiently and effectively.

Activity 2.2   *Critical thinking*

Think about a time when you were involved in working in a team. This could be the experience you thought of in Activity 2.1 if it fits the definition of a team. Write down the main aim or purpose of the team. Find out if the team/organisation has a values and vision statement or area philosophy. Consider the behaviours in the team that reflect these values/vision/philosophy and therefore if the statement contributed to the success or otherwise of the team.

There are some possible answers and thoughts at the end of the chapter.

It is often said of teams that the team as a whole is more effective than the sum of its parts; that is to say, a team can get more done and get it done effectively than the same number of individuals undertaking the task alone or in an unco-ordinated fashion. What do you think it is about teams that makes them more efficient and effective?

Team effectiveness

When a team works well together there is a conspicuous difference in the work atmosphere. This is noticeable in several different ways, for example when team members:

- have a shared understanding of team goals and tasks;
- are willing to listen to each other;
- feel comfortable discussing their work with each other;
- handle disagreements positively and openly;
- give and receive feedback with respect for each other's feelings.

Activity 2.3   *Reflection*

Compare the list of issue of attributes of an effective team, listed above, to the list of problems which Francis (2013) identified in the *Report of the Mid Staffordshire NHS Foundation Trust Public Inquiry*, discussed in Chapter 1.

Reflect on what this means for the role of values in the creation and effective working of teams.

There are some possible answers and thoughts at the end of the chapter.

In contrast, an ineffective team can be dominated by a few members with strong views and opinions. This can mean other members feel isolated from the main purpose of the team, which in turn can lead to feelings such as disenfranchisement, boredom and a lack of engagement and commitment.

An overuse of rules and regulations can lead to a stifling of informal relationship building, a process that is necessary to achieve team harmony and a supportive atmosphere. For example, each team will have a set of norms to guide it on how each person should be addressed – whether by organisational title and family name, or by first name. Another example might occur when a team has devised a specific method of dealing with patients' personal effects that fits fundamentally with the principles of the organisation's policy but which has been tested and proven to be less than practical given the nature of the unit – such as an emergency care unit, where people are constantly being moved around. On the other hand, a leader needs to know which institutional or legal regulations have to be followed for procedures and patient safety to be maintained. Individual team members should also be aware of their own professional responsibilities, guided by professional codes of conduct such as the Nursing and Midwifery Council (NMC) *Code* (NMC, 2015). Acknowledging individuals' responsibility also reinforces a sense of professional autonomy that can contribute positively to (or indeed detract from) team working.

Conflicts and disagreements are uncomfortable situations to deal with in a team. However, if not dealt with, these situations can lead to team members avoiding each other and suppressing negative feelings. This, in turn, can lead to resentment and frustration. So it is important to look at disagreements as opportunities for improving team relationships, by talking through differences and discussing alternative ways of working together. Team leaders can facilitate these discussions or they can be between the individuals provided ground rules are established and resolution of the differences is made a focal objective. A helpful team activity for dealing with differences is for the team to develop a team code of co-operation. (See the useful websites section at the end of this chapter, as well as Chapter 4, for further information on dealing with conflict.)

Giving feedback on performance to team members (whether you are a leader or from one co-worker to another) is an activity that, for an effective team, needs to be integrated into discussions about work. Effective feedback can enhance performance and improve the outcomes for the team. But it can so easily seem like negative criticism. This is especially so when it may be about the work of a senior, a more experienced colleague or towards a less experienced colleague who is developing their confidence in participating in the team. Chapter 3 looks more closely at working with individuals within teams, and Chapter 5 at issues around coaching and mentoring colleagues.

Negative or destructive criticism that is personal and hurtful has the potential to erupt and create discordant relationships that in turn lead to resentment and hidden feelings. One way for a team to learn to work with constructive feedback is to practise, or role play, in a simulated situation by giving feedback to one another to experience what it feels like; and to generate or become accustomed to phrases that are acceptable to convey feedback to one another in a respectful manner, as shown in Table 2.1.

Team dynamics and processes

The manner in which team members engage with each other and the factors that affect the team functioning well together are crucial aspects of effective team working. It is customary for there to be a designated team leader who will guide the team's performance and set the tone for how a team will work together. There are occasions, however, when a team will be self-directed and led jointly by members who have similar status or responsibilities, such as in a multidisciplinary group.

Characteristic	Effective	Ineffective
Leadership	Has a clear idea of what the team needs to do to achieve its goals, facilitates team working in a supportive atmosphere	Unclear idea of direction, does not allow team members to express ideas, does not capitalise on individual strengths in the team, overly autocratic
Environment	Informal, open	Indifferent, tense, strained
Discussion	Shared, focused on getting the job done and making improvements, actively listening to each other	Unfocused, dominated by a few strong characters, no active listening
Response to points of view	Respectful, encouraging, trusting each other's judgement	Patronising and judgemental, overly critical, mistrustful
Decision making	Reached by consensus, general agreement acceptable, dissenters tolerated, diverse views accepted	Lack of consensus and discussion, lack of flexibility or appreciation of differing perceptions, reliance on only majority acceptance as basis for agreement
Feedback	Constructive, honest, directed towards problem solving	Personal, destructive, aimed at creating embarrassment
Tasks, responsibilities	Clear, agreed by all despite some disagreement	Unclear, resented by dissenting members
Feelings	Open for discussion, exploration and support	Hidden, potentially explosive

Table 2.1: Summary of effective and ineffective team characteristics

Source: Adapted from Yoder-Wise (2007), page 345.

Norms

Most teams develop norms, which are the informal rules of behaviour shared and enforced by team members. These norms are developed by the team as a form of self-regulation to enable stable team functioning and survival. Norms are often linked to expected contributions from individual performances. For example, a student nurse's contribution to the team will be bounded by him or her being supernumerary or by how far s/he is into training. A healthcare assistant will have expectations of the role of a qualified nurse and will support the qualified nurse with agreed activities or parameters.

However, these parameters may vary from unit to unit and ward to ward, depending on the nature of the work or the experience of the team members. Trying to adapt to these different parameters can sometimes lead to misunderstandings because of the variations between teams, and student nurses, or new team members, will need to find out the norms of any group by discussion and reference to unit protocols. Examples of norms may include when breaks are taken, how shifts are negotiated, how to prevent embarrassment by being loyal to the team, and how collectively held values or principles are best expressed.

Roles

A role is an expected set of behaviours that is characteristic of a specific function in the team. Individuals may have an inherent tendency to perform a role, such as a nurturing role; alternatively, roles may be informally ascribed by the group or formally designated by the leader. Sullivan and Decker (2009, page 152) suggest roles can be divided into either task roles or nurturing roles and they are set out in Tables 2.2 and 2.3.

Initiator	Redefines problems and offers solutions, clarifies objectives
Contributor	Suggests agenda items and maintains time limits
Information seeker	Pursues descriptive baseline information for the team's work
Information giver	Expands information given by sharing experiences and making inferences
Opinion seeker	Explores viewpoints that clarify or reflect the values of other members' suggestions
Opinion giver	Conveys to group members what their essential values should be
Elaborator	Predicts outcomes and provides illustrations or expands suggestions, clarifying how they could work
Co-ordinator	Links ideas or suggestions offered by others
Orienter	Summarises the group's discussions and actions
Evaluator critic	Appraises the quantity and quality of the team's accomplishments against set standards
Energiser	Motivates the group to accomplish, qualitatively and quantitatively, the team's goals
Procedural technician	Supports team activity by arranging the environment and providing necessary equipment
Recorder	Documents the team's progress, actions and achievements

Table 2.2: Task roles

Encourager	Compliments members for their opinions and contributions to the team
Harmoniser	Relieves tensions and conflicts
Compromiser	Sets aside own position or views to maintain team harmony
Gate keeper	Stimulates discussion to enable all team members to communicate and participate, without allowing any one member to dominate
Group observer	Notices team processes and dynamics and informs the team of them
Follower	Passively attends meetings, listens to discussions and accepts the team's decisions

Table 2.3: Nurturing roles

Task roles keep the team focused on the objectives or functions of the team, whereas nurturing roles are facilitative or concerned with meeting interpersonal needs. Team members may adopt more than one role. A team leader may wish to accentuate one role in place of another to improve team functioning or alternatively to suppress a role that becomes over-emphasised. This is where the team leader assumes the nature of a conductor of an orchestra to utilise the different talents of the team, possibly at different times, to achieve a successful performance.

Meredith Belbin (2010) continues to be one of the major contributors to team role theory. Based on research into dysfunctional teams in the 1970s, Belbin found that effective teams were founded upon individual behaviours. The research was originally contrived to examine ways to control team dynamics; however, the researchers found that the difference between success and failure in a team was not based on intellect but on separate clusters of behaviour, each behaviour making a specific contribution to effective team working.

Belbin went on to identify nine team roles, each equally essential to the team and necessary to create a balance of roles. Of note, each identified role also displays some potential weaknesses which can interfere with team productivity but which are tolerated because of the positives that role also brings to the team. (See the useful websites at the end of the chapter for more information on Belbin's work.)

Influence of social systems on teams

Teams do not work in isolation. In healthcare they are often located in organisations or as subsets of other larger team structures such as departments or divisions. These background factors need to be taken into consideration for a full analysis of team dynamics (personal relationships) and processes (actions directed towards a specific aim). The sociologist George Homans (1961) used a systemic model to describe what he determined as the *internal systems* facing *external systems* and the impact of systems or feedback loops on team dynamics and consequently the effectiveness of teams.

An example of a system is the water cycle. Water is condensed from the atmosphere into clouds. It falls on to the earth and is collected into some form of reservoir. Humans channel the water into homes, factories and buildings. It is then utilised and transformed into waste water, which travels into rivers and seas to be evaporated back into the clouds, thus beginning the cycle all over again. At each stage, there are factors that influence the system, such as drought, over-usage and contamination. Equally, social systems can be affected by political, economic, social, techno-logical, legislative or environmental factors and therefore indicate the complexity and vulnera-bility of any system, as well as an ability to adapt to change. Understanding systems and how they work can have an impact on problem solving, team working and the management of change (see useful websites for more information on management application of systems thinking and PESTLE analyses).

While the importance of Homans' focus on individuals in small groups is now quoted less often, the fundamental findings of his work help to illuminate the factors that influence small-group functioning as a system and the consequences of those interactions, such as the impact of the manager's leadership style and external organisational infrastructures. Homans considered the essential elements of a group system to be the activities, processes, interactions, interpersonal relationships and attitudes of team members towards the goals of the team. See Figure 2.1 for a contemporary version of Homans' conceptual scheme.

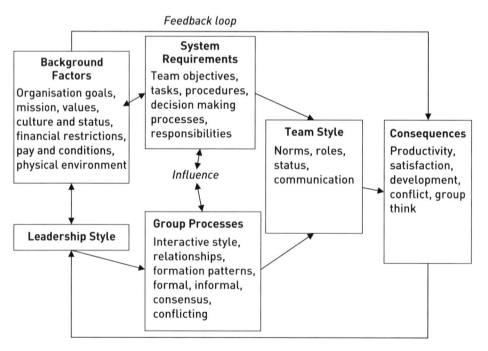

Figure 2.1: Homans' (1961) conceptual scheme of a small social system modified to reflect external and internal influences on consequences or effective outputs of a team in the twenty-first century

The conceptual feedback loop scheme Homans designed can help us to analyse groups and pinpoint problem areas when teams are ineffective. The importance of this work is to acknowledge that each action has an effect on another part of the process in a system, which is a major characteristic of systems theory and also of any small-group interaction. Homans' studies led to the development of social exchange theory and the premise that social interaction is based on the exchange of rewards.

Theory summary: Social exchange theory

This theory is predicated on establishing and sustaining reciprocity in social relationships, or mutual gratification between individuals, and the comparison of alternatives. The theory relies on the assumption that humans are rational and willing to exchange items, material or emotional, that are important to them for the benefit of other people. Integral concepts of the theory are the notions of justice and fairness. If the perceived costs of a relationship outweigh the benefits, the theory predicts that a person will leave the relationship. However, criticisms of the theory are that it favours an economic model, whereby all human interaction is likened to a process of cost–benefit analysis. Furthermore, there are opportunities for coercion and power tactics through the use of punishments and rewards if benefits are withdrawn. This is particularly evident in hierarchical or highly structured environments and groupings. The perceived effect of social obligations versus the amount of freedom of choice to exchange commodities can also negatively affect relationships. Understanding the intricacies of social exchange theory can help you understand social relationships in a team, when some people are more willing to help others, for example. (See the useful websites listed at the end of the chapter for further information.)

Creating effective team working

There has been much emphasis in the management literature on team-building activities to enhance team effectiveness by focusing on both task and relationship aspects of team working. The aims of team building are generally to:

- establish goals or specific objectives;
- clarify the values, purpose and functions of the team;
- allocate or re-allocate work roles and responsibilities;
- establish or revive communication patterns;
- clarify the group norms or expected behaviours of the team;
- identify the decision-making processes, responsibilities and hierarchies to define interteam relationships.

Team-building strategies can be used to help integrate individuals into teams, for example at induction, thereby creating effectiveness from the beginning of a team's lifetime. This may require funding and time away from the work situation. Alternatively, the team leader can undertake an analysis of the team's functioning if the team only needs finetuning (see the useful websites at the end of the chapter for team-building ideas). Team leaders can undertake an objective observation of team activities and then take this to team meetings for an open and self-aware evaluation and discussion. The team leader will need to take the emotional temperature of the team to decide if this will be appropriate.

Where the leader has to intervene because a team is not functioning effectively, there will need to be preliminary preparation aimed at analysing and defining the problems. This involves four steps:

1. Gathering information through different means, such as:
   (a) individual interviews;
   (b) anonymous surveys;
   (c) focus groups;
   (d) team meetings;
   (e) team supervision.

2. Identifying the team's strengths and areas for development.
3. Creating a plan of action to present to the team.
4. Identifying time to work on the issues identified in steps 1 and 2 above.

Background information can also be gathered about the structures of the organisation in which the team works, the current work climate and culture (e.g. financial constraints, status consciousness), team goals, professional characteristics of the team's work settings (e.g. mental health, community nursing, interdisciplinary, stroke rehabilitation, infection control), extent to which members work as autonomous individuals who link to a team, if based in a unit or spread out over a geographical area, complexity of roles and responsibilities, problem-solving styles, interpersonal relationships and relations with other groups in the organisation.

Sullivan and Decker (2009) suggest that the following eight questions should be asked:

1. To what extent does the team accept the goals of the organisation?
2. What, if any, hidden agendas interfere with the team's performance?
3. How effective is the team leadership?
4. To what extent do team members understand and accept their roles and responsibilities?
5. How does the team make a decision?
6. How does the team handle conflict? Are conflicts dealt with through avoidance or denial, force, accommodation, compromise, competition or collaboration?
7. What personal feelings do members have about each other?
8. To what extent do members trust and respect each other?

You can see that many of these questions relate to the characteristics of an effective team, discussed earlier in the chapter.

Strategies for managing team problems

We have discussed how to create effective team working, and we go into more detail by studying different styles of leadership and management elsewhere in this text. There are, however, a few pointers from Antai-Otong (1997) that are worth considering at this stage. These are aimed at specific team problems in nursing that a team leader will need to consider.

If the member is not a team player:

- consider carefully whether or not you want the person on the team;
- interact with the member assertively;
- give the person an opportunity to provide feedback on problematic situations;
- if communication with other team members is part of the problem, speak to the person one to one;
- listen actively when the person speaks, assessing verbal and non-verbal messages to identify any underlying issues or anxieties;
- avoid blaming and shaming, which tends to create defensiveness and arguments.

If the member seems to lack a sense of personal accountability:

- explain how failure to take responsibility affects the whole team (and give an example);
- without blaming or shaming, provide feedback from all team members.

If the team lacks clear goals:

- brainstorm activity to clarify short-term goals and develop an action plan with the team;
- strive for consensus regarding mission and goals;
- define member responsibilities;
- determine resources to accomplish goals (e.g. staffing expertise, financial, administrator support, time and equipment);
- periodically review team progress and achievements.

If team roles and boundaries are unclear:

- clarify role boundaries with the team's input;
- define all roles in the team, including the leader's;
- periodically review the team's staff or professional development needs.

Communication in the team

One of the most frequent causes of poor team work is failing communication. A major problem in busy units and departments is dealing with distractions if essential information is to be communicated. Most distractions are through sensory perceptions, such as poor lighting or background noise, talking, music, ringing phones and interruptions. Moving to a quieter environment or agreeing a time to speak when all parties can concentrate will help to minimise distractions. Anxieties around reporting, heavy workloads and keeping up to date can also be distracting.

Different levels of knowledge can create frustration between staff and misunderstandings over expectations if a standard of knowledge is not met. This requires a culture of openness in the team so that members feel free to ask questions and are not embarrassed to admit to not having specific information.

Good communication in teams requires a rhythm of reciprocation and team engagement. When spontaneous decisions have to be made, individuals can feel left out of the loop. All organisational and planning decisions should be agreed by consensus. However, an understanding that in exceptional circumstances there may be no time to communicate should also be agreed. Building in protected time or a mechanism to debrief the team on situations that fall outside the usual can help.

Differences in perception can misrepresent messages. The same message can be distorted through a lens of individual biases and preconceptions, sociocultural, ethnic and educational differences. Teams need to develop tolerance and awareness of individual perceptual filters – that is, how various team members see the world.

Distress, anxiety, high emotional states and certain personality traits, such as neuroticism, which is one of five key personality traits typified by excessive anxiety or indecision, can interfere with message communications. (If you are interested in finding out more about personality traits and identifying your own traits, see the useful websites at the end of the chapter.) As all members of any team are only human, home life stresses may be brought to the workplace. Team members need to feel safe to express their anxieties and have support from colleagues and the leader. However, if the stresses are interfering with effective working, occupational health support should be sought.

Dealing with meetings and committees

When you have a busy day ahead with many things on your to-do list, the last thing you may feel like spending time on is either going to a meeting or leading one. Meetings have a reputation for being boring and ineffective. But a well-led meeting can produce some very satisfying results and ensure everyone uses their time efficiently and purposively. Meetings are the processes by which organisations conduct their business through committee structures. There are different types of committees with distinct responsibilities and decision-making powers. Formal committees that are part of the governance structures of an organisation have different levels of authority and scope to make decisions. The highest level of committee structure is board level (see useful websites for further information). The responsibilities and functions of any committee are outlined in their **terms of reference** along with the membership, frequency and quorate requirements (minimum numbers attending allowing for decisions to be made). Very often committees have subcommittees that are convened to deal with specific tasks or matters that need specialist and focused attention.

Other committees may have an advisory remit but no authority or power, although they may have a strong influence on decisions. Committees are also set up to undertake specific tasks to be completed in a defined time span. An example is to develop a proposal for service development. The committee may then be tasked with implementing the developments or alternatively charged with investigating problems that require recommendations to be sent to a formal committee for action. Another form of committee will monitor activities such as standards or quality enhancement.

At ward or unit level the team meetings, where staff get together to discuss issues and problems and formulate local policies and procedures, are the focal point of work life. These meetings need to be seen as the pivotal place for decisions, discussions and forward planning to enhance the work environment and service delivery. It is the team leader's responsibility to ensure that the relevance and role of the meetings are understood and valued by team members. It should also be a time to enjoy being with colleagues who have a shared vision of their working lives.

Preparation; place and time; participation

The key to successful meetings is to follow the three Ps: preparation, place and time, and participation.

- *Preparation* is about clearly identifying the *purpose* of the meeting. Even if it is a short meeting, there should be an agenda with items to be discussed plainly stated and an indication as to whether the item is for discussion, decision or information. The leader needs to think ahead about the agenda items and undertake pre-reading, so that s/he is ready to respond to questions and has potential solutions to problems ready as well as an idea of delegated responsibilities if this is required.
- *Place and time*: advance information about venue and duration is vital. Meetings are work and not social gatherings, so an emphasis on getting things done and an action-oriented approach are needed to encourage effective use of time. Members will also think it worthwhile attending if their time is not wasted.
- *Participation*: your knowledge of team dynamics and the roles your team members play, whether nurturing or task-oriented, will be valuable in understanding how team members participate in the meeting. Their ability to contribute will also depend on their level of skills and knowledge. However, this could be detrimentally affected by the phenomenon known as **group think**, which is a particular concern if you have a philosophy of self-directedness in a group of experienced professionals. The ability to chair meetings, take notes if necessary, delegate activities and follow up on actions are key elements of an effective meeting.

Theory summary: From group think to team think

In the 1970s social psychologist Irving Janis identified the phenomenon of group think that happens when a group makes faulty decisions (Janis, 1972, 1982). This is due to pressures from within the group whose members ignore alternatives and make irrational decisions that ignore the humanising factors present in other groups or sections of an organisation or community. When group members are from the same background, are insulated from outside influences and there are no clear decision-making structures, they are particularly susceptible to group think. There are eight documented symptoms of group think:

1. An illusion of invulnerability creates excessive optimism that encourages taking extreme risks.

2. Belief in collective rationalisation – members discount warnings and do not reconsider their assumptions.

3. Belief in inherent morality – members believe in the rightness of their cause and therefore ignore the ethical or moral consequences of their decisions.

4. Stereotyped views of other groups lead to negative views of 'the enemy', which make effective responses to conflict seem unnecessary.

5. Direct pressure on dissenters involves putting members under pressure to avoid expressing arguments against any of the group's views.

6. Self-censorship means that doubts and deviations from the perceived group consensus are not expressed.

7. Illusion of unanimity – the majority view and judgements are assumed to be unanimous.

8. Self-appointed 'mind guards' involve members protecting the group and the leader from information that is problematic or contradictory to the group's cohesiveness, view and/or decisions.

When groups are tightly knit and under pressure to make decisions, irrational decisions are likely as alternatives are not considered. Failure to discuss options and potential outcomes leads to carelessness and a need to achieve unanimity. The overall outcome is groups that have a low probability of successful decision making.

To move towards 'team think', team leaders need to facilitate discussions in teams that are not reliant only on members of the team, by introducing observers to the team or other specialists to give a point of view. Dealing with dominant members, as discussed previously, and not putting the team under pressure will also offset these effects. One of the main factors is always to consider alternative perspectives and the viewpoints or goals of other teams or activities in the organisation to gain a wider viewpoint of how decisions fit into the whole picture before making final decisions.

Interdisciplinary team working

Up until now this chapter has focused on team working within a professional group or disciplinary area, although it is acknowledged that there are many different types of teams working within nursing. In healthcare today there is an increasing need for professionals from different disciplines to work together to improve patient services for seamless care. Nurses, physicians, dieticians, social workers, pharmacists, physiotherapists, administrators and technicians, among others, may all find themselves working together with a common aim but a different perspective on how to achieve this aim.

Activity 2.4　　　　　　　　　　　　*Evidence-based practice and research*

In your most recent practice placement, were you aware of any interdisciplinary teams functioning in the organisation? Next time you are in practice ask your mentor if there are any interdisciplinary teams and find out what the objectives are for these teams. You might like to ask your mentor if you can sit in on an interprofessional meeting so that you can listen to the ways in which the professions interact.

At the beginning of this chapter, Competency 7 of the NMC Standards domain Leadership, management and team working sets out specifically nurses' requirements for interdisciplinary working. Use this as a guide to analyse one interdisciplinary team's activity in your placement area. You may want to make notes for your assessment portfolio.

There is no right or wrong answer to this activity.

According to Hewison and Sim (1998), interprofessional working requires co-operation and mutual understanding, yet there are many barriers that can prevent this from happening. They explored the role of professional codes of ethics and the potential to foster professional distinctiveness and exclusivity. By identifying areas of common ground, in particular around **whistle blowing**, they felt multidisciplinary working could develop. To achieve effective interprofessional working they argued that the role of management was crucial in leading teams in order to minimise professional rivalries and retain a central focus on patient need.

In common with all elements of good leadership, working with other professions requires that the leader is clear about the values of the team. In the care setting this will mean a desire to achieve positive outcomes for patients or clients; what different professionals view as a positive outcome and how this is achieved is not as important as the fact that they all support achieving a positive outcome, as described by the patient.

The following is an account of a study to examine the effectiveness of a team and the multidisciplinary working processes.

Research summary: The impact of team processes on psychiatric case management

This is a study undertaken to identify the structures and interactions within community mental health teams that facilitate or impede effective teamwork and psychiatric case management. The view of the researchers was that effective case management requires close collaboration between case managers or care co-ordinators and other members of the multidisciplinary mental health team, yet there has been little research into this relationship. A multiple case study of seven UK community mental health teams was conducted between 1999 and 2001, using qualitative methods of participant observation, semi-structured interviews and document review. Factors were identified from the study that impacted on the ability of care co-ordinators to act effectively. These were *structure and procedures; disrespect and withdrawal; humour and undermining; safety and disclosure.*

Care co-ordination was enhanced when team structures and policies were in place and where team interactions were respectful. Where members felt disrespected or undermined, communication, information sharing and collaboration were impaired, with a negative impact on the care provided to service users. The researchers concluded that teams require clear operating procedures alongside trust and respect across the professions if there is to be open, safe and reflective participation.

Chapter summary

This chapter has given you an overview of how teams work and how you might better understand the way in which individuals in teams work together. There are strategies in the chapter to help you work more effectively with others in a leadership capacity or collegiate manner in teams. The chapter has only touched the surface and you are strongly recommended to access the useful websites or further reading to provide you with more detailed guidance.

Activities: brief outline answers

Activity 2.2 Critical thinking

Teams utilise all of the skills of the people in the team and can therefore solve more complex problems than individuals can manage alone. Because people have different skills, then the breadth of work they can achieve in teams is increased, but so is the complexity, as individuals solve the problems facing others within the team as they exercise their skills sets in different ways.

Activity 2.3 Reflection

Teams are not effective just because they are; rather they are effective because the people within the teams want them to be, share common goals and values and put these into practice. When values are relegated to second place after targets, then the quality of the work of the team is affected, as described in the Francis report.

Further reading

Bach, S and Grant, A (2015) *Communication and Interpersonal Skills in Nursing* (3rd edition). London: SAGE/Learning Matters.

Two chapters deal with effective team working and the working environment – Chapter 5: Understanding Potential Barriers, and Chapter 7: The Environmental Context.

Goodwin, B and Clemow, R (2010) *Nursing and Interprofessional Practice* (2nd edition). Exeter: Learning Matters.

Chapter 6: Teamwork is about interdisciplinary team work.

Useful websites

www.acas.org.uk/index.aspx?articleid=1218

Advisory, Conciliation and Arbitration Service (ACAS), dealing with conflict at work.

www.managementhelp.org/grp_skll/meetings/meetings.htm

Free Management Library information on preparing, planning, leading and evaluating meetings.

http://managementhelp.org/systems/systems.htm#anchor6759

Free Management Library on the development and application of systems theory to analyse problems and influence change management.

www.businessballs.com/teambuilding.htm

This site provides ideas for team building and also discussion around corporate social responsibility and ethical organisations.

www.belbin.com

Home page for Belbin's team role theory, role descriptors and explanations of the theory.

www.infed.org/thinkers/george_homans.htm

www.angelfire.com/bug/theory_project/Exchange_Theory.htm

These two websites both provide background to the work of the sociologist George Homans and the development of social exchange theory.

www.the-happy-manager.com/tips/pestle-analysis

A short and clear overview of the PESTLE analysis tool.

Chapter 3
Working with individuals in teams

NMC Standards for Pre-registration Nursing Education

This chapter will address the following competencies:

Domain 1: Professional values

6. All nurses must understand the roles and responsibilities of other health and social care professionals, and seek to work with them collaboratively for the benefit of all who need care.

Domain 3: Nursing practice and decision making

10. All nurses must evaluate their care to improve clinical decision making, quality and outcomes, using a range of methods, amending the plan of care, where necessary, and communicating changes to others.

Essential Skills Clusters

This chapter will address the following ESCs:

Cluster: Organisational aspects of care

12. People can trust the newly registered graduate nurse to respond to their feedback and a wide range of other sources to learn, develop and improve services.
14. People can trust the newly registered graduate nurse to be an autonomous and confident member of the multi-disciplinary or multi-agency team and to inspire confidence in others.
15. People can trust the newly registered graduate nurse to safely delegate to others and to respond appropriately when a task is delegated to them.
16. People can trust the newly registered graduate nurse to safely lead, co-ordinate and manage care.
17. People can trust the newly registered graduate nurse to work safely under pressure and maintain the safety of service users at all times.
19. People can trust the newly registered graduate nurse to work to prevent and resolve conflict and maintain a safe environment.

Chapter aims

After reading this chapter, you will be able to:

- understand the significance of the concepts 'responsibility' and 'accountability' in relation to individuals in teams;
- evaluate the factors affecting the delegation of work to others in a team;
- evaluate the role of personal development plans (PDPs) for an individual in a team;
- understand the relevance of individual, organisational, generational and cultural differences to team working.

Introduction

In this chapter topics such as individual roles, responsibility and accountability with reference to the Nursing and Midwifery Council (NMC) *Code* (NMC, 2015) will be discussed along with techniques for delegating. PDPs, performance appraisal and staff development principles will be explored. Cultural and generational differences will be discussed. Employment issues such as health and safety legislation and risk management will be included in this chapter. How to recruit, select and retain staff to work in teams will be covered briefly in Chapter 7. In addition, you will find it helpful to look at the NMC (2015) *Code*, which has specific guidance for nurses and midwives working with others. A number of key areas are covered in this guidance, including:

1. Communicate clearly.
2. Work cooperatively.
3. Share your skills, knowledge and experience for the benefit of people receiving care and your colleagues.
4. Be accountable for your decisions to delegate tasks and duties to other people.

Activity 3.1   *Evidence-based practice and research*

Go to the NMC web page (**http://www.nmc-uk.org**) and review the underpinning principles of these themes proposed by the NMC.

These principles and themes are further discussed throughout this chapter.

The 2010 NMC *Standards for Pre-registration Nursing Education* and *The Code* (2015) place considerable emphasis on team working and the responsibility of both the individual in the team and the team leader. In this chapter we will be focusing on the leadership role in supporting individuals in the team.

Individual roles, responsibility and accountability

In the previous chapter we looked at the many different forms and types of team and the ways in which teams can work together. In this chapter we will be concentrating on the individuals in the team and begin by looking at roles and responsibilities. Each team will have a defined purpose, indicated in the two scenarios below.

Scenarios: Different examples of teams

Team A is brought together for a short-term activity such as the length of a shift. This could be a band 5 nurse caring for six patients in a section of a ward with possibly, and depending on the acuity of the needs of the patients or the seriousness of the illnesses, another band 5 colleague and two healthcare assistants (HCAs) from 7 a.m. to 3 p.m.

Team B is a multidisciplinary team convened to work together for a longer duration to implement a new service initiative to improve patient care. In this example it is a project group to ensure patients receive dignified care.

Within each of these teams an individual team member will have a role or a part to play in completing a task and in the overall remit of the team and be responsible for various actions. It is worth reminding ourselves of the meaning of the word 'responsible' and how that relates to the concept of accountability.

Activity 3.2   *Critical thinking*

Write out your definitions of 'responsible' and 'accountable' without referring to a dictionary. Think about the differences between the two concepts.

Then think about what the difference is for those who are leading teams and for those who are being led. The exercise should be about leadership styles and priorities, not accountability.

Further guidance is given on this activity at the end of the chapter.

The next step is to ensure that team members understand their responsibilities in relation to a task. A team leader is expected to assign responsibility for activities and this can become a mine-field of emotions and hurt feelings if communicated inappropriately or to a person with the wrong skill set or knowledge. We will discuss this in more detail later in the chapter under the heading of delegation, but in this discussion we are focusing on conveying a sense of responsibility to complete team work successfully. This is not achieved by magic or guesswork or estimates of a team member's capabilities. It requires clear thinking about what is expected and clear communication as well as checking progress throughout the task. If this is not done, leaders are responsible for less than satisfactory results and cannot hold team members accountable for any shortfalls. To ensure responsibilities are understood and carried out:

- identify the appropriate team member with the skills and knowledge to carry out the task;
- ensure resources are available for the task to be completed or advise the team member how to obtain resources;
- explain and assign the task;
- identify the level of support to be given to the team member (e.g. is the person novice or experienced?);
- set the standards;
- check progress;
- make sure the standards are met and the task completed.

Delegation

As a team leader you can only delegate those tasks for which you are responsible. As we have seen in the discussion above and in the activity, the delegator remains accountable for the task, whereas the delegate is accountable to the delegator and has responsibilities for the task being assigned.

Delegation is a means of dividing up the workload in a team. It is also a way for leaders to help team members develop or enhance their abilities and skills. It can promote team working, foster collaboration and increase the amount of work achievable in a given time when compared with a person working alone.

Delegation is not a means of escaping tasks or responsibilities that you do not want. Nor is it work or task allocation. Allocating tasks is to transfer a task from one person to another, whereas delegation gives someone the authority to carry out a task in place of the person who would normally undertake that task. By transferring authority, the person has the right to act and is empowered to undertake the task (i.e. this could be to ask others to undertake subtasks as part of the overall activity). This difference should be made explicit to the delegatee when a task is delegated.

Scenarios

Let's return to the scenario of Team B. Within this group there are representatives from different wards in a hospital as the initiative is to be undertaken across the organisation. The team also includes representatives of different disciplines. Once a plan of action has been agreed, to ensure dignity is implemented on the wards, the representatives will go back to their bases and initiate changes in the ward to bring about a successful outcome. They will need the collaboration of their peers, subordinates and, possibly,

continued . . .

seniors to carry out subtasks. They may be experts in change management strategies and be able to charm the birds from the trees, but they will also need the authority to undertake this task and have that recognised by the teams they are going to be working with. Multidisciplinary workers may have to work with professions other than their own. To be successful, they will also need their personal skills and the support of the authority invested in the group to bring about these changes. The authority invested in the project group, probably by a senior member of the directorate or division, will provide the legitimate authority for the project to carry out adjustments in the wards.

In the case of Team A, where tasks are being divided amongst the team, the aim is to assign relevant activities to the appropriately qualified or grade of staff. The team leader will have the authority to assign the tasks and the responsibility to match activities to grade or competence. However, the team member has the responsibility for his or her own activities and the care of the patient.

Delegation decisions

Who to delegate to and how to delegate are, for the novice, quite daunting decisions. There are several potential competing thoughts and feelings impacting these decisions, such as:

- guilt in asking someone else to do a job that you are well qualified or competent to undertake;
- reluctance to delegate if you think you can do a task better or quicker;
- having to ask someone you are equal to in grade or who you haven't worked with before.

Activity 3.3   Reflection

Consider the last time someone delegated responsibility to you. How did you feel? What reasons might you have had for wanting to do the task? What reasons might you have had for not wanting to undertake the task?

Further guidance is given on this activity at the end of the chapter.

Working with skill mix

Changing care needs and priorities mean care leaders have to get used to thinking about and adapting to the changing **skill mix** in their teams. In NHS acute care settings, increasing numbers of HCAs will be working alongside qualified nurses undertaking whole-patient care and not just tasks such as observations of temperature, pulse and respirations (Gainsborough, 2009). The majority of HCAs are employed on band 3 grades and you may want to request a copy of the generic job description for this grade to understand the scope of practice for this grade. The job description should link to the NHS Agenda for Change band and the NHS Knowledge and Skills Framework national clinical grading criteria. Some HCAs will take up assistant or associate practitioner roles, with many having completed a specialised Foundation degree in healthcare. These were introduced by the Skills for Health organisation in 2000. HCAs with this specialist qualification can move from the Agenda for Change band 3 grade to band 4. It would be worth your while looking at the difference between these two grades and the difference in the roles and responsibilities of an associate practitioner and a registered practitioner. Each band has a corresponding list of likely responsibilities and roles (**www.NHSemployers.org**).

In addition, some HCAs will have achieved National Vocational Qualifications (NVQs) at level 3 or 4. NVQs are a competency-based qualification and there are five levels. Although NVQs are not usually compared directly to conventional academic qualifications, approximate equivalences have been established. Additionally, NVQs are currently in the process of being replaced by the new Qualifications Credit Framework. See the useful websites at the end of the chapter for more information.

In mixed teams providing acute care to adult patients, qualified nurses will need to delegate care to HCAs and other non-professionally registered staff such as domestic or ancillary personnel. In community settings health visitors delegate care to nursery nurses and band 5 nurses (staff nurses) who undertake some developmental screening. In some teams, such as intermediate care in the community, community practitioners are band 5 staff nurses working with specialist community practice home nurses. In acute mental health settings assistant practitioners work with registered mental health nurses. In child care nursery nurses work with staff nurses and in learning disability settings registered learning disability nurses work with nursing assistants.

All this points to the fact that the leader has to have an awareness not only of the work which needs to be done by the team, but also the skills sets available from within the team. Knowing the team and the skill mix within the team will enable the leader to make appropriate decisions about task delegation and will help to promote effective care provision.

Enabling staff development through delegation

By delegating tasks and responsibilities to other members of the team, opportunities can be provided for staff development, increased job satisfaction and promotion. It has been understood for some considerable time that one of the key motivators of people in the workplace lies in giving them responsibility to undertake tasks which stretch them professionally (Herzberg, 1959). People also have a need to undertake tasks which they see as worthwhile and which might contribute to their advancement both personally and professionally (Herzberg, 1959). It should be clear by now that one of the criteria for role satisfaction for all team members has to be that they are doing something which aligns with their values. Factors such as a positive organisational culture encourage delegation, as well as the expression of personal qualities that engender co-operation and a willingness to collaborate, the appropriate use of resources (equipment and learning environment) and appropriate supervision or guidance for the task.

Selecting the right person to delegate to requires a corresponding leadership style. It is often assumed that delegation is a management role; however, recognising the talents and strengths of individuals and working to meet their developmental stages require leadership qualities. Kotter (1990) recognised this and developed a scheme for matching the appropriate leadership style to the individual's levels of commitment and competence. This enables leaders to draw out the best in their team members and identify where development needs to take place. Table 3.1 outlines an adaptation of Kotter's ideas. We discuss coaching in Chapter 5.

Developmental level of individuals	Appropriate leadership style
Low competence – high commitment	Directing
Some competence – low commitment	Coaching
High competence – variable commitment	Supporting
High competence – high commitment	Delegating

Table 3.1: Matching individual levels of competence and motivation for tasks with leadership style
Source: Adapted from Kotter (1990).

Personal development plans

We have just talked about developing staff, so it would seem timely to introduce the topic of development planning. The PDP (sometimes called individual development plan or staff review) is intended to help employees enhance existing skills or knowledge and develop new skills to fulfil an existing role. If responsibilities have increased, the PDP may be utilised to identify a level that requires a regrading to a higher grade. Alternatively, it can be used to identify a role at a grade equivalent to a previous role. In NHS settings the PDP should be carried out annually and is a method of ensuring staff maintain their skills and knowledge to perform their roles.

The PDP provides a framework for:

- prioritising developmental support;
- planning related activities, such as attending study days, seminars or courses, in an appropriate sequence and within agreed timescales;
- monitoring progress within those timescales;
- evaluating outcomes in terms of skills, knowledge and expertise;
- developing individual career plans and identifying organisational succession plans.

A specifically designed e-platform for working with PDPs in healthcare settings can be found on the Knowledge Skills Framework website (see the useful websites at the end of the chapter). As a student you may have completed a PDP that looks at your personal growth and development during your course. As a newly qualified nurse you will be expected to follow a period of preceptorship which will give you the opportunity to identify areas you want to concentrate on during your preceptorship to extend your confidence in specific skills and knowledge. As you progress in experience and seniority you may be involved in undertaking PDPs for HCAs and you would be advised to look out for any training being offered, as all organisations have a slightly different emphasis on how they conduct the PDP process. As a registered practitioner you will be required to maintain your professional knowledge to remain on the NMC register. Known as PREP (Post Registration Education and Practice), you are required to declare you have completed the following every 3 years:

- 450 hours of registered practice in the previous 3 years;
- 35 hours of learning activity (continuing professional development) in the previous 3 years.

The practice element can be met through administrative, supervisory, teaching, research and managerial roles as well as providing direct patient care.

Activity 3.4   *Reflection*

Look at the learning objectives you set with your mentor at the start of your last placement. Consider how the allocation of work which you undertook allowed you to meet the targets for development which you set. If you are newly qualified you might like to do this activity with your preceptor or line manager, considering how your skills sets are growing to help meet the needs of the service in which you are working.

As this answer is based on your own observation, there is no outline answer at the end of the chapter.

Performance appraisal

Redshaw (2008) investigated the role and extent of appraisal in nursing. At the time, only six out of ten staff in the NHS received a formal appraisal. There is a distinction between appraisal – the judgement and assessment of the worth or value of an employee's performance at work – and personal development – a process of mutually planning (between staff member and senior staff in the organisation) supporting activities for individuals to undertake their role in the workplace. Appraisal does not always have a good press as staff can feel that it is a waste of time or does not measure accurately their contribution to the work. Alternatively, some staff want to know how they are performing and have some measure of performance as a yardstick to improve, for their own satisfaction or to progress in their career or work roles. Chapter 7 gives more information about performance appraisal.

There are different forms of appraisal scheme: top-down (the most common), self-appraisal and peer appraisal, upward appraisal where appraiser reports on management's performance (the least common) and multi-rater appraisal, which is usually in the form of 360-degree feedback about an individual from a variety of peers, subordinates, external and internal appraisers and superiors.

There are difficulties with performance appraisal both in the implementation and management of appraisal schemes. Some appraisal systems can be time consuming both in terms of the interview and form completion. The objective of appraisal is to identify and reward performance. If this is not achieved in practice, the scheme will lack merit. If there is an appraisal system alongside a development-planning scheme, the allocation of rewards can undermine the personal developmental aspects as the emphasis will be on organisational aims and outputs. There are also concerns about the subjectivity of making appraisals that can be influenced by personal attributes of the appraiser or employee and environmental or situational factors such as individual health or organisational changes.

Support for staff – including performance review – can raise standards in the workplace. However, the quest for better performance has not always been accompanied by a better system of appraisal. According to Redshaw (2008), the most important process for improved performance is not to set goals and order staff to achieve them, but to improve relationships so that staff feel highly valued and have a sense of belonging. So, the development of positive manager–employee relationships is an effective way of improving the appraisals process. Conflicts, lack of understanding of the aims of the process and mutual distrust will have a negative effect, resulting in staff finding it difficult to accept criticism and feedback. This in turn will have a wider impact on staff performance. This is especially relevant in team-based work where the style of the leader can influence colleagues' performance and attitudes towards appraisal. Another factor is the way in which feedback is handed to employees. Giving feedback can be challenging and managers need good communication skills to ensure feedback is constructive and helpful. Feedback that is focused on blame damages self-confidence, whereas constructive criticism to recognise and improve poor performance is appropriate.

Case study: Ensuring adequate nutrition

The setting is a busy acute female medical ward. In a six-bedded bay, Mary, a slight 72-year-old who was originally admitted with unstable type 2 diabetes, is waiting to be discharged home. Although the ward staff have told her she won't be leaving until after lunch, Mary has had her bags packed since 7 a.m. as she is keen to leave the ward. Mary is a quiet and undemanding person who rarely complains. The band 5 team leader for the shift, Sandy, passes by the bed and sees that Mary has been provided with her lunch of soup and a sandwich. Nutrition is an important part of Mary's recovery plan to treat her diabetes and also to help her restore her body mass index to within normal limits. Mary should be having fortified soups and not the usual soup, as she has been given in this instance, from the hospital menu. Fortified soups are available for patients in the ward kitchen. Sandy has spoken to the HCAs and ward hostess before about ensuring that Mary has fortified soups and that she receives reinforcing messages when she has her meals of the relevance and importance of maintaining her nutrition once she is at home. Sandy believes the HCAs are capable of giving health education as well as ensuring patients receive the appropriate nutrition. This would be in line with the NHS Knowledge and Skills Framework section on health and well-being and appropriate for an HCA to undertake. She also believes that the HCA, Joanna in this case, should have responsibility for ensuring the ward hostess provides the correct soup and that Joanna should monitor this. Sandy resolves to speak to the HCA to provide feedback on her performance and what she expects the HCA's role to be in this respect.

Fowler (1996) suggests the following principles when giving feedback:

1. Be specific and give examples.
2. Be constructive and focus on what can be learnt from the event.
3. Avoid comments about attitude or personality that cannot realistically be changed and concentrate on behaviour and how it affects performance.
4. Give feedback regularly and do not wait for annual reviews; it should be timely and as close to the event as possible.
5. Encourage self-reflection – feedback is not just about telling.
6. Avoid argument – a practical discussion about differences of opinion on performance is much more helpful. Listen to the other person's point of view.
7. Explain the reasons for the request for a change that may be needed and encourage the development of an action plan.
8. Take feedback yourself – the discussion should be two-way and there may be lessons to learn from your own performance.
9. Encourage openness and this will lead to the other person seeking regular feedback as part of the culture of the unit/department and your leadership style.

Activity 3.5 — *Decision making*

Imagine that you are Sandy, the band 5 staff nurse on this shift, who is leading the team. Make a draft plan of how you would give feedback to Joanna. What points would you make? What would be the principles upon which you would base your feedback for Joanna? When would you go about giving the feedback?

Further guidance is given on this activity at the end of the chapter.

Individual, cultural and generational differences

Working with individuals in teams, the team leader will encounter individual differences in the team members that have to be acknowledged and worked with to ensure effective working relationships.

In Chapter 1, we examined different roles that individuals assume in a team by individual differences. The chapter concentrates on the individual traits and personality that a person has. In Chapter 2, we had a brief look at these characteristics and now we can further explore personal characteristics that fall within the 'big five personality theory'.

Research summary: Five-factor model of personality

In 1991 Barrick and Mount reported on a study that they undertook to examine the relationships between workplace roles and individual personality characteristics, defined in the 'big five personality theory' or 'five-factor model of personality', as it is known theoretically. The personality dimensions are:

1. extroversion;
2. emotional stability;
3. agreeableness;
4. conscientiousness;
5. openness to experience.

These were matched to three job performance criteria (job proficiency, training proficiency and personnel data – i.e. age, time in occupation) for five occupational groups (professionals such as teachers, nurses and doctors; police; managers; sales; skilled/semi-skilled occupations).

The results of their analysis indicated that one dimension of personality, conscientiousness, showed consistent relations with all job performance criteria for all occupational groups. For the remaining personality dimensions, the correlations varied by occupational group and professional criteria.

Extroversion was a valid predictor for two occupations involving social interaction: managers and sales (across criterion types). Also, both openness to experience and extroversion were valid predictors of the training proficiency criterion (i.e. those persons who had a role as educators and this was across all professions in the study). Other personality dimensions were also found to be valid predictors for some occupations and some criterion types, but the correlation between the occupation and criterion was small.

Overall, the results illustrated the benefits of using the five-factor model of personality to predict suitability for job performance. The findings were thought to have numerous implications for research and practice, especially in the subfields of personnel selection, training and development, and performance appraisal. This means that there is some substance to the theory that certain personal characteristics are better suited to certain occupational roles.

Organisational culture

Another factor to influence individual behaviour in teams is cultural mores. Culture is not so much about what an organisation does; rather, in the sense we are thinking about it in this book, culture is about how staff experience their place of work (Kohn and O'Connell, 2005). The philosophies, social and historical background to an organisation all shape the prevailing culture. In addition, practices within an organisation that are derived from leadership or management style have an impact. Examples include whether an organisation is people- or task-oriented; if there is an emphasis on control and command; the extent of tolerance to risk taking; if there is a reward culture or a blame culture; the manner in which an organisation responds to change – rapidly or at snail pace – and finally, the extent to which an individual willingly signs up to the philosophy of the organisation.

Activity 3.6   *Reflection*

Take a moment to reflect on the culture of the organisation you have worked in, or had practice experience in, most recently. Can you recognise any of the characteristics mentioned above? How do they relate to the culture of the organisation? Then think about what kind of culture you would want to foster if you were leading a team.

As this answer is based on your own observation, there is no outline answer at the end of the chapter.

Cultural diversity

The other aspect of culture is the sociological phenomenon of culture, which affects our lives in a complex and multifaceted manner in our culturally diverse society. To work collaboratively in teams, nurses have to understand and respect unfamiliar behaviour patterns and attitudes without dismissing or devaluing them. Yet, this diversity needs to be harnessed to be effective and to meet patients' needs. Bach and Grant (2015) consider the relevance of focusing on cultural diversity and communication, as this is often the first barrier to overcome.

There are thought to be four cultural dimensions along which cultures differ in the workplace:

1. directness – getting to the point ↔ implying the messages;
2. hierarchy – following orders ↔ engaging in debate;
3. consensus – dissenting is accepted ↔ unanimity is needed;
4. individualism – individual winners are acceptable ↔ team effectiveness is paramount.

Different attitudes to authority, culturally embedded notions of authority and power, perceptions of gender stereotypes and acceptance of directness or expectations of hidden meanings in communications all influence these cultural dimensions. A team leader will need to be observant to recognise at which point of these dimensions individuals are expected to behave in the team and how each individual will be interpreting these dimensions, depending on their social and cultural background and the norms they are accustomed to. In addition, the philosophy of the organisation and the nature of the tasks undertaken (e.g. the perceived status of those tasks) will have an influence.

Generational differences

Every generation is affected by the time in which they are growing up. Influences such as economic (e.g. post World War II thriftiness), political (e.g. Thatcherism and individualistic political policies), social events (Bob Geldof Live Aid concerts), feminist ideology and technological advances will play a significant part in forming the context for attitudes to be formed about work. While the cusp years can vary depending on the individual, here's how the generations are typically described:

- traditionalists or veterans: born before 1946;
- baby boomers: born between 1946 and 1964;
- generation X: born between 1965 and 1980;
- generation Y or millennials: born after 1980.

Patterson (2005) has gathered together observations from her work as an organisational psychologist and the business management literature to assemble impressions of the main characteristics associated with generations since the early part of the last century (Table 3.2).

Traditionalists (1925–1945)	Baby boomers (1946–1964)	Generation X (1965–1980)	Millennials (1981 to present)
Practical	Optimistic	Sceptical	Hopeful
Patient, loyal and hardworking	Teamwork and co-operation	Self-reliant	Meaningful work
Respectful of authority	Ambitious	Risk taking	Diversity and change valued
Rule followers	Workaholic	Balances work and personal life	Technology-savvy

Table 3.2: Defining work characteristics
Source: Adapted from Patterson (2005).

While not everyone will fall into a defined category, taking note of generational diversity is important as intergenerational conflict, or lack of understanding of different generational mores, can impede plans, team work and ideas for service improvement. For example, a baby boomer manager may not be familiar with social networking and the impact technologies have had on social relationships. The manager's ideas on how relationships are communicated and sustained might involve paper notices on notice boards, whereas the millennial team members will be likely to expect messages to be posted on a social networking site.

Research summary: Generational differences

Smola and Sutton (2002) surveyed 350 baby boomers and generation Xers in 1974 and 1999 and found an overall change in work values as generations matured, such as giving work a lower priority in life and placing less value on feeling a sense of pride at work. In particular, the younger women tend to question workplace expectations more often, such as long work hours or taking work home, and they are often more open about their parenting obligations and commitments. The study also found generational differences, for example, generation Xers report less loyalty to their companies, wanting to be promoted more quickly and being more 'me-oriented' than baby boomers. It is suggested that such differences are, in part, accounted for by workers' values shifting as they age.

Working in teams can cause clashes between individuals in the workplace. Baby boomers, traditionalists, generation Xers and millennials all represent different cultural norms as far as respecting tradition, social manners, speaking frankly about personal issues and attitudes to hierarchy are concerned. The generations will respond to change in different ways – fear of change can be expressed in one way if it results from being too used to certain ways of doing things, and in another way completely if it results from immaturity and insecurity. Baby boomers may find traditionalists inflexible, and themselves be perceived as self-absorbed in return. Generation Xers, on the other hand, may find themselves criticised for being cynical and negative while seeing baby boomers as having their own conventional rigidity, and millennials as spoiled upstarts. Such clashes may be reduced if there are opportunities for facilitated discussion in team meetings, helping the various participants to explore the benefits and disadvantages of different approaches to working methods. A team leader will have the role of encouraging effective listening between team members, reducing ambiguity and misunderstandings, supporting the sharing of expertise and recognition of individuals' contributions to the team. It is helpful if the various generational groups can be encouraged to understand why each might respond in a particular fashion, and how patients might benefit in each case.

This approach is even more useful in interdisciplinary teams if misunderstandings are to be avoided. Team members can then work towards seeking a balance between building on traditional procedures and supporting newer ideas to blend the different work ethics of the generational groups.

According to Patterson (2005), effective, or similar, messages are for:

- traditionalists: 'Your experience is respected' or 'It is valuable to hear what has worked in the past';
- baby boomers: 'You are valuable, worthy' or 'Your contribution is unique and important to our success';

- generation Xers: 'Let's explore some options outside of the box' or 'Your technical expertise is a big asset';
- millennials: 'You will have an opportunity to collaborate with other bright, creative people' or 'You have really rescued this situation with your commitment'.

What this research shows, and the important message for the leader, is that different people view the world in different ways. This will mean that differing members of a team will have different needs and wants, as well as different abilities, and being aware of, and responding to, this in an appropriate way will mean the manager will get the most from individual team members and as a result from the team as a whole.

Chapter summary

This chapter has given you an overview of how teams work and how you might better understand the way in which individuals in teams work together. There are strategies to help you work more effectively with others in a leadership capacity or collegiate manner in teams. The chapter has only touched the surface and you are strongly recommended to access the useful websites or further reading to provide you with more detailed guidance.

Activities: brief outline answers

Activity 3.2 Critical thinking

The term 'responsible' can be understood from two perspectives:

1. being the cause of something, usually something wrong or disapproved of;
2. being answerable to someone for an action or the successful carrying out of a duty.

In a team, the team member has responsibility for carrying out an activity to the standard required by the team leader. To avoid perspective number 1 above, where misunderstandings, inaccuracies and disappointments may have occurred, the required standard should be explained to the person who is responsible for the task. In this situation it is the team leader's responsibility to be clear about what is expected in a task and the team member's responsibility to accomplish the task. Spending time explaining to a team member what is required can save time later and also enables the team member to carry out the task up to the level required. It may be a peer who is in the team and in this case it would be helpful to clarify that both of you are working towards the same goal or outcome. If it is a subordinate or someone with untested skills or knowledge of the situation, an example or demonstration may be necessary to indicate the standard required for the task.

The term 'accountable' can also be understood from two perspectives:

1. the obligations to report, explain or justify a behaviour or activity that has taken place and take responsibility for this activity. In this sense a person is answerable to, or responsible to, another person, organisation or professional body for the manner in which an activity has been undertaken. A key factor here is the word obligation, which can be interpreted as the legal responsibility or employment responsibility of the grade in which a person is employed. In this sense it is accepting ownership for the results, or lack thereof;
2. the capability of explaining why something has taken place (i.e. to give an account of something with reasons and/or evidence).

In nursing, we more often use the first perspective rather than the second perspective as the concept of accountability is blended with responsibility. Therefore, the team leader is both accountable to the employer with the responsibility for carrying out the task through the activities of the team members. The team members are accountable to the team leader and have responsibility to the team leader to carry out the required activity. However, the second perspective may be drawn upon if a person is required to give an account of the failure or success of a task.

Activity 3.3 Reflection

You may have wanted to do the task because it made you feel special, it may have been a good learning opportunity or because you just wanted to be helpful. Reasons you might not have wanted to undertake the task include a lack of confidence, fear of failure or a dislike of taking responsibility.

Activity 3.5 Decision making

The points you make may include the following:

1. Importance and rationale for nutrition in:

   (a) treatment of type 2 diabetes;
   (b) weight maintenance.

2. Importance of health education information about maintaining diet when patient goes home.
3. Ensure the ward hostess gives the correct type of soup to Mary by monitoring delivery.
4. Ensure Mary drinks the soup, even though she is keen to go home and not make a fuss.
5. Has Joanna had any additional training in diet and nutrition, and in particular with type 2 diabetes? If not, is there a training day coming up soon that she could attend?
6. Is Joanna comfortable monitoring the ward hostess? Does she see this as part of her role and her work in the team on this section of the ward? If not, explain that you have this expectation and you will support Joanna to do this by mentioning this as the expectation for all HCAs in the next team meeting.

When giving Joanna feedback, what principles would you be thinking of, drawn from Fowler's (1996) list in the section on giving feedback in the text above?

When would you go about giving the feedback? It is suggested that feedback should be given at a time close to the event occurring. You will have to balance this decision with an evaluation of the suitability of the time available during a shift, at the end of the shift or at a pre-arranged time other than during the day of the shift. It depends on how busy you are and any other situational factors. However, do not let these factors obstruct you from your task. If this is the first time you are to give feedback you may want to let your ward manager know and practise how you are going to handle the situation with her/him. She/he can also give you support when the issue is raised in the team meeting.

Further reading

Bach, S and Grant, A (2015) *Communication and Interpersonal Skills in Nursing* (3rd edition). London: SAGE/Learning Matters.

An accessible introduction to the subject.

Sullivan, EJ and Decker, PJ (2009) *Effective Leadership and Management in Nursing* (7th edition). Harlow: Pearson International Edition. Chapter 10, Delegating Successfully.

Although this book is written for the USA, the principles are transferable and this chapter provides some indepth analysis of the difficulties and methods to overcome the art of delegation.

Useful websites

http://www.nhsemployers.org/~/media/Employers/Publications/NHS_Job_Evaluation_Handbook.pdf

Provides information on the Agenda for Change bands – see especially Chapter 6.

http://www.nhsemployers.org/PayAndContracts/AgendaForChange/KSF/Simplified-KSF/Pages/SimplifiedKSF.aspx

Introduction to the NHS Knowledge and Skills Framework and its links to the NHS Agenda for Change National Pay Agreement.

http://rapidbi.com/created/personaldevelopmentplan.html# formonthejobdevelopmentrecord

Link to an example of a personal development plan from a commercial organisation.

http://www.nmc-uk.org/Documents/Standards/NMC_Prep-handbook_2011.pdf

Nursing and midwifery PREP requirements, as stated by the NMC.

http://www.qca.org.uk

Website of the Qualifications and Curriculum Authority.

www.skillsforhealth.org.uk/getting-the-right-qualifications/vocational-qualifications

Skills for Health website giving information on QCF qualifications and foundation degrees.

http://www.nhsemployers.org/your-workforce/retain-and-improve/managing-your-workforce/appraisals/appraisal-tools-and-tips

NHS Employers appraisal tools and tips.

Chapter 4
Conflict management and negotiation skills

NMC Standards for Pre-registration Nursing Education

This chapter will address the following NMC competencies:

Domain 1: Professional values

2. All nurses must practise in a holistic, non-judgmental, caring and sensitive manner that avoids assumptions, supports social inclusion; recognises and respects individual choice; and acknowledges diversity. Where necessary, they must challenge inequality, discrimination and exclusion from access to care.

Domain 2: Communication and interpersonal skills

4. All nurses must recognise when people are anxious or in distress and respond effectively, using therapeutic principles, to promote their well-being, manage personal safety and resolve conflict. They must use effective communication strategies and negotiation techniques to achieve best outcomes, respecting the dignity and human rights of all concerned. They must know when to consult a third party and how to make referrals for advocacy, mediation or arbitration.

5. All nurses must use therapeutic principles to engage, maintain and, where appropriate, disengage from professional caring relationships, and must always respect professional boundaries.

Domain 4: Leadership, management and team working

4. All nurses must be self-aware and recognise how their own values, principles and assumptions may affect their practice. They must maintain their own personal and professional development, learning from experience, through supervision, feedback, reflection and evaluation.

Essential Skills Clusters

This chapter will address the following ESCs:

Cluster: Care, compassion and communication

1. As partners in the care process, people can trust a newly registered graduate nurse to provide collaborative care based on the highest standards, knowledge and competence.

continued . . .

At entry to the register

9. Is self aware and self confident, knows own limitations and is able to take appropriate action.

11. Acts as a role model in developing trusting relationships, within professional boundaries.

12. Recognises and acts to overcome barriers in developing effective relationships with service users and carers.

4. People can trust a newly qualified graduate nurse to engage with them and their family or carers within their cultural environments in an acceptable and anti-discriminatory manner free from harassment and exploitation.

At entry to the register

6. Acts autonomously and proactively in promoting care environments that are culturally sensitive and free from discrimination, harassment and exploitation.

7. Manages and diffuses challenging situations effectively.

Cluster: Organisational aspects of care

19. People can trust the newly registered graduate nurse to work to prevent and resolve conflict and maintain a safe environment.

At entry to the register

3. Selects and applies appropriate strategies and techniques for conflict resolution, de-escalation and physical intervention in the management of potential violence and aggression.

Chapter aims

After reading this chapter, you will be able to:

- identify situations during which conflict might arise;
- discuss strategies for preventing conflict arising;
- demonstrate awareness of methods of managing conflict;
- comment on your own ability to understand and manage yourself in difficult situations involving interpersonal conflict.

Introduction

Nursing involves caring for people during some of the most emotionally difficult times of their lives. As well as patients, nurses come into contact with relatives, friends and carers of patients who are themselves distressed and anxious. In some circumstances, nurses and other care staff can become upset or angry themselves.

Within any clinical setting there is the potential for anxiety, confusion, distress, hurt and pain to erupt into conflict. Sometimes distress arises as a result of a patient's physical condition.

At other times, frustration may surface as a result of apparent failures within systems, poor communication or lack of understanding.

Conflict may arise between patients and care staff; between patients; between care staff; between patients and significant others; or between staff and patients' significant others. Recognising the potential for conflict and learning how to prevent and manage conflict are all key skills in leadership and management. Perhaps the most important skill aspiring nurse leaders can have however is the ability to understand and manage themselves in such situations.

The purpose of this chapter is to enable you to explore some of the issues that contribute to the development of conflict in the clinical setting, and to examine strategies to prevent these occurring or to defuse such situations when they do occur.

What is conflict?

Understanding what conflict is and why it arises is fundamentally important in understanding both how to prevent it from occurring and how to manage it once it has arisen. Conflict is the expression of a disagreement between two or more parties that arises out of a difference in opinion, needs or desires. It is important to recognise that conflict is not usually about the individual him- or herself; it is more likely to arise as a response to an individual's perception of a situation or circumstance. The prevention of conflict, therefore, has as much, if not more, to do with the management of perception as with anything else.

Not all conflict is physical in nature, although what started as a disagreement, a heated discussion or an argument can soon escalate to violence if it is not handled well. The following example encourages you to think through an everyday situation in a hospital to increase your understanding of how easily a confrontational situation can develop.

Case study: The protracted wait

Stan is a busy man who has to attend hospital regularly for monitoring of his emphysema. The hospital is quite old and Stan is forced to wait in the corridor along with the rest of the people attending the clinic because there is no waiting room. The corridor is cold and draughty, and has a constant stream of people through it. Stan has waited over an hour past his allotted appointment time and is fed up, not only with the hanging around but with having to sit in the corridor. Stan approaches the receptionist and demands to know how much longer he will have to wait. The receptionist's response, while polite, is not helpful as she does not know why the appointments are running so far behind. Stan is upset by the lack of information he is given and the seemingly poor communication within the team. He shouts at the receptionist for being 'incompetent'.

This case study illustrates how perception and the physical environment can contribute to bad feeling. Stan is aggrieved at having to wait in an environment that is not designed for the purpose for which it is being used. He is forced to wait for a protracted period of time but does not know why. When Stan tries to find out why he is waiting, he does not get what he considers to be a reasonable response. The receptionist is not being rude, but Stan's perception of the fact she is unable to give him a reason for the delay is that his needs are not being met and this is unacceptable.

We can imagine the same scenario acted out in various different ways which may lead to different outcomes. The receptionist might tell Stan to sit down and wait, thus escalating the situation to one of open conflict. She might apologise for the delay and say that she will find out what is happening and come back to him, thus meeting his need to feel that he is being taken seriously. She might empathise with Stan about his situation and say how bad it is for her as well; while this may distract Stan from shouting at her, it may lead to his anger being focused at other staff in the hospital. Evidently there may be little that she, or indeed many leaders or managers, can do about the physical surroundings (since this may require a considerable investment of money) but they can and must exercise control over the psychosocial, interpersonal environment of care. This is a reflection of values in action and demonstrates the leader's compassion, respect for people and person-centredness.

What is also clear from this scenario is that prevention of conflict is everyone's business. It may seem to some that it is the role of managers, senior staff and security to deal with issues of conflict when they arise. What the protracted-wait scenario shows is this perception is wrong. Being polite and appearing to be helpful is the role of all staff, whether they be care professionals, students or support workers. Clearly, and as is explored later in the chapter, one of the roles of the manager in this sort of scenario is to look for ways in which such situations can be managed better in the future to achieve better **outcomes** for patients.

Why managing conflict is important

The need to manage conflict effectively may seem obvious: conflict is just not nice. There are good reasons why managing conflict is important in the context of leadership and management, and these go beyond merely preventing an unpleasant situation.

The first reason that conflict management in care environments is important is it can negatively affect the experiences of patients and clients (Northam, 2009a). This applies equally to those involved in the conflict and those forced to witness it. The same is true of the staff in a department or team when conflict occurs regularly. The negative experiences of staff will almost certainly affect their ability to care and may give rise to absence through sickness associated with stress. Continued poor management of conflict may cause some staff to leave their posts, creating recruitment and retention issues.

Managing complaints and conflicts properly can lead to benefits for the team and the organisation. Recurrent complaints arising from the provision of care may be turned around to create opportunities for development. If conflict and complaints arise out of people's perceptions of the care they receive then these can be used to help redesign both the ways in which care is delivered and the nature of the care itself. A key message for leaders and managers in the management of conflict is therefore about learning from it. Properly managed, perhaps through the use of **clinical supervision** (see Chapter 5) and individual reflection (Hocking, 2006), conflict may prove to be a catalyst for innovation and creativity. **Total quality management** requires nurse leaders and managers to recognise and engage in practices which improve both the processes and practices of healthcare; this includes responding to complaints, criticism and compliments from clients.

While there is no specific legislation in the UK covering workplace conflict, bullying and the like, the Health and Safety at Work Act (1974) makes it quite plain that employers are responsible for the health of their employees – this includes their mental well-being. Legislation against discrimination on the grounds of age, sex, disability or ethnicity does exist and requires that managers behave in an equitable manner towards all of their employees, as required in the Equality Act (Her Majesty's Government, 2010), and that they protect employees from harassment in the workplace. This requires managers, leaders and all care staff to be aware of situations which might lead to conflict and to manage them and the behaviour of staff effectively.

Consider the following case study, where conflict arising out of the way in which a service is provided is reflected on and used to develop a better way of working with potential to improve patients' experience.

Case study: The pain clinic

The pain clinic in the local district general hospital provides many services to local people, one of which is minor pain-relieving procedures requiring a short period of sedation. Each morning ten people are admitted to the clinic to undergo procedures such as facet joint injections and selective nerve root blocks. Each procedure is quite short but requires a small amount of sedation so it usually takes about 3 hours to get through the whole procedures list.

Tom is asked to attend the clinic at 8 a.m. in order to have an injection to help manage his back pain. Tom duly arrives at 8 a.m. and sits in a waiting room along with the other nine people. By 9.30 a.m. Tom is still waiting to be admitted as he is the last on the procedures list for that day. Tom is irritated by the wait as he is in pain and the chairs in the waiting area are uncomfortable. He asks Emma, the nurse admitting the patients, why he has been brought in so early when it is clear he will not need to be in a bed until about 11 a.m. Emma responds that it is just the way the clinic runs. Tom protests loudly that this is silly and that there has to be a better way of running things. Another patient joins in, saying he feels as if they are being treated like cattle, being forced to wait for no apparent good reason. Both Tom and the other patient become quite excited and start to talk loudly about how ridiculous it all is until they are both called in to be admitted.

continued . . .

> *Emma is quite intimidated by what has happened. She reflects that this is a regular occurrence and perhaps the patients have a point about the way in which the clinic is run. She decides to talk to Hamida, the clinical nurse manager, about the complaints.*
>
> *Hamida points out that the orthopaedic day unit in the same hospital sends out different appointments for admissions on surgery days, with an hour between patients. The staggered admission times mean one nurse can comfortably admit and prepare three or four people for surgery on the same day and no one is kept waiting unnecessarily. Emma reflects on this and decides she should go and see what the orthopaedic unit are doing to understand the pros and cons of their approach with a view to adopting the practice in the pain clinic.*

What we can see in this case study is that patients have a real issue with being kept waiting, especially if they are in pain. Rather than ignoring this, hiding away or perhaps leaving the clinic, Emma takes on a leadership role and seeks to turn a problem into something that works for everyone's benefit. She reflects on the situation and then seeks help and support from a more experienced member of the team.

Perhaps the second key message of managing potential conflict is to listen to what is being said, rather than just to how it is being said. A third lesson might be to seek help in understanding and solving potential issues.

Again, this case study shows the value of learning from and acting upon complaints to improve the quality of care provision. If we can do this, we demonstrate our engagement, both as nurses and as leaders, with improving the lives of our patients.

Identifying potential sources of conflict

Conflict is a constant possibility in any organisation where there are human interactions (Johnson, 1994). The potential for conflict to arise in the hospital or other clinical setting is compounded by the type of work that occurs there. People visiting hospitals or other healthcare facilities, either as patients or visitors, are in physical and psychological distress. This means they are vulnerable, particularly if they do not understand what is happening. The fact that healthcare is often delivered in an autocratic manner also makes people feel vulnerable.

This vulnerability is perhaps not, in itself, something which nurses can eliminate. However, recognising it and doing something about it may make the difference between conflict arising or not. What is clear is that feeling vulnerable makes some people defensive and aggressive and in identifying this nurses, along with all care professionals, can do a lot to avert conflict.

Taking a leadership role in the management of conflict is every nurse's role. As we saw in Chapter 1 on the experience of leadership, this involves seeing the bigger picture and understanding how the structures within which we work affect both us and the people we work with. In good part these sentiments are reflected in the increasing importance of user consultation and patient involvement forums. Clearly the best way to understand how care is experienced is to ask the people experiencing it and the best way to improve how care is experienced is again to involve those in receipt of care.

It is worth reflecting on the effect a lack of understanding can have on how we feel about ourselves and others around us, and how this lack of understanding can create a real sense of vulnerability.

Activity 4.1   *Reflection*

Cast your mind back to your first day on your most recent clinical placement. Think about the feelings that you had about working in a team of people you did not know, in an area with which you were unfamiliar and with patients whose conditions you perhaps did not fully understand. Think about how all these unknowns made you feel. How did you react? Who made you feel less at ease? Who made you feel more at ease? What did people do that made you feel more or less at ease? What lessons can you draw from this experience to help you to understand how patients might feel and behave in unfamiliar circumstances?

There are some possible answers and thoughts at the end of the chapter.

This activity emphasises that fear is a natural response to the unknown, and what people do and say can have a great impact. Understanding what may create feelings of vulnerability in ourselves can help us to understand which issues might create vulnerability in others. Managing our encounters with others and recognising the potential for conflict that arises out of our interactions allows us to demonstrate the important, people-centred aspects of leadership.

The potential for conflict can be heightened by the amount of specialisation and organisational hierarchy that is present in many clinical teams (Swansburg and Swansburg, 2002) (for more on managing conflict in teams, see Chapter 2). The manner in which we choose to present ourselves to others can heighten feelings of inadequacy and fear. The specialist knowledge we have in an area and the position we hold can be used to create barriers between us, our team and our patients. The idea of separation created by titles and roles is well demonstrated in the theory of **binary thinking** which demonstrates how we can create our own identities by comparing and contrasting ourselves with others (Davies, 2004).

We like to identify ourselves in various different ways as perhaps a parent, a partner, a nurse or a student. While these identities mean that we can explain who we are and what we do, they can also create a sense of difference between us and other people.

Concept summary: Binary thinking

Exploring the notion of binary identity and how this might apply in the clinical setting may help us to understand some of the ways in which conflict might arise. Within binary logic, 'A' is 'A' and anything that is not 'A' is 'something else'. Translated into the nursing workplace this may be seen as operating as: 'I am a nurse; you are not'; 'I know what is happening here; you do not'; 'I am the powerful professional; you are the compliant patient'; 'I know best; you do not'. You may have experienced this type of feeling yourself perhaps as a student nurse, or in relation to another more 'powerful' professional.

In this sense binary is seen as one of only two options, as in the code used to program computers where the only options available are 0 and 1. This tends to suggest strongly a sense of them and us – when someone is not one of us, they are something else.

In part, the differences expressed here represent some of the more negative aspects of creating for ourselves a professional identity which excludes others who do not share our identity (as a nurse, say) – sometimes called **othering**. This way of looking at ourselves creates a scheme whereby we see patients and non-nursing colleagues as 'other'. It is a small step from seeing ourselves as something different and set apart to the creation of conflict. Acting in ways which can be seen as highlighting and exploiting the differences between us as nurse and 'others' as patients, or us as leaders and 'others' as followers runs counter to everything we identified as important in the way of exercising our common values in Chapter 1.

Conflict often arises because of perceived, if not real, differences between the needs, wants and desires of individuals. When we as nurses, and nurse leaders, remember that we are people first and nurses second it will allow us to start to see something of the nature of the fear that being 'the other' brings. This realisation will help enable us not only to respond to, but to pre-empt, some of the conflict that arises as a result of fear and perceived isolation.

Activity 4.2 — *Critical thinking*

Think about what binary thinking says about professional image and presentation of self to others in the care setting. How is binary identity used in the care setting to advantage the professional? Can you think of times someone has made you feel different or excluded by their behaviour? Have you used binary thinking to your own advantage? What approaches to self-presentation and leadership can stop these sorts of situations arising?

There are some possible answers and thoughts at the end of the chapter.

It is worth thinking critically about binary thinking here, not because it is a clever way of understanding how we create identities but because it reflects a way in which conflict may be generated. Quite clearly, using binary thinking theory, we can see divisions between individuals are readily created when we start to see ourselves as something other than fellow human beings. This idea translates well into how we might think about preventing conflict as well as how we lead others by example in the ways in which we interact with our managers, peers, those who work under our leadership and our patients.

Conflict may also arise in the clinical setting when staff disagree about the care and management of a particular patient. Sometimes conflict may arise because of an ethical dilemma, such as a family requesting that a loved one is not told her diagnosis when it appears she should be (Ellis, 2014). When ethical dilemmas occur, they can give rise to conflict between people with different views about how the issue should be resolved. Differences of views may then arise along professional boundaries, or between professionals and patients. Alternatively, they may result as a consequence of age, gender, status, culture, religion or experience (Northam, 2009a).

Binary theory helps us to understand what is going on in such situations where conflict arises. People who disagree with our point of view, instead of being accepted as people with another viewpoint, are regarded as 'other' and therefore become a legitimate target of attack. The role of the leader or manager in such situations is to focus the discussions back to the issue under dispute and away from the personalities involved.

The Chartered Institute of Personnel and Development (2007) identified general behaviour, disputes about performance, attendance at work and relationships between colleagues as being the main causes of conflict at work. Of note, people in public-sector employment rated relationships, bullying and harassment and all forms of discriminatory behaviour as being among the major causes of conflict at work.

Bullying takes many forms in the healthcare sector and can involve staff bullying other staff, staff bullying patients, patients bullying staff and visitors and relatives bullying staff. In a survey of NHS staff in England, 23 per cent reported having been bullied, harassed or abused in the last year by other NHS staff (NHS Employers, 2013).

Bullying can take many forms. Some bullying is deliberate, whereas other bullying arises out of differences in perception and poor communication. Gossiping about someone, spreading rumours, ridiculing someone as well as being consistently rude or abusive, all constitute bullying behaviour.

Case study: Bullying

Steve was a newly qualified nurse who prior to becoming a nurse had undertaken a first degree and Master's degree in biology. Steve joined the team in the intensive care unit at his local hospital as a junior staff nurse and greatly enjoyed his job.

continued . . .

Amanda was one of the unit sisters who had been qualified for many years and was a very experienced nurse. When Steve was on shift with Amanda he was often allocated the patient in the isolation room. Steve got the feeling that Amanda did not like him and noticed that he was often overlooked for breaks and was never allowed to look after unusual cases in the main unit when she was on duty.

Steve felt that he was being bullied and started to become very unhappy at work. Steve raised his concerns with one of the unit charge nurses, Des. Des had also noticed the behaviours that Steve described and advised Steve to have a word with Amanda about it. When Steve asked to talk to Amanda, she was dismissive but Steve persisted. In the office Steve raised his concerns, saying he had joined the team to learn how to nurse in the intensive therapy unit and he was keen to be useful. He said he felt excluded by Amanda and that she appeared to have taken a dislike to him for no apparent reason. Amanda started to cry.

Amanda admitted that she felt intimidated by Steve as she had found out he had two degrees and she did not even have a diploma. Amanda admitted she was worried about her position in the team with bright young things threatening her status.

In this real-life case study, we can see that Amanda's behaviour has arisen out of her own fears about her position in the team. It could have all been so different, however; she might have treated Steve in the manner she did because she did not like men, he was gay, from a different ethnic background or she did not like his religious views. Quite clearly, any one of these alternative explanations is unacceptable, as is the fact that she was using her position to bully him because she felt threatened.

Activity 4.3   *Evidence-based practice and research*

Unfortunately, bullying and harassment are common workplace occurrences (see the statistic cited earlier). When you are next at work, find a copy of the local bullying and harassment policy and familiarise yourself with the definitions it contains as well as the local practices in relation to it. You may want to repeat this exercise when you are in university: you may find these policies on the local intranet.

As the answers to this activity will depend on the policy available in your own workplace, no outline answer is given.

What all of the examples of how conflict could emerge in the clinical setting have in common is that they all come about as a result of communication issues. Handling communication, perception and relationships is therefore an important element of conflict management.

Managing to reduce the potential for conflict

What we have seen so far in this chapter points to the fact that much conflict can be avoided. From the leadership and management perspective, as well as from the perspective of individual behaviours, there are a number of strategies which can be used to help prevent conflict. The key to reducing the potential for conflict lies in managing the environment of care in such a way that it is focused on achieving high-quality patient outcomes. Hocking (2006, page 250) suggests that the route to achieving this is *through open communication, trust, and accountability.*

There is good reason to think as a leader or manager that treating the staff in our team as people first and as staff second can lead to an increase in the level of trust and reduce the potential for conflict – as well as signposting the values we want the staff to display in their interactions with each other and patients. A meta-analysis by Dirks and Ferrin (2002, page 621) demonstrated that when team members trust a leader, they are more likely to work co-operatively and are less likely to act negatively towards each other and those around them: *As predicted, trust in leadership was most strongly related to work attitudes, followed by most of the citizenship behaviors, and finally job performance.*

In his widely cited piece of work, Scholtes (1998) identifies two elements to the generation of trust in leaders: first, that leaders are competent and able to do their job and second, they demonstrate that they care for the staff who work with them (see also page 110). It is in the demonstration of caring about the welfare of staff, the exercise of the value of *person-centredness,* that the leader sets the tone for how the team will work with each other and patients.

The strategies for managing to reduce the potential for conflict are, like so many issues and ideas in leadership and management, heavily interlinked. The culture of the organisation, department or team all contribute to the ways in which conflict arises, is prevented, recognised and dealt with. Creating a culture where we learn from our mistakes and create environments which allow people to develop and grow as individuals and professionals will have a great impact on the likelihood of conflict arising in a team. While **learning organisations** are explored in more depth in Chapter 8, it is worth noting here that an organisation which allows people to make mistakes, learn from their mistakes and develop is more likely to minimise the likelihood of conflict arising and to handle conflict in a meaningful way. The same message translates well down to team level where a manager who encourages and supports learning enables members of the team to understand the root causes of conflict and how to deal with them.

Managing situations where conflict arises

When conflict does arise, there are a number of approaches that can be taken to manage it. The choice of which approaches to use will depend on the nature of the conflict: who is involved, where it is taking place and whether the conflict is physical or purely verbal in nature. The choice of approach to managing the situation will make a great deal of difference to the potential outcome of the situation. Thought should always be given to what strategy is right in any given situation, but if this is not possible it is always best to start with the minimum intervention required and scale up.

Table 4.1 gives some ideas about general approaches to managing conflict, along with when to use them and their pros and cons.

Collaboration: creates a potential situation where everyone can win and allows for creative solutions. It requires that the situation is worked through and a solution found which addresses concerns. This is useful where the conflict arises between individuals who either trust each other a lot or where there is pre-existing enmity. Collaboration, while it may be an effective means of managing conflict, can be time consuming and is open to abuse if both parties are not really committed to it

Compromising: leads to a situation where everyone involved has to give a little ground. This may prove beneficial where the parties in the dispute are equally committed to their own point of view and where they are of similar status. It can speed up the process of resolving a dispute, but only when the exact outcome is not too important. Compromise may lead to a solution that is not acceptable to anyone and may not work if the sides are too far apart at the start

Accommodating: is useful when one side of a conflict realises the issue is more important to the other side, or that s/he is wrong. Accommodating allows for **social capital** to be built up and called upon later and helps maintain relationships which may be more important than the disagreement. The problem with being accommodating is that people may see it as a sign of weakness and take advantage

Competing: sometimes other avenues of reaching agreement have been exhausted, so when the point being made is correct it is important not to give in easily. On other occasions when someone is trying to forcibly get his or her way it is best to challenge the person. The experienced leader or manager will recognise that competition can escalate some conflicts and it may not be wise when the conflict is or may become physical in nature

Dodging: is perhaps the best strategy when the conflict is not important, you are too busy to deal with an issue at that time, you need to cool off or there is no chance of winning. Dodging the issue can, however, make matters worse in the long run and may allow a transgressor to win. Dodging can be used as a short-term strategy by the manager but rarely results in a satisfactory solution to the issue of conflict

Table 4.1: General approaches to managing conflict situations

Source: Adapted from Thomas and Kilmann (1974).

What seems clear from the strategies in Table 4.1 is that different approaches will suit different scenarios. Constant use of one strategy will lead people to thinking that you do not have the **emotional intelligence** to work out when to change what you do in response to different situations. Knowing what strategy to employ is not something that is easily taught and, like emotional intelligence, it is something that comes with time, experience and reflection.

Activity 4.4	*Critical thinking*

Sue has been admitted to the orthopaedic ward following a fall in which she broke her arm. It is late evening and, just as visiting is about to finish, Dave, Sue's husband, arrives to visit her. You are asked by the ward sister to tell Dave that he must leave in 5 minutes, despite him having just arrived. Dutifully you tell Dave that visiting is nearly over and he must leave. Dave is angered by this and aggressively states that he has only just been able to get there and he should be allowed to see his wife and that the rules are ridiculous.

Use the strategies identified in Table 4.1 to think about the alternative approaches you might use to handle this situation. Which approach(es) best fit this particular scenario? Why?

There are some possible answers and thoughts at the end of the chapter.

This activity, drawn from a real-life experience, demonstrates how rigid adherence to rules can be construed as insensitivity and so inflames what must already be a worrying situation. Clearly the right approach would have been not to provoke conflict in the first place, but to ask whether Dave knew the visiting times and why he had been so late. Perhaps a compromise might then have been reached without the need for generating bad feeling.

There is a key message for the novice manager – that rules are sometimes there more as guidelines to follow than rigid policy. The emotionally intelligent manager will realise that on occasions breaking the rules is the right thing to do and that in exercising wise choices such as this s/he is demonstrating leadership rather than being weak.

Negotiation

Although it is easy to imagine **negotiation** is the starting point for dealing with all conflicts, in some instances it is not. Negotiation means trying to reach an agreement with another party when both parties share the same overall objective but perhaps differ on how this objective might be achieved. Negotiating is the process that is undertaken in order to reach a compromise solution to an issue. One of the fringe benefits of successful negotiation is that the relationship that builds up in a successful negotiation may lead to future collaboration.

The first rule of negotiation is to know what it is you want to achieve – the outcome that is acceptable to you. Once you know what is acceptable as a solution you know what ground you can give in the process and what you need to defend to achieve your goal. This is also the time to decide what the points of conflict are: why do you and the other party not agree?

The second most important negotiating skill is listening (Northam, 2009b). Listening not only allows you to understand the other person's point of view; it also creates opportunity for you to ask sensible questions about what they are saying.

The third rule of negotiation is to build on small successes, get agreement on small issues and then work up towards the main issue of the conflict. This allows for an environment of collaboration and agreement to be created and built upon. What are you willing to give up, and what is the other party willing to give up as part of the process?

Activity 4.5   *Evidence-based practice and research*

Start a discussion with your leadership tutor about how to manage situations in which conflict can arise. Ask if you can rehearse these sorts of situations through the use of role play in the classroom. Use the role play to explore the kinds of issues which give rise to conflict, how you feel about being involved in conflict and how a change in the way in which you choose to interact can alter the pattern of the conversation.

As this activity is based on what you manage to do in the classroom, there are no specimen answers at the end of the chapter.

Mediation

Sometimes a dispute or conflict between individuals cannot be resolved by the individuals themselves. At this stage there is a need for a third party to help find a resolution to the issue. One approach to conflict resolution is the use of **mediation**. Mediation is not about the settlement of a dispute by the imposition of an agreement; rather, it is a means of facilitating a resolution that both parties can agree to. A mediator's role is that of an impartial third party who helps progress a solution to a problem.

In mediation, the mediator listens to both sides of an issue, sometimes in private, and then brings the two sides together to discuss their grievances. The mediator will try to identify common ground, things the two parties can agree on, and uses these in order to start building a resolution to a problem. Fundamental to the process of mediation is that both sides in a dispute agree to take part in the mediation process and that they are both willing to seek agreement. Reaching agreement is not simply about compromise, or one side backing down; instead, mediation seeks to build on small agreements until a consensus is reached.

Mediation is especially useful where two sides have a history of not working together as it helps to build relationships which allow for future development and joint working. For a leader, this may mean facilitating discussions between two members of a team who do not get on or who are in conflict about some aspect of their working life.

Arbitration

When the processes of negotiation or mediation fail, it may become necessary to look for other ways of resolving a dispute between two parties. Arbitration and conciliation, like mediation, employ the services of a third, impartial individual to help reach a resolution.

In arbitration, the role of the third party is to decide on and impose a final solution to the conflict. The decision that is reached is based on the third party gathering together all of the facts and coming to some conclusion about what should be done to resolve the issue. An arbitrator has the authority to impose the decision on those in dispute – however, there may be instances when one or both sides in a dispute feel unhappy about the result, creating continued tensions in the workplace. Leaders who have to arbitrate will therefore need to stick to their values and demonstrate emotional intelligence in managing such situations.

Case study: The rota

Ann and Claire are junior staff nurses on the same ward. There is a concert by a well-known band in the town in a couple of weekends' time and both Ann and Claire want to go. Both nurses are rostered to be at work at the time of the concert and so both approach the ward sister and ask for an early shift or the day off instead. The sister says that she needs one of them to work and that they must sort it out between them.

Ann and Claire, who aren't the best of friends anyway, soon get into a verbal fight about who should have the opportunity to go to the concert. The argument spills over from the staff room to the ward and the sister has to take them both into her office. Both Ann and Claire claim they need to have the evening off the most and again begin to squabble. The sister has to intervene and suggests that she will have to make the decision and they will have to abide by it as that is what is required. Reluctantly they both agree. The sister says that, as she cannot choose between them, then the original rota which was written without any knowledge of the concert must stand.

Whistle blowing

So far, the examples we have used all have some reasonable explanation and resolving the issues they create is relatively easy. Sadly, this is not always the case. Sometimes there are situations of conflict, bullying or harassment which are not amenable to being dealt with locally. Whistle blowing offers one avenue for people who witness, or who are experiencing, conflict or bullying in the workplace to get help.

Essentially, whistle blowing is the act of bringing an important issue to the attention of someone in authority. Sometimes whistle blowing occurs within a team or organisation. If there are issues with an organisation, however, whistle blowing may need to be external. Within the NHS there are policies in place for both forms of whistle blowing. In certain circumstances, these allow the whistle blower to remain anonymous.

The Public Information Disclosures Act 1998 protects people who blow the whistle about poor practices specifically where the worker has real concerns about any one of a number of issues (**www.legislation.gov.uk/ukpga/1998/23/contents**). Such issues for the manager or leader may include the health and safety of workers. As discussed earlier, this includes protecting staff from abuse and conflict and the subsequent impact of this on their health.

Activity 4.6　　　　　　　　*Evidence-based practice and research*

When you are next at work find a copy of the local whistle-blowing policy and familiarise yourself with what it says. You may want to repeat this exercise when you are in university: you may find these policies on the local intranet.

As the answers to this activity will depend on the policy available in your own workplace, no outline answer is given.

Deciding to blow the whistle is a big step for anyone involved in conflict or bullying. In all such situations it is better, if possible, to try to come to some solution more locally. However, there are times, perhaps involving a legal or ethical issue, where whistle blowing may be the right thing to do. One example is to be found within the key findings of the Francis report (2013), which demonstrated too great a degree of tolerance of poor standards and of risk to patients, along with assumptions that monitoring, performance management or intervention was the responsibility of someone else.

These key findings suggest the culture prevented good practice in both care and in the communication of the lack of good care. Good care and intolerance of poor standards and risk to patients is everyone's concern and the need to do something about it, potentially by blowing the whistle, is something all nurse leaders should encourage.

Managing yourself

It may seem strange to say this towards the end of a chapter dealing with conflict, but the first point of reference for anyone involved in conflict is to ask if they, themselves, are the problem. Management of yourself and your relationships with other people is an important step on the road to becoming an effective leader and manager of others. Who wants to be led by a person who cannot manage him- or herself?

Since differences of opinion, perception and power all play a role in creating conflict situations, it is important for prospective leaders and managers to be aware of the influences on their thinking as well as how they come across to others. It may be tempting to think that this can be achieved purely through reflection, but reflection alone is likely to produce a flawed view. Self-management is as much about self-development as it is about being aware of your own opinions, and if you are to develop you need to take on board feedback from other individuals.

It would be easy to say that, in order to avoid unnecessary conflict, you should always follow what you believe to be the moral and ethical thing to do. This oversimplifies the case for self-management, however. Evidently there are some ethical and moral principles which, if you believe in them and act on them, will mean you can usually justify your actions – it is the exercise of the principles that allows others to see the sorts of values we hold dear and what sort of person we therefore are. Such principles might include treating others as equals and always trying to be fair. Rigid adherence to rules, as we saw in Activity 4.4, can lead to problems and so part of managing yourself is to learn when to adapt what you do to the situation. This means being open to the views of others and being able to adapt your behaviours when necessary, while not abandoning important ethical principles.

In essence this is about good communication, awareness of how others see you and how you behave and being aware of the perceptions of others. Mayer and Salovey (1993, page 433) termed this ability emotional intelligence and described it as *a type of social intelligence that involves the ability to monitor one's own and others' emotions, to discriminate among them, and to use the information to guide one's thinking and actions.* There are essentially four elements to the Mayer–Salovey model of emotional intelligence: (1) the ability to identify emotions in yourself and others; (2) the ability to use emotion to communicate; (3) the ability to understand how emotional information is used to construct meaning; and (4) the ability to manage your own emotions.

Being able to read and understand the emotions that lie behind your own behaviours and the behaviours of others is helpful in identifying whether conflict is a result of your behaviours or a reasonable response to the behaviours of others. To grow your emotional intelligence, it is important to reflect on your own motivations, to ask others about their motivations, and to put this in the context of the situation in which you find yourself. The essence of conflict management, therefore, is honest communication with yourself and with others.

Chapter summary

In this chapter we have identified some of the causes of conflict which arise in the clinical setting. We have identified that perception plays a large part in how people feel about a situation and that poor management of a situation, often the result of poor or non-existent communication, is often the root cause of conflict.

We have identified that there are a number of strategies that can be employed by the nurse leader to prevent conflict from arising, to identify situations in which conflict may arise and to manage conflict when it does occur. The fundamental messages for the management of conflict appear to lie in the need for good communication, management of self and treating others as equals.

We have seen that not all conflict can be dealt with by the individuals involved in the conflict, and that it is sometimes necessary to involve a third party either to help those in conflict come to a negotiated settlement or to have a settlement imposed. As with all aspects of nursing and interpersonal relationships, the key skill of reflection (both alone and with others) is helpful in resolving situations that arise.

Activity: brief outine answers

Activity 4.1 Reflection

Entering a new clinical area for the first time may have made you feel quite unsure about yourself and your own abilities and capacity to fit into the team. You may have been uncertain about where everything is kept and what the routine of the area is, as well as what would be expected of you. Some kind staff would tell you not to worry and might perhaps show you where things were and explain what they expected of you, while others might ignore you or make it quite plain that they were not happy about someone who was unable to pull his or her weight. The people you most admired and who most put you at your ease would probably be the staff who wanted to share their knowledge with you and who reassured you that in time you would understand what was expected of you as well as how to work effectively within the team.

Patients and visitors feel the same emotions. They are worried about what might happen, what is expected of them, who they will meet and how they will be treated. They also have the concerns that accompany being a consumer of healthcare, what the long-term outcomes might be, how they will be treated and who will be caring for them. Unlike the staff, they do not have the luxury of going home at the end of the shift or of having an education and training that prepare them to understand and make sense of their care. Because of this, they may well feel frightened and vulnerable; some may become aggressive or confrontational in order to hide their vulnerability.

Activity 4.2 Critical thinking

The answers to this issue lie in the way in which we choose to present ourselves to others, as well as the values we hold and the ways in which we choose to express these values. If we are quite clear in our interactions with patients and more junior staff that we are the knowledgeable professional and they are not, we will cause antagonism. If we choose to remember, as nurses and leaders of people, that we too are people and that we are dealing with people, then the ways in which we interact will demonstrate this, and will be less likely to give rise to behaviours that cause conflict to occur.

Activity 4.4 Critical thinking

- Collaboration will require a discussion to take place about Dave's concerns and that you show understanding in reaching a solution which addresses them.
- Compromising will allow you to reach a mutually agreeable solution with Dave – perhaps allowing him to stay a little longer, but only on this occasion.
- Accommodating: allowing Dave to stay because of the circumstances would perhaps seem reasonable and will defuse the situation, but it may mean he abuses the system in the future.
- Competing would mean demanding Dave leaves and perhaps calling security. This would alienate both Dave and Sue, and may not be a good idea in the long run.
- Dodging: just walking away and hoping Dave will leave is not really an option as other patients in the ward will see what has happened and may choose to do the same with their visitors or may be disturbed by Dave's continued presence.

Further reading

Bach, S and Gilbert, A (2015) *Communication and Interpersonal Skills in Nursing* (3rd edition). London: SAGE/Learning Matters.
See especially Chapter 4 on Understanding Potential Barriers to Safe and Effective Practice.

Benson, G, Ploeg, J and Brown, B (2010) A Cross-Sectional Study of Emotional Intelligence in Baccalaureate Nursing Students. *Nurse Education Today*, 30 (1): 49–53.

A study of emotional intelligence in nursing students and how it changes across the years of training.

Hocking, BA (2006) Using Reflection to Resolve Conflict. *Journal of the Association of Operating Room Nurses*, 84 (2): 249–59.

A helpful view of conflict management.

Thomas, J (2006) *Survival Guide for Ward Managers, Sisters and Charge Nurses.* London: Churchill Livingstone, Elsevier.

See especially the chapter on dealing with complaints.

Wedderburn Tate, C (2006) The Art of Managing Difficult People. *Nursing Standard*, 20 (19): 72.

A brief but interesting look at managing difficult people.

Useful websites

www.cipd.co.uk/NR/rdonlyres/1EB2AE66-D1A8-4641-AB8B-B6C67D38E6D9/0/4334Managing conflictWEB.pdf
From the Chartered Institute of Personnel and Development, an easily understood guide to managing conflict at the personal and team level.

www.acas.org.uk/index.aspx?articleid=1364
The Advisory, Conciliation and Arbitration Service's guide to managing conflict at work.

www.nmc-uk.org/Nurses-and-midwives/Raising-and-escalating-concerns
The Nursing and Midwifery Council's guidance on raising concerns and whistle blowing.

www.pcaw.co.uk
Public Concern at Work is the independent charitable authority on public-interest whistle blowing.

www.gov.uk/whistleblowing
UK governmental whistle-blowing guidance.

www.danielgoleman.info/topics/emotional-intelligence
The website of the most widely cited writer on emotional intelligence.

Chapter 5
Coaching, mentoring and clinical supervision

Introduction

The main emphasis in this chapter is on the support of staff through leadership and management techniques such as coaching, mentoring and clinical supervision. This chapter will investigate when to coach to improve performance or achievements. Different forms of coaching and mentoring, whether in an educational role or as a supporting role model, will be discussed and compared as methods of staff support. Problem-solving and decision-making frameworks are included in the discussion on coaching techniques. Clinical supervision models will also be introduced and discussed. The concept of a **learning culture** will be explored. The detrimental effects of staff burnout will be considered here, as will the notion of establishing a workplace environment that embraces the philosophy of work–life balance.

Coaching to improve performance

The term 'coaching' is more often used in the UK when referring to the training of athletes or performers, and may be caricatured by a person with a whistle and clipboard.

Increasingly the term refers to an approach to encouraging the improved performance of skills based upon an interpersonal relationship between a manager or team leader and a team member. In Chapter 3, we spoke about staff development and touched on performance appraisal as a means of planning and supporting staff to improve their knowledge and skills. Coaching is one method of supporting others to improve in an individually tailored manner. It is based upon a belief that individuals can develop skills and knowledge through frequent interactions (often called one-to-one meetings or 1:1s) that are planned and carried out with an agreed outcome in mind.

The notion of coaching in organisations, and mentoring, which we will look at later in the chapter, as a management tool began with the introduction of the people management and development literature. It can be traced back to the situational leadership model developed by Hersey and Blanchard in the 1960s (Hersey et al., 2007). The model is composed of four quadrants

(Figure 5.1). Hersey and Blanchard's use of the term coaching is meant to convey leading and persuading to adopt a solution to the situation. In this way the member of staff is included in the decision making and involved in suggestions for completing the task. It is an approach that encourages motivation as well as building competence.

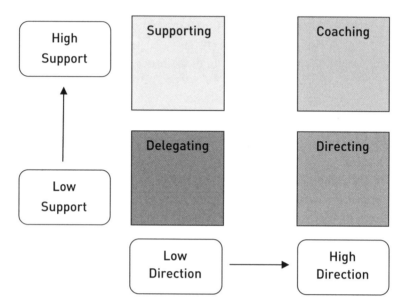

Figure 5.1: Hersey and Blanchard's situational leadership model

Source: Adapted from Hersey et al. (2007).

In Chapter 3 we explored the work of Kotter (1990), who recognised the importance of matching the approach with the characteristics of the individual. He developed a scheme for matching the appropriate leadership style to an individual's levels of commitment and competence to identify when and how tasks should be passed on to the team member. This enables a leader to draw out the best in team members and identify where development needs to take place. The Hersey and Blanchard model extends this approach and stresses that the leader has to be flexible and have at the forefront the developmental needs of the individual and not only the appropriate delegation method.

The leader needs to select an approach, or combination of approaches, from one of four leadership styles:

1. telling/directing;
2. selling/coaching;
3. participating/supporting;
4. delegating.

These are matched, respectively, with one of four follower styles, or developmental level of maturity in the individual:

1. high competence/high commitment;
2. high competence/variable commitment;

3. some competence/low commitment;
4. low competence/high commitment.

Depending on the maturational level of the person the leader provides high to low support along an axis of low to high direction. For example, the person with high commitment/high competence requires the least support and direction and can assume delegated tasks with minimal interference from the leader.

Case study: Teaching a procedure

David is a band 6 staff nurse, and Jasmine a new healthcare assistant. On Jasmine's second day, David spends 30 minutes telling her how to carry out a procedure to clean and redress a wound with the expectation that she will do this herself once the knowledge and skills required for the task have been thoroughly explained. David gives Jasmine instructions on what to use, why, when, where and to whom. Then he tells her he will come back in 2 hours' time to see how she is getting on.

When David returns, the wound has not been dressed with the appropriate dressing and he has to redo the dressing. This causes unnecessary discomfort to the patient and wastes time.

Although David may feel frustrated about this, questions have to be asked about the process of instruction that took place and whether it can be improved. Hersey and Blanchard would say that leaders have to match the style of leadership to the maturity (or developmental style) and readiness (i.e. competence and motivation) of the person or team they are leading to perform a task. Thus, a simple telling and instruction session will not be sufficient. There needs to be an assessment of the individual's learning style, level of comprehension, confidence, motivation and a relationship established or developed between the leader and the 'follower'.

This means that David, as the senior, might be advised to take the following steps:

1. *Make an overall assessment of Jasmine's scope of current tasks and activities. Determine her current workload and how she is coping with it.*
2. *Assess Jasmine's development level on the requested task by questioning and/or demonstration.*
3. *Decide on the leadership style.*
4. *Discuss with Jasmine the approach to be taken.*
5. *Follow up and discuss progress; correct where necessary.*

Activity 5.1   *Reflection*

Reading the case study above, imagine that you are the leader of the team on a shift in a busy female medical ward and are asking a junior member of staff to undertake a task similar to the one delegated to Jasmine in the scenario. Write out an imaginary short story of how you *continued* . . . •

would have tackled the five steps above. What factors would you take into account? You may want to revise your knowledge of Mumford's (1999) learning styles to help you consider how individuals learn. A web link is in the useful websites section at the end of the chapter to help you here. Which leadership approach would you take to coach the junior member of staff based upon your version of events? Try to see it from the junior staff's point of view as well as the senior's perspective.

As this answer is based on your own reflection, there is no outline answer at the end of the chapter.

Since the introduction of situational leadership, other approaches have been developed in coaching methods for work improvement. In the UK, the notion of coaching as a metaphor for improving performance came to prominence with the publication of *The Inner Game of Tennis* (1974), by Tim Gallway, who went on to publish *The Inner Game of Work* (2000). The latter drew on a philosophy summarised as *Performance = Potential minus Interference.* Thus the coach's job was to release the self-knowledge and potential that everyone possesses rather than deliberately instructing an individual towards achievements. The key ingredient was to develop greater self-awareness and a sense of responsibility in the performer. Since these early proposals, and a call for more evidence-based approaches utilising such philosophies, a body of literature has grown to support the coaching approach (Grant, 2001).

The GROW technique

Developed from the original Gallway texts is a coaching technique that relies on using questions and which follows a structure to involve the person in problem solving as well as learning. Known as the GROW technique, the idea is to use a simple guided set of questions that can form the basis of a discussion in a coaching session or as a means of establishing the developmental level of a person to be supported. The aim is to assist the person to think about the problem/task at hand and identify a solution or range of options.

An easy way to remember the structure of the questions is to refer to the mnemonic that summarises the GROW technique in this way:

- Establish the *goal.*
- Examine the *reality.*
- Consider all *options.*
- Confirm the *will* to act.

This approach has been found to be helpful in improving motivation with a person who has basic knowledge, expertise and enthusiasm. However, with inexperienced learners this can be time consuming and not practical for day-to-day work-based situations (Parsloe and Leedham, 2009). For this approach to be effective the questions need to be expanded, undertaken over a period of time and yet remain focused on the main goal to be achieved. The prominent factor is that the coaching is undertaken as a conversation, with two-way communication between the person and the leader or manager.

The 3 D technique

A more rapid approach is known as the 3 D technique. When time is really short and a solution to a problem has to be identified quickly the technique is to identify elements on three dimensions:

1. the situation – for example timescales, lack of resources, lack of expertise;
2. people involved – for example, unhappy, impatient, unreliable, over-confident;
3. you – lack of knowledge, conflicting priorities, general attitude.

From this analysis it is possible, by using questioning techniques around the dimensions, to draw out potential actions or plans.

Activity 5.2 *Reflection*

This activity is designed to help you with rapid coaching and skill building.

Practise the 3 D technique on yourself to coach yourself through a problem by following the following steps:

1. Define a current problem in a single sentence.
2. List three general issues relating to the problem situation.
3. List three issues relating to the people involved.
4. List three issues that relate specifically to you and the problem.
5. Choose one issue from each of your three lists of three issues.
6. Now identify one or more actions/options that are most likely to make progress in solving the problem.

As you are going through the steps, imagine you are asking yourself questions and make a note of the coaching questions you ask, to reflect later if they were the right questions to ask.

You may want to gain further skills in this approach by working with a fellow student or friend on a problem either you or s/he wishes to solve. In this way you not only develop your own skills; you can also ask for feedback on the different types of questions you need to ask to elicit answers that are helpful from your colleague or friend.

As this answer is based on your own reflection, there is no outline answer at the end of the chapter.

You may now be thinking that there is an overlap between the role of coach and the mentorship role you are experiencing in your practice learning and you would be right. However, there are subtle differences, which we will look at in the next section.

Mentoring

Mentor was the name of a character in Greek mythology, the tutor of Odysseus' son Telemachus in Homer's *Odyssey*. So he could hardly be more different from the person with a whistle and clipboard described earlier in this chapter.

The tutoring Mentor offered was not restricted to the giving of information; rather he encouraged the exploration of subjects such as virtue, integrity, responsibility and character development. He was a trusted and wise counsellor. This historical meaning has remained in use over time and is still used today for someone who has acted as a role model or who has had a significant influence on a person's career or professional outlook on life. The term 'coach' is a more recent one and is used specifically to describe the growth in skills and knowledge towards a higher or improved level.

Confusingly, coaching can also be incorporated into a mentoring role. The term mentoring, today, can cover several roles, such as coach, adviser, guide, confidant/e, teacher, role model, counsellor, friend, consultant, critic and advocate. The Nursing and Midwifery Council (NMC) has identified standards for mentors of nursing and midwifery students. There is no definition of mentoring in the NMC Standards; however, there are criteria that have to be met to support learning and assessing of students in practice.

Activity 5.3   *Evidence-based practice and research*

Go to the website address in the useful websites section for the NMC *Standards to Support Learning and Assessing in Practice* and review the standards in section 2 for mentoring. Think about how you will undertake this role when you become a qualified nurse and how you will plan to take a recognised mentorship education programme.

This activity aims to help you understand more fully the role of mentoring nursing students but also encourages you to think about your own personal development plan as well as your engagement with the notion of lifelong learning.

You may want to discuss with your mentor his or her experience of taking the mentoring course and of being a mentor to students. Reflect on what you can learn from your mentor's experiences.

As a final part of this research activity, ask your mentor if s/he had or has a mentor now that s/he is qualified and, if so, what impact this has had on your mentor's working life.

As this answer is based on your own research and reflections, there is no outline answer at the end of the chapter.

Research summary: Multiprofessional views of mentorship

Bray and Nettleton (2007) researched the role of the mentor in nursing, midwifery and medicine using questionnaires and semi-structured telephone interviews with both mentors and mentees. They were interested in any differences in the professional perceptions of the role. They were also interested in the potential dilemma that mentors, who are perceived as wise guides, have to become assessors and make judgements on their mentees' abilities. This could be viewed as a conflict of interest. They found that for nurse mentors the roles of teacher, supporter and role model were most important, with only 5 per cent indicating assessor as part of the role. By contrast, in midwifery the role of facilitator came higher than teacher and similarly few regarded assessor as part of the role. Within medicine, advisor and supporter were regarded as most important, with only 2 per cent regarding assessing as important.

When asked about any aspect of the role they found most difficult, both nurses and midwives reported difficulties in being objective towards their students when they had become 'supportive friends'. In medicine, less difficulty was reported with the assessor role. The biggest difficulty was finding time to commit to the role and all its aspects.

Bray and Nettleton found that across the professions there was a lack of clarity about the combination of the role of assessor with mentor. They admit that they had a small sample and have reservations about the generalisability of their findings. Yet, they make an interesting observation that, as we move towards further collaboration within multidisciplinary professional teams, a multiprofessional approach should be adopted towards defining the role and function of mentoring in healthcare professional education.

Mentoring in other contexts

While we may be familiar with mentoring in healthcare settings, it is worth noting that mentoring takes place in other sectors and organisations outside of healthcare education. We can learn from these relationships as they provide a contrast to the mentoring experienced in healthcare, as well as ideas for opportunities for service development and relationships. This could be to develop entrepreneurial or business skills (see Chapter 7), or alternatively to enhance working in community settings or with third-sector or voluntary services groups in the fields of mental health and learning disabilities. One example can be in business-to-business relationships where a mentor from a large organisation may work with a small organisation to advise on economic regeneration. In business-to-social-enterprise relationships, organisations like the Prince's Youth Business Trust have mentors to guide young starters who have received grants from the Trust. Similar to this are training schemes supported by the government.

Providing mentoring to special needs or community projects has become an important part of community university engagement schemes, where more personal or individually tailored mentors are matched to individuals (Schuetze and Inman, 2010). Working the other way around, business people can work with education (e.g. head teachers, universities and students) to advise on business skills. There are also 'buddying' schemes between first- and third-year students, which are another version of mentoring.

Broadly speaking there are three main types:

1. the corporate mentor, who is a guide or counsellor in someone's career from orientation into the company to senior management;
2. the qualification mentor, who is required by a professional organisation – such as the NMC – to guide candidates towards achieving a qualification, including NVQs;
3. the community mentor, who acts as a guide or counsellor to individuals who may be disadvantaged, experiencing social inclusion or in a distressing situation (see the Mentoring and Befriending Foundation in the useful websites section at the end of this chapter).

Throughout these discussions there has been a tacit acknowledgement that everyone needs access to guidance or experienced advice at some point in their professional lives. The notion of lifelong learning was mentioned earlier and it is highly relevant in nursing, where care may not change but clinical treatments are constantly evolving. Consequently, we need to be prepared to update our practice and ensure that our practice is meeting the needs of the client group with whom we work. Gaining experience in a given field is one way to add to our skills and knowledge. Seeking the guidance of a clinically experienced practitioner is another means of reflecting and learning from everyday practice. Often termed clinical supervision, it is the focus of the next section.

Clinical supervision

Thomas (2006) says that some nurses have become too focused on definitions of clinical supervision and that it is simply someone who is more expert than you, with whom you can have regular contact to help reflect and learn (for a more detailed literature review, see further reading). She suggests this could be a nurse specialist, a consultant doctor, a nurse consultant or another more experienced ward manager. Thomas maintains that all nurses in a team should have access to clinical supervision. A more junior nurse can be matched with a more experienced nurse who is not a direct assessor or appraiser, thus providing a basis for a trusting relationship to develop. The aim is to build up a relationship so that the clinical supervisor can be contacted in times of need, rather than you just meeting them at set times. This model may be suitable for busy acute adult care environments but may not suit all situations, specialties and fields of practice.

Supervision can be on a one-to-one basis or in groups. Think about the advantages and disadvantages of each approach and draw up a list to compare.

Further guidance is given on this activity at the end of the chapter.

There are very specific and different statutory requirements for supervision of midwives and the NMC has standards for the selection and activities of supervisors of midwives. In mental health settings, clinical supervision was introduced into pre-registration education in 1994 and in 1995 the UK Council for Nursing and Midwifery (forerunner of the NMC) declared clinical supervision should be in all fields of nursing and midwifery. The literature suggests that the number of nurses receiving clinical supervision varies between regions and specialties. Similarly, the length of time and training for providing supervision is variable.

There do seem to have been technical advances made in the delivery of clinical supervision in community settings using telephone conferencing and similar techniques. However, the majority of research literature concerns the educational provision of clinical supervision in pre-registration nursing courses (Butterworth et al., 2007). Employer organisations and their influence on implementing a culture for clinical supervision are seen as crucial themes in the literature. The factors influencing levels of engagement in organisations appear to be culture, availability of time, supervisor numbers and many local factors. The role of the organisation in creating a culture of learning will be discussed next.

The learning organisation

The concept of the **learning organisation** is seen by many as the way in which organisations will have to organise their structures for the twenty-first century. Up until the mid-1980s it was quite possible to have a successful organisation without mentioning the word *learning*. As we steer ourselves deeply into the territory of the twenty-first century, there is a world of global information and technologically driven organisations. Speed will be important to communicate changes and information management systems become key, which means people and organisations will need to learn to do things differently and quickly. New information is constantly becoming available, requiring new ideas to be adopted and skills and knowledge to be continuously updated.

In healthcare we have seen the implementation in the last ten years of developments such as telemedicine, microsurgery, stem cell research, patient-held records, shared patient management systems and many other technological and pharmacological advances. In addition, there are constant pressures to reduce costs and maximise efficiencies, which have led to a short-term focus on immediate results and constant efforts to rationalise the number of employees in organisations.

There is a conflict, therefore, between the organisation's need to manage the learning potential of its employees actively and the pressures to change employment practices and professional roles. Not surprisingly, there is a culture of resistance to change if professional status and roles are eroded or services are seen to be reduced.

Case study: Changing the skill mix

The scene is a community healthcare setting. Two new roles have been introduced into the health visiting team to improve the skill mix. Joan, a nursery nurse, is employed to carry out focused parenting skills training over 6 weeks with families, providing weekly support to learn new skills. Joan is also available for advice at child health clinics. Usha is a staff nurse who used to work on a children's ward. She has a children's nursing qualification and experience, and is now employed to perform 3-month developmental checks in the home. She is also available for pre-school checks to work with the school nurses. This frees up time for Liz, Jamil and Frances (the three health visitors in the team) to deal with complex family cases and public health initiatives. These kinds of cases have become much more prevalent in their caseloads and, while they would like to continue with providing a service to all mothers and their families, they realise that they need to focus their specialist expertise on more complicated cases where they can give extra time. Liz, Jamil and Frances are encouraged to undertake specialist, post-qualifying courses in child protection and public health. Joan (the nursery nurse) and Usha (the staff nurse) are also given the opportunity to go on to further training: Joan to become a registered nurse and Usha to become a registered community health visitor and public health nurse. The team manager and the organisation (as part of its staff development strategy) are prepared to sponsor them for future training for career development. This also supports the organisation's strategy for succession planning and maintaining a learning culture.

This is an example of where new roles have been introduced into the team that are less costly than the health visitors to employ, which means efficiencies have been made. But Joan and Usha have the potential and ability to make a significant contribution to the work of the team as well as supporting the notion of a learning culture. At the same time the experience and skills of the health visitors, Liz, Jamil and Frances, are maximised and not diminished by the inclusion of new roles into the team.

It is always worth your while looking into the staff development strategy of the organisation you will go to work for after you qualify to see what opportunities there are for you to develop promotion opportunities or a career pathway.

The main features of a learning organisation are:

- an increased focus on learning and development to ensure organisational effectiveness and a sustainable future;
- encouraging as many people as possible to become coaches, mentors or clinical supervisors to ensure learning takes place in the workplace;
- establishing training programmes in coaching, mentoring and clinical supervision;
- generating a culture that accepts the need to move from current standards of performance to higher levels to ensure continuous improvements in performance;
- supporting individuals to manage their own learning to develop their skills, maximise potential and enable a satisfactory work–life balance (adapted from Parsloe and Leedham, 2009).

Activity 5.5   *Critical thinking*

Imagine you are working in a hospice and your manager has asked you to take on responsibility for managing all student placements. This role means you have to think about the learning needs of students from a variety of professional backgrounds, paying special consideration to what they might need to learn while on placement with you. How will you develop the culture of the team so that your hospice becomes a *learning environment*?

Hints

1. Would you first find out what kind of students attend the hospice and who the mentors are?
2. Would you undertake an informal survey of their views on how to create a learning environment and one that considers, and that would benefit, multidisciplinary team working if more than one profession is represented?
3. Would you draw on any of your positive learning experiences as a student in other settings?
4. Would you look for any evidence in the literature of other initiatives to create learning environments or evidence to support your initiative?
5. Would you draw up your ideas into a proposal, citing the advantages and disadvantages of your ideas and a plan of implementation for discussion in the team meeting?

As this answer is based on your own research and reflections, there is no outline answer at the end of the chapter.

The adoption of a learning culture in the health and social care workplace is in essence a reflection on the values of the workplace. Workplaces which value people, and their development, are likely to be workplaces which attain good standards in patient care, as opposed to workplaces where staff are not valued and therefore the work they do is valueless to them as well. One of the values which underpins nursing is the desire to provide the best care possible: this is best achieved by a motivated workforce working in an environment which rapidly adopts improved ways of working and new practices, such as that found in a learning organisation. In this respect then creating a learning organisation as a nurse leader is a reflection of the core values of nursing.

Burnout and work–life balance

Throughout this chapter we have been discussing ways that leaders and managers can support team members and colleagues. With increasingly complex workloads and demanding resource pressures we have to consider the effects this can have on the working life of the individual. In extreme cases many staff experience degrees of burnout. It is important to recognise the early signs of burnout before it takes a hold and also to look at ways to create a work setting that has a philosophy of work–life balance.

Burnout

Burnout is defined as a prolonged response to chronic emotional and interpersonal stressors on the job and is defined by the three overwhelming dimensions of exhaustion, cynicism and sense of inefficacy (Maslach, 2003). Unlike acute stress reactions, which develop in response to specific situations, burnout is a cumulative reaction to work stressors. The emphasis is on the process of gradual psychological erosion and the social outcomes rather than physical outcomes of this chronic exposure. Burnout is therefore the result of prolonged exposure to chronic interpersonal stressors. Exhaustion, cynicism and a sense of inefficacy are the predictors; however, other workplace factors, such as working in care-giving environments where there is a sense of giving with little regard for self, as well as reduced resources, have been found to compound the likelihood of burnout.

Research summary: Burnout

In 2002, as part of a larger survey into the relationship between qualified nursing staff and quality of patient care outcomes, Aiken et al. studied the relationship of burnout to qualified nurse/patient ratios. They found that higher emotional exhaustion and increased job dissatisfaction were strongly and significantly associated with nurse/patient ratios. Their findings indicated that increasing a ratio of patients to nurses by one patient could increase emotional exhaustion. This implied that nurses in hospitals with patient:nurse ratios of 8:1 would be 2.29 times as likely as ratios of 4:1 to show signs of high emotional exhaustion.

In 2006, Edwards and colleagues surveyed community mental health nurses using the Maslach Burnout Inventory (MBI) and the Manchester Clinical Supervision Scale (MCSS) to identify whether effective clinical supervision could have a positive effect on burnout. Their findings indicated on the MBI that 36 per cent of staff had high levels of emotional exhaustion, 12 per cent had high levels of depersonalisation and 10 per cent had low levels of personal accomplishment. Those nurses who had completed six sessions of clinical supervision scored lower MBI scores and higher scores on the MCSS, which indicated effective supervision (Edwards et al., 2006).

These two studies are examples of the extensive research undertaken in this area and which offer means of early detection and solutions to minimise effects in the workplace.

Work–life balance

Linked to the subject of burnout is the more recent concept of work–life balance. This is about people having a measure of control over when, where and how they work. It is achieved when an individual's right to a fulfilled life inside and outside paid work is accepted and respected as the norm, to the mutual benefit of the individual, business and society. Striking a balance between the needs of the individual employee, customer and organisation demands the following:

- For employees: Different individuals will have different expectations and needs at different times in their life.
- For customers: Organisations need to respond to the demands of their customers if they are to continue to be successful.
- For organisations: Organisations need to be able to manage costs, maintain profitability and ensure that teams work effectively together.

In 2010, an estimated one in five UK workers were mothers, 25 per cent of all families were single-parent families, and up to ten million people were caring for elderly relatives. By 2022 there will be one million fewer workers under 50 and three million more over 50. We now live in a 'service' world where customers increasingly expect a personalised, 24/7 service (The Work Foundation, 2008). The demands on workers to juggle home life, health and happiness are even greater in the twenty-first century than ever before.

Case study: Work–life balance

This example is from the Work Foundation, a not-for-profit organisation that has the aim of improving working life. The Good Hope Hospital in Birmingham had a project to improve work–life balance through improving recruitment and retention. The hospital had 2,841 employees, with 81 per cent women and 14 per cent ethnic minorities. Staff turnover was high, at 18 per cent (this includes 12 per cent voluntary leavers but excludes completed contracts such as doctors on 6 months). Eighty-five per cent of women returned to work after maternity leave.

continued . . . .

The NHS in general, including Good Hope Hospital, was facing a recruitment and retention crisis. The response was to introduce a system of self-rostering, whereby nurses choose the shifts they want to work rather than the traditional off-duty system of nurses writing down the shifts they cannot work. The off-duty system, apart from being extremely time consuming, was open to abuse and favouritism and was well recognised as being a cause of friction on wards.

The computerised RosterPro system turned the whole process on its head, and removed the administrative burden from the nurse manager. Once a month nurses simply enter the shifts they want to work on to the computer. As well as identifying their availability, the nurses are able to assign a preference rating to each shift. RosterPro does the rest, with the system allocating shifts on a fair and equitable basis.

Overall benefits were:

- *improved staff morale;*
- *boost in recruitment rates;*
- *reduction in staff turnover from 14.4 per cent to 9.3 per cent;*
- *huge administrative burden released from ward managers;*
- *sickness and absenteeism rates greatly reduced;*
- *average sickness at Good Hope reduced from 6 per cent to 5 per cent (against an increase on wards with no self-rostering);*
- *better customer care, due to staff having a better work–life balance;*
- *15 per cent increase in staff being able to work the hours of their choosing in the space of 1 year;*
- *improvement in computer literacy amongst nursing staff in practice.*

An example of a nurse who has benefited from the introduction of self-rostering is Auveen, a ward sister and mother. Auveen's story can be found on the Work Foundation website (see the useful websites at the end of this chapter), but in short, the flexibility of self-rostering allows her to manage her work–life balance so she has time for her husband and children, and her work. Auveen works 37½ hours a week and, using RosterPro, chooses her shifts to allow her to make time for activities with her two young children. For example, if her children have after-school activities or an appointment with the dentist, Auveen can work an early shift to accommodate this. The Work Foundation's account quotes her as saying: 'Whether I'm providing an after-school taxi service or spending time doing homework with the children, I love the fact that my job now allows me this flexibility. I firmly believe that young minds need to be nourished and my working pattern allows me to spend quality time with the children that a fixed-hours job just wouldn't allow.'

It may not always be possible to introduce the flexible work scheduling in the example above; however, working creatively with the philosophy of creating a work–life balance in the workplace will go some way to improving difficult working lives. In the useful websites section you will find further ideas which you may wish to take to your workplaces and discuss with your teams.

Chapter summary

In this chapter you have explored three different methods of staff support that can improve staff performance as well as improve work–life balance. Coaching can be used to improve performance and problem solving. It does not have to be undertaken by an expert in the field of practice. Mentoring has many different forms and can include coaching. Clinical supervision is usually undertaken by an expert in the field around a very specific area of knowledge.

It is essential for twenty-first-century organisations to create a learning culture if they are to keep abreast of innovations, support staff morale and encourage personal development options. In addition, the pressures of contemporary life need to be supported by initiatives to bring about a balance between work and personal life. Leaders at all levels in the organisation have a part to play in creating these environments. Environments of care are influenced directly by the way in which leaders exercise their values, which need to remain central to everything which they do.

Activity: brief outine answers

Activity 5.4 Critical thinking

Clinical supervision	Advantages	Disadvantages
Group supervision	• More people seen at one time, saving time • A variety of ideas can be offered from different perspectives • Helps with team building	• Takes more people away from the clinical area at one time • Requires an experienced/ trained facilitator • May not meet everyone's specific needs
One-to-one	• More personal and focused • Deeper trusting relationship can be established • Can specifically match specialty advice	• Could become too intense • Personalities may not match • More resources required for time

Further reading

Cummins, A (2009) Clinical Supervision: The Way Forward? A Review of the Literature. *Nurse Education in Practice*, 9: 215–20.

This article gives a more recent review of the clinical supervision literature and how it complements mentorship and preceptorship programmes postqualification.

Parsloe, E and Leedham, M (2009) *Coaching and Mentoring: Practical Conversations to Improve Learning*. London: Kogan Page.

Gives useful detail on how to conduct the coaching conversation and advice on how to deal with difficult conversations.

Thomas, J (2006) *Survival Guide for Ward Managers, Sisters and Charge Nurses*. London: Churchill Livingstone/Elsevier.

A pocket-sized, practically focused guide to surviving in a new managerial role. It does what it says in the title and is a very easy, quick reference guide.

Useful websites

http://rapidbi.com/created/learningstyles.html#honeymumfordlearningstyleslsq

Learning styles review: several learning styles theories are displayed on this url; however, the overview of Honey and Mumford's four learning styles – activist, reflector, theorist and pragmatist – will be particularly helpful for Activity 5.1.

www.nmc-uk.org/Educators/Standards-for-education/Standards-to-support-learning-and-assessment-in-practice

This link will take you to the NMC *Standards to Support Learning and Assessing in Practice*. See section 2.1 for the standards for mentorship.

www.mandbf.org

Website of the Mentoring and Befriending Foundation.

www.princes-trust.org.uk

The Prince's Youth Business Trust, which has mentors to guide young starters who have received grants from the Trust.

www.gov.uk/browse/working/finding-job

Similar to the above are training schemes supported by the government, as detailed on this site.

www.theworkfoundation.com/DownloadPublication/Report/155_155_unison.pdf

The Work Foundation's report on maintaining a work–life balance. The case study from the Good Hope Hospital cited in this chapter can be found at: **www.theworkfoundation.com/DownloadPublication/Report/98_GoodHopeHospital.pdf**.

Chapter 6
Frameworks for management and leadership

continued . . . .

16. People can trust the newly registered graduate nurse to safely lead, co-ordinate and manage care.

At entry to the register
1. Inspires confidence and provides clear direction to others.
2. Takes decisions and is able to answer for these decisions when required.
4. Acts as a positive role model for others.

Chapter aims

After reading this chapter, you will be able to:

*   identify the features of leadership and management;
*   discuss what features of management and leadership are appropriate in nursing;
*   relate some management and leadership theories to your own experiences of practice;
*   consider which aspects of leadership and management you would like to develop in yourself.

Introduction

The purpose of this chapter is to lay bare some of the key definitions and understandings of what it means to be a leader or manager in the health and social care sector. To appreciate leadership and management for nursing fully it is important that any definition of the roles that leaders and managers hold includes not just a theoretical explanation of what they do, but also some explanation of why they are important to practice.

This chapter will advance some of the ideas seen in Chapter 1, where the key characteristics of leaders and managers as might be experienced by student nurses were explored.

Are leadership and management different?

Some commentators on leadership and management regard them to be mutually exclusive ideas; that is, a manager is a manager and a leader is a leader. More commonly, and in our view more correctly, it is perhaps true to say that leadership is one of the roles of a manager in health and social care, whereas leadership can be everyone's responsibility depending on their position, the roles they are given and the situations in which they find themselves.

This may seem a difficult idea to grasp, but consider all the people who display leadership qualities, or who undertake leadership roles, in the clinical setting. These people may include individuals who have responsibility for leading a small team, some of whom may be at the same grade. Other leaders may have specific roles in the team, such as a wound care or moving and handling co-ordinator. On occasions people may have to show leadership because of a situation that arises. Such individuals are not perhaps always managers, but they are leaders.

Managers on the other hand are most often defined by their position and job title, e.g. a ward manager, community team manager or outpatients manager. While such individuals are managers, part of their role will include displaying some of the activities of leadership, as described later in the chapter.

Pascale (1990, page 65) suggests that: *Managers do things right, while leaders do the right thing.* The suggestion here is that managers are bound by and follow local policy and procedures, while leaders follow their intuition and understanding of people to get things done. In 1989, Bennis famously explored the comparisons between what he saw as the key features of leadership and he listed 12 key differences between managers and leaders:

1. Managers administer; leaders innovate.
2. The manager is a copy; the leader is an original.
3. Managers maintain; leaders develop.
4. Managers focus on systems and structure; leaders focus on people.
5. Managers rely on control; leaders inspire trust.
6. Managers have a short-range view; leaders have a long-range perspective.
7. Managers ask how and when; leaders ask what and why.
8. Managers have their eye always on the bottom line; the leader's eye is on the horizon.
9. Managers imitate; leaders originate.
10. Managers accept the status quo; leaders challenge it.
11. Managers are the classic good soldier; leaders are their own person.
12. Managers do things right; leaders do the right thing.

We can see in these comparisons that managers are regarded as having the interests of the organisation at heart and that they achieve this by following the rules and maintaining the status quo.

Daft (2001) further expands on Bennis' ideas:

13. Managers plan and budget; leaders create vision and set direction.
14. Managers generally direct and control; leaders allow room for others to grow, and change them in the process.
15. Managers create boundaries; leaders reduce them.
16. The manager's relationship with people is based on position power; the leader's relationship and influence are based on personal power.
17. Managers act as boss; leaders act as coaches, facilitators and servants.
18. Managers exhibit and focus on: emotional distance, expert mind, talking, conformity and insight into the organisation; leaders exhibit and focus on: emotional connectedness, open-mindedness, listening, non-conformity and insight into self.
19. Managers maintain stability; leaders create change.
20. Managers create a culture of efficiency; leaders create a culture of integrity.

What we can see in these definitions is the focus on emotional connections with the team on the part of the leader, and remoteness and a controlling attitude from the manager. What seems clear from these distinctions is that some of these qualities will suit some situations at different times, but it is unlikely that one or the other approach will always be the right way to deal with all situations that arise in nursing.

It is worth noting again that leadership is also one of the roles of the manager and so the distinctions drawn here may be somewhat artificial. Clearly within the care setting there is a need for nurses to demonstrate the qualities of both leaders and managers.

Activity 6.1 — *Reflection*

Think back to some of your experiences in clinical practice and consider the types of leaders and managers you encountered while there. What were the characteristics of the people in charge you admired? Why did you admire these characteristics?

There are some possible answers and thoughts at the end of the chapter.

Considering the differences in the above comparisons and the answers you gave to the activity, you may start to form the opinion that leaders are better than managers in the ways in which they connect with people. You may feel that managers perhaps miss the bigger picture and are more remote and removed from the realities of practice. You may also note that some situations require management and therefore some of the key skills of management are appropriate to certain situations.

In exploring different management and leadership theories in the rest of the chapter, we hope that you will start to see, as we have already suggested, that leadership and management styles and activities can co-exist in, and be practised by, the same person. We further hope that you will also come to the conclusion that perhaps the art of good leadership and management is knowing what style of supervision to apply in what situation. So being a good manager may also mean being a good leader.

You may find it useful to look at the answers you gave to some of the activities in Chapter 1 (especially Activities 1.2, 1.5 and 1.6) at this point and consider what role values play in helping to shape leadership and management behaviours. Consideration of the 2010 Nursing and Midwifery Council (NMC) Standards of proficiency, notably in the domain of 'Leadership, management and team working', competency 4 (see the start of this chapter), should be at the forefront of your mind as you read the rest of the chapter and engage with the activities and case studies.

While we argue that leadership and management cannot be divorced from each other, it is worth considering theories of management and theories of leadership to see what we, as nurses, can gain from them and when it might be appropriate to adopt one approach or the other in supervising care.

Theories of management

There are almost as many theories of what it is to be a manager as there are people in management positions. The purpose of the theories in this sense is to act as a guide to the key tasks and role functions of the manager. Interestingly for nursing, a profession that is increasingly driven by an emphasis on evidence-based practice, little of the work of the manager, especially the health and social care manager, is informed by any meaningful research. What this means is that we have theory and observation for guidance, but there is a large amount of scope within these theories for personal interpretation and adjustment to the individual management tasks and contexts within which these are applied. There is a large amount of research into leadership and management styles and behaviours from disciplines other than nursing which can be used to inform your thinking.

In part, the lack of meaningful research into the management function is itself a product of the diversity of people, staff, managers and settings in which nurse management takes place. The uniqueness of each individual, manager, team, group and organisation, as well as the ever-changing political, social and technological climate in which they work, mean it is difficult to produce research-informed strategies for management that have any real, long-lasting meaning. This means that being a manager requires a constant engagement with the people being managed, the organisation and the wider political and social context.

What this implies for theories of management is that they are just that, theories. Theories are ideas about a topic which are supported by some evidence; they are not substantively proven. Even if management theories were proven, they would not all apply in the same way in every management situation.

Mintzberg's role theory

Mintzberg (1975) produced one of the most enduring descriptions of the roles of the manager. Mintzberg suggests strongly that if managers are to be effective at what they do, they need to recognise the nature and scope of the work they are undertaking and they must apply their own natural abilities to it. Mintzberg further suggests that the management function is complex and involves an intricate balance of three key roles. The power which the manager possesses arises from a recognition of his or her formal authority and status within the organisation. The three key roles of the manager, as Mintzberg describes them, are the *interpersonal*, the *informational* and the *decisional*. Within each of these roles there are a number of subroles which together constitute the larger role.

Interpersonal roles

- Figurehead – the manager performs some more basic functions which may be part of the routine of day-to-day work.
- Leader – including recruitment, staff development and motivating staff.
- Liaison – including communication with people and organisations not directly related to the immediate team.

continued . . .

Informational roles

- Monitor – in this role the manager collects information about the team and the wider environment in which the team works. Some of this information comes from official sources and some from sources such as staff room gossip.
- Disseminator – managers share some of the information they have gathered from formal and informal sources from inside and outside the team with the team. There is a need for discretion here as to what information is shared, with whom and when.
- Spokesperson – essentially information sharing outside of the direct team and organisation.

Decisional roles

- Entrepreneur – the manager seeks opportunities to improve what s/he does.
- Disturbance handler – the manager has to respond to external pressures and make changes that have not come from within the team.
- Resource allocator – as well as managing his or her own time, the manager allocates tasks, equipment and jobs to the team.
- Negotiator – this may mean within the team, with service users, other professions or other agencies. Sometimes this is planned; sometimes it is a response to immediate pressures.

Source: Adapted from Mintzberg (1975).

What is apparent from the description of the manager Mintzberg presents is that the role requires a fair degree of adaptability on the part of the manager. Mintzberg sees the interpersonal elements of the role as being integral to the task of managing and places leadership within the description of the functions of management.

Activity 6.2	*Reflection*

Consider how the manager on your last placement/current place of work exercises the various functions of the manager as described by Mintzberg. How does the manager adopting a particular role at a particular time affect you and the rest of the team? What happens when a member of the team misunderstands what it is that the manager is trying to do?

As this activity is based on your own reflection, there is no specimen answer at the end of the chapter.

Theories such as Mintzberg's can help to add some clarity to what it is managers actually do. In Chapter 1, the case study 'The newly qualified nurse' demonstrated that the student (Julius) had little idea about what it was that the ward sister (Deirdre) did all day. Sometimes an understanding of the roles and pressures others have to work under allows us to understand better what it is they do and therefore our place in the team.

Contingency theory

Contingency theory refers to the idea that managers have to take into account a number of factors when making management decisions; that is, decisions are situation-dependent. Management decisions are therefore seen as being dependent on what is happening, where it is happening and who is involved. This is perhaps best thought of as applying as much to the way in which a decision is made as to the decision that is made. Such an idea fits well within Mintzberg's scheme, where the manager is busy juggling a number of roles in order to fulfil the task of managing.

Activity 6.3   *Reflection*

Reflect on the management decisions made on a day-to-day basis in the area in which you are/have most recently been on placement. What are the factors that influence the way in which these decisions are made/communicated and therefore the impact they have on the team? Are these decisions always communicated in an appropriate way? How does the team respond to the manner of the communication?

Since this is based on your own experiences, there is no specimen answer at the end of the chapter.

Contingency theory is similar to the different ways in which you will interact with clients and their relatives according to the nature of the care they are receiving, their age, mental capacity and how well you know them as individuals. As a manager, successful action relies on your understanding of a situation which in turn relies on good communication. Griffin (1999) makes the useful point that what works as a manager in one situation cannot be generalised to all such situations. As such, managers have to be adaptable to the demands of their various roles as well as the environment they work in and the people they work with.

Systems theory

Systems theory identifies that managing people, resources and care delivery requires the manager to recognise the contribution all of these elements make to the effective running of an organisation or team. Systems theorists see the world of work as a set of interdependent subsystems which interconnect to form what is a whole (or holistic) system. Von Bertalanffy (1968), the initial and most famous system theorist, recognised that systems (teams, groups, organisations) are characterised by the interactions of their components (people and their environments) and the unpredictability of those interactions.

What this means for the management of people is that the role each plays within the functioning of a team has to be recognised, supported and directed with one eye on the bigger picture. When one part of the system fails, then the whole system is affected. It is important therefore for the leader or manager to consider the role of each member of the team in achieving the team's goals.

The Hawthorne experiments (see the useful websites at the end of this chapter) provide an interesting insight into how people are motivated at work by the feelings of belonging and of being paid attention to: the so-called **Hawthorne effect**. Essentially the experiments undertaken at the Hawthorne factory involved making both positive and negative changes to people's working conditions and recording the impact this had on productivity. What the experiments demonstrated is that what is done is not as important as the fact that workers are being paid attention to, which alters their behaviour. A similar effect is seen in research, where people react in ways which they believe a researcher wants them to because they are under scrutiny (Ellis, 2013).

Activity 6.4   *Researching and finding out*

Consider the practice area you are most recently familiar with. Make a list of all of the people you have come into contact with who play a role in the day-to-day activity of the area. List what these people do and who is affected by this. Ask a colleague or your mentor to do a similar list so that you can compare. Consider together what difficulties the rest of the team face when individual members of the wider team are away from work. What does this say about the way in which that system works?

Since this is based on your own experiences, there is no specimen answer at the end of the chapter.

The important message for the manager here is the need to demonstrate to all members of the team that the role they play, however minor it may seem, can have a much wider impact.

Case study: The wrong mop

George is a new ward orderly who is responsible for cleaning Juniper ward. The ward has three side rooms. In side room two is a patient with methicillin-resistant Staphylococcus aureus *(MRSA), who is being nursed in isolation. George mops side room two and then continues to use the same mop to clean the open ward areas. Within a few days there is an outbreak of MRSA on the ward.*

This case study reminds us that even the most mundane task can have a significant impact not only on the nursing team, but also the patients that we care for. The nurses on the ward may have been meticulous in their hygiene and infection control procedures when caring for the MRSA-positive patient, but one component of the system, in this case George, was not and so the system, which includes the ward and the hospital at large, is affected by this single action. Of course, there are a number of potential explanations for George's lack of understanding about the impact of his actions, which include poor training, poor leadership or perhaps his feeling of not belonging in the ward team.

Workload management

Within the role of the manager there are a number of tasks which need to be undertaken. Some of these tasks reflect on the roles identified in the model by Mintzberg discussed earlier; others are more singular and are worthy of some discussion here.

The role of the manager in co-ordinating the work of a team was alluded to in Chapter 1, especially in the case study 'The newly qualified nurse'. The management of workload is perhaps one of the key skills for the new or aspiring nurse manager who needs to satisfy his or her own developmental and work–life balance needs; the needs of the team members; the needs of the organisation; and the needs of the people who use the service.

To achieve this balance the nurse manager must learn and consolidate a number of skills and, while this is not an exhaustive list, some of these skills are discussed here:

- Learn to say 'no'! The need to prioritise workloads as a manager is very real. Taking on more than you or the team can manage will mean that no one is satisfied.
- Learn to delegate. People are the greatest resource for the nurse leader and manager. Knowing your team, what they are capable of and what individuals enjoy doing means that you can delegate tasks and everyone benefits (Ellis and Abbott, 2010).
- Learn to kick the door shut. When you have a pressing task to attend to, an open-door policy (which allows anyone in at any time for any reason) means you cannot concentrate on what is in front of you and so are unable to finish anything. Clearly this is not always appropriate; emergency situations may require immediate attention and shutting yourself away during a crisis is not appropriate.
- Learn to go home. If your job cannot be done in the time allotted to it, you have too much work. A tired nurse manager is likely to make mistakes and be unhappy. This is no good to anyone. Failure to achieve everything in the allotted time may also indicate the need to become more organised, delegate more effectively and manage time more wisely.

By managing their time through prioritising, saying no and sensible delegation, managers can achieve their goals and develop team members at the same time.

Of the roles of the nurse manager, drawing up the roster is one which can often lead to disagreement and create disharmony in the team (as we saw in the case study 'The rota' in Chapter 4). For the manager who is concerned with doing things right, there are a few simple rules to follow in undertaking this task and which contribute to successful workload. The lessons from these translate well into other management tasks.

There is a need to be open and honest about the process: people have no need to speculate, and gossip, about what they can see. An open process will involve observing two important principles: being fair and being consistent. The morally active manager is described by Dawson and Butler (2004, page 237) as acting *on the basis of internal values, or standards, rather than (or as well as) … on the basis of externally imposed codes of conduct.* Clearly, as well as being transparent in the process of work allocation, it is important for the manager to allocate staff so that there are appropriate levels (the skill mix) and numbers of staff on duty at any one time.

The sorts of principles associated with moral management are also the sorts of principles associated with moral and ethical nursing practice. Fairness dictates that all staff are given equal opportunity to request days off and consistency that these are all considered according to the same criteria. Whatever tasks the manager faces, be this acting as a spokesperson or as a role model, there is a need to demonstrate moral and ethical awareness. Managers who are unable to demonstrate moral activity in their day-to-day management practice cannot reasonably require the same from their team. Moral and professional conduct is one of the cornerstones of good nursing and good management practice.

Resilience and management

One of the features of modern nursing management is the need to be resilient. Resilience is the ability to cope with, and even thrive as a result of, the stresses and challenges that being a twenty-first-century nurse manager throw up. In Chapter 9, we will discuss strategies for developing confidence as a leader or manager and how this will enable you to make the transitions from student to qualified nurse and nurse leader and thereby develop the ability to cope with the challenges that nurse management and leadership create.

There are some key strategies that enable nurse managers to become more resilient and in so doing role model to their team how to cope with the challenges that nursing creates. Where a manager is able to deal with situations clearly, fairly and ethically, there will be trust within the team.

The most important strategy in being resilient is your own ability to make sense of what is happening in the world around you. In part, this ability comes from a strong understanding and belief in your core values (as discussed in Chapter 1). A positive attitude to reflecting on and learning from situations, changes and challenges is a core element of being a good nurse and later a good nurse manager. This understanding is exercised and communicated through the use of emotional intelligence (as described in Chapter 4, as well as later in this chapter) in which the leader recognises and responds to his or her own, and other people's, emotional responses to a situation rather than dealing with it on purely a cognitive (thinking) level.

Being positive and using new situations as opportunities to learn mean in turn that you will develop problem-solving abilities. The ability to solve problems means that you are in control, not only of the situation, but also of yourself. Understanding the effects of stress on yourself and on others is a key element of emotional intelligence, discussed further later, which is a necessary skill for successful managers and leaders.

Activity 6.5 — Reflection

Consider how reflection on critical incidents throughout your training as a nurse has enabled you to make sense of some aspects of nursing practice. What strategies did you find helpful during this process – perhaps discussion with peers, tutors, mentors or managers, reading articles, textbooks or attending lectures? How did this process help you to develop? What was it about reflection that enabled you to cope in untoward circumstances? How might these strategies translate to the need for resilience as a leader or manager?

There are some possible answers and thoughts at the end of the chapter.

Your reflections on this activity will have led you to the conclusion that being prepared emotionally and intellectually is one of the key strategies for surviving as a student, as a nurse and in the long term as a manager. As with all aspects of leadership and management, understanding your own responses to a situation will mean you are better prepared for, and more understanding of, the emotional responses of others. That is one of the fundamental requirements of effective people management.

Theories of leadership

Leadership can be regarded as one facet of the management role or as an entity in itself. It is a people-focused activity that requires engagement with a team – the followers. House (2004) describes leadership as the ability to motivate and enable other people to achieve the goals of the organisation for which they work.

Being a leader can arise out of an individual's position within an organisation or team, or it may result from a natural ability a person has to inspire other people to follow him or her (charisma, perhaps). There are a number of approaches to leadership, some of which take account of the nature of the interaction between the leader and followers and others which take a more comprehensive view of the nature of leadership and the tasks of the leader as well as the interpersonal aspect of the role.

Transactional leadership

Transactional leadership is leadership at its most basic. As the name implies, there is a transaction taking place. The followers do what the leader asks of them in return for a reward, at its most basic a salary. The role of the leader in this model is to state what needs to be done and who will do it and then allow them to get the job done.

This approach to leadership is very much focused on getting a task done, rather than on the people undertaking the task. It is easy to imagine how this approach to leadership may be appealing when there are serious time constraints or in an emergency situation. In nursing, it does hark back to the days of task allocation, when patient care was perhaps less holistic than is common today.

Relating the theory to good leadership practice, the leader who understands and communicates effectively with the team will gain the respect and trust of that team and for the team the reward for getting the job done will come from the sense of shared purpose and belonging that co-operative working brings.

Transformational leadership

Transformational leadership is about having a vision (a view of how things should or could be) and being able to communicate this idea effectively to others. The vision of how things should be may come from leaders themselves, from their managers or following discussion within a group or team. What is important about transformational leaders is that they believe, and are seen to believe, the vision.

For transformational leadership to work, there are some assumptions which need to be made and need to be true. First, people will follow a leader who can inspire them; second, a passionate leader with vision can get things done; and third, getting things done is a matter of instilling energy and enthusiasm into a group.

Transformational leadership requires there to be a relationship of trust between the leader and the followers. This trust means that the followers will do whatever it is that the leader envisions for them. As in all relationships, the best way to generate trust is to show people you care about them and be consistent in your approach.

Transformational leaders succeed in what they do by having faith, not only in what they want to achieve and what they do, but also by generating and displaying trust in those they work with. Clearly one of the central focuses of the transformational leader is change. Transformational leaders who are successful in sharing their vision with their team will doubtless be able to lead their team through change more successfully than a leader who does not have the full support of the team.

It is worth thinking about whether transformational leadership is suited to health and social care, and more specifically within nursing. The simple answer to this is that the most successful nurse leaders will retain a vision of how things should be in terms of high-quality and successful patient care provision. The shared values of care and compassion are the key to generating the trust which transformational leaders need in order to improve (transform) care provision.

Of course, having the faith and trust of the team is not of itself enough to make a person a transformational leader. There is also a real need for a vision that is correct and workable as well as inspiring. If we can agree that all improvement is a change, but not all change is an improvement, we can see that enthusiasm and vision without some foundation in reality are perhaps not all that helpful. Trust is generated when followers believe both that a leader cares about them as individuals and that the same leader is capable of delivering whatever it is s/he says s/he will deliver. Liking someone as an individual and trusting that person as a leader are not the same thing.

Think about some occasion when you have met a mentor or lecturer who you have liked because s/he was inspirational. Now think about whether s/he delivered what you expected. Did you learn what you thought you would learn? What was the difference between successful learning and less successful learning? Is a good relationship as important for learning as the content of the learning?

There are some possible answers and thoughts at the end of the chapter.

What this reflection shows is that there is more than one dimension to being an effective leader of people. Being nice is not really enough; there is a need for some substance to underpin activity.

Bass (1985), one of the leading writers on transformational leadership, suggests four essential components of effective transformational leadership. First, leaders must provide intellectual stimulation, challenging the way things are and encouraging creativity among the team. Second, they must demonstrate individualised consideration and by using good communication skills make followers feel able to share ideas and gain direct recognition for their unique contributions. Third, they need to demonstrate inspirational motivation which enables followers to experience the same passion and motivation as the leader to meet the team goals. Fourth, they need to have idealised influence; that is, they must act as a role model who followers wish to emulate while taking on the values of the leader.

Reflecting on the nature of the leaders we respect and trust, the sorts of people we choose as role models, we can see they have many of the characteristics which suggest them to be exercising values which are central to nursing. The requirement of a transformational leader closely reflect what Jane Cummings, the Chief Nurse for NHS England, in 2012 coined as the 6 Cs (see the useful websites at the end of the chapter).

1. care;
2. compassion;
3. competence;
4. communication;
5. courage;
6. commitment.

Transformational leaders who have the ability to exercise, and be seen to exercise, these essential values in their dealings with colleagues and service users can expect others to see these as a template for how they ought to act. One of the core learning points for anyone moving into a leadership or management position in the caring professions is not to put aside all of the qualities and values (as embodied in the 6 Cs), since their continued exercise reflects strongly on who we are and putting aside our values, as we discussed in Chapter 1, especially in the scenario about Julius and Deirdre, can lead to dire consequences for all concerned.

> ## Activity 6.7   *Researching and finding out*
>
> With some colleagues go online and find some more information about the 6 Cs. Using this information as a guide, consider how you have seen the 6 Cs in action in your practice setting. What examples can you find of them being used and who is using them? What does this say about the culture of the workplace?
>
> *Since this is based on your own experiences, there is no specimen answer at the end of the chapter.*

Adair's action-centred leadership

Adair (2010) describes leadership as being made up of three interlocking and interdependent activities (often portrayed as interconnected circles) which leaders must pay attention to in their role: the task, the team and the individual. The role of the leader is to achieve the task (in nursing, this may be the provision of good-quality care) through building and developing the team while developing the individuals that make up the team.

The functions of the leader, as described by Adair (2010), which enable them to achieve the task are defining the task, planning how the task will be achieved, briefing the team and controlling the process. In order to achieve the task the leader also needs to pay attention to the human elements of what they are doing through evaluating, motivating, organising and providing an example to both the team as a whole and the individuals in it. The elements of the various activities include:

Task

- organising duties;
- focusing on goals;
- controlling quality;
- checking performance;
- reviewing progress.

Team

- building and maintaining morale;
- maintaining communication;
- setting standards;
- supporting the team.

Individual

- praise and recognition;
- developing and training;
- meeting human needs.

Ignoring or underemphasising any one of these areas of activity will mean the leader is not doing what the team, individual or task require. Overemphasis on any one element of these three leadership activities will lead to imbalances in the ways in which work is done and can be to the detriment of all concerned. Leaders need to learn to balance all three activity areas as a general rule, increasing their attention in any one area for short periods as required. So, for instance, if there are problems with the team the effort put into this needs to increase but – and this is important – this should not mean the leader neglects the task or the individuals within the team as a result.

The servant leader

Many classic models of leadership identify the leader as the individual out in front with the followers coming along behind. Some modern theories of leadership take a different view of the role of leaders, who have a more interdependent relationship with their team (Howatson-Jones, 2004). The role of the leader in this view is that of a leader who also has the ability to follow. This idea of the 'servant leader' is described as an individual who wants to serve first and to whom the decision to lead comes later. Servant leaders seek leadership as a means of expanding their ability to serve.

Throughout history there have been a number of individuals who can be said to have been servant leaders. Well-known examples include the Dalai Lama, Mahatma Gandhi and Mother Teresa. These individuals, whose motivation lies in serving others, have managed to expand their ability to do so by taking on leadership roles. While it can be argued that each was motivated by religion or political change, they share the common value of care for other people, which is a value common to many healthcare managers and leaders.

Activity 6.8   *Critical thinking*

Think about the nurses, and other health professionals, who you have worked with and who hold positions of power. Consider those individuals you most admire. Think about what it was that you admired about them most. Consider whether they were the sort of individuals who got their hands dirty, who led by example, who seemed to lead so that they could improve the care of the people that they care for. Now think what this means for you as a nurse and how you might continue to hold the focus on patient care you have now as you progress into more senior roles.

As this is based on your own thoughts and reflections, there is no specimen answer at the end of the chapter.

What we can see from this example is that servant leadership could be a natural progression for nurses who start their career in positions where they deliver patient care. This model of leadership allows there to be some consistency in who they are and what they do as their career progresses.

This should not be seen as justification for leaders and managers who continue to deliver nursing care much of the time while neglecting the role which they are paid to perform. While we have highlighted the person-centred nature of health and social care, this does not always mean for leaders or managers that they have to deliver face-to-face patient care. What it does mean is that they need to support their staff to do so by leading by example, providing environments condu- cive to learning and improving care (see Chapter 8) and by creating and supporting policies which underpin person-centred care.

The NHS Leadership Model

Partly in response to the Francis report (2013) and partly to update an old leadership framework, the NHS Leadership Academy launched the new Healthcare Leadership Model in 2013. The emphasis of the model is on personal qualities and behaviours. The authors make the argument that:

> *The way that we manage ourselves is a central part of being an effective leader. It is vital to recognise that personal qualities like self-awareness, self-confidence, self-control, self-knowledge, personal reflection, resilience and determination are the foundation of how we behave. Being aware of your strengths and limitations in these areas will have a direct effect on how you behave and interact with others, and they with you.*
(NHS Leadership Academy, 2013)

The argument continues to highlight how the behaviours of the leader set the culture of the workplace and subsequently, the tone of patient care. In their view, workplace culture is partly a product of the behaviours and dispositions of the leader. Ideas regarding personal qualities are not explicit in the model but are a core theme throughout. Being able to lead with reference to personal qualities and exhibited behaviours requires self-awareness and emotional intelligence. The model is divided into nine interdependent and interlocked dimensions.

The nine dimensions of the Healthcare Leadership Model

1. Inspiring shared purpose
2. Leading with care
3. Evaluating information
4. Connecting our service
5. Sharing the vision
6. Engaging the team
7. Holding to account
8. Developing capability
9. Influencing for results

These dimensions all contain some challenge for the leader and, if you visit the online pages in which this model is described, you can do some of the activities for yourself (see the useful websites at the end of this chapter).

The role of emotional intelligence

The concept of emotional intelligence has gained an increasing following over recent years. Emotional intelligence in relation to leadership and management refers to the ability of leaders or managers to understand the role that their emotions play in their decision making and the ability to recognise the emotions of the individuals within the team and how this affects the work they do (Goleman, 1996).

Recognising the influence of emotions on decision making means that leaders and managers may be in a better position to understand what motivates and what constrains staff in their work. Leaders and managers who have well-developed emotional intelligence are said to be better at communicating with their team and therefore at achieving better outcomes.

Goleman (1998, page 317) defines emotional intelligence as *the capacity for recognizing our own feelings and those of others, for motivating ourselves, and for managing emotions well in ourselves and in our relationships.* He further states that emotional intelligence is a *learned capability.* Goleman's emotional intelligence framework comprises five elements: self-awareness, motivation, self-regulation, empathy and social skills. It is probably fair to comment that emotional intelligence is one dimension of what it is to be a good nurse and that this learned skill translates well into leadership and management roles.

It follows from this, however, that people who rely heavily on their emotions to guide their actions will tend to base their decisions on their emotional responses to a situation rather than on more objective empirical evidence and that in some situations this may be detrimental to the decisions they make (Croskerry and Norman, 2008). That said, the failure of leaders and managers to understand the role of their own emotions and those of their staff in shaping decision making and behaviours at work will mean that important issues are overlooked which may affect patient care.

Case study: The grieving staff nurse

Blossom had always been a self-confident and able staff nurse. She was friendly with staff and patients, but on the whole tended to keep very much to herself. Blossom had seemed a little withdrawn in recent weeks, but had said nothing to anyone until one day she went into an unexplained rage. Blossom shouted at the students and her fellow staff nurses and was rude and abrasive towards patients and visitors. Kathy, a fellow staff nurse, decided she should take control of the situation and took Blossom to one side. Once in the ward office Blossom started to cry. She confided to Kathy that her father had died some weeks previously and she was finding it hard to cope.

There are two interesting elements to this case study: first, Blossom had not shared her grief with anyone and did not know how to deal with it herself; second, no one on the ward team had picked up on her distress. On two levels, then, emotional intelligence was seen to be lacking: in Blossom recognising the effects of grief on her behaviour and in her colleagues recognising that Blossom was grieving. Clearly, for emotional intelligence to work for leaders or managers of people, they need to develop an awareness of the effects of their own emotions before they can recognise and respond to the emotions of others.

Chapter 4 looks at emotional intelligence in the context of conflict management.

Gaining support

What we have seen in this chapter is that one of the key roles of leaders or managers in nursing is working with and through their team. In order to achieve this, nurse managers and leaders need the support of their team. How this support is gained and maintained is through a mixture of good communication, good interpersonal skills and developing a sense of achievement. The team will support a leader that they trust.

Scholtes (1998) identifies trust as arising out of the feeling that leaders or managers both care for their staff and are capable of doing the job (Figure 6.1).

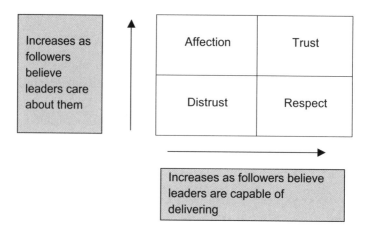

Figure 6.1: Trust, respect and affection

Source: Adapted from Scholtes (1998).

The model presented in Figure 6.1 demonstrates to novice leaders or managers the importance not only of getting the technical, procedural and policy elements of their role right, but also the need to take their team with them. This returns us to one of the key themes of the chapter – that to be a successful nurse manager there is a clear need not only to know what you are doing, but also to nurture and develop your staff and team while you are doing it – good management and good leadership.

Chapter summary

This chapter has introduced some of the different theories of management and leadership as well as some of the ways of acting that contribute to their success. We have seen that leadership and management, while often viewed as separate entities, can co-exist in the same individual and that when they do they can add to the success of the manager.

This chapter has identified that some of the key values of nursing translate well into good nurse leadership and we have identified that for managers or leaders to be successful they need both resilience and the ability to influence people. The need for resilience clearly comes from the requirement for managers and leaders to manage what can be difficult situations, and that part of the toolkit of successful leadership and management in terms of resilience is the ability to connect with people on the human level and thereby influence what they do and how they do it.

For nurses, who enter the profession to care for others, we have suggested that maintaining the focus on care as a fundamental part of developing as a leader and manager both sets a good role model to the team and helps to develop trust. Developing trust means that nurse leaders or managers can effectively lead their team in the delivery of high-quality nursing care.

Activities: brief outline answers

Activity 6.1 Reflection

You may remember meeting senior nurses who were able to let you know what they were doing and why you should do things in the way they wanted. Other nurses may have told you to do things because that is how things are done here. The first example is of leadership, as the senior nurse lets you see why and how you should behave in a certain way. The second example is more managerial in telling you what to do because this is policy. The best senior staff will be able to swap between being a leader and manager according to the situation and this change will appear appropriate; for example, during an emergency situation it may be best to be told what to do rather than why.

Activity 6.5 Reflection

Using reflection as a tool and utilising the experience and understanding of others allow us to see situations in a context. Understanding the context of a situation and why things happen as they do enables us to make sense of them, and cope emotionally with things which might otherwise prove too difficult. Part of the reflection process is planning how we will meet challenges in the future – action planning, that is how we become prepared. When we are prepared, we know not only how we will feel, but also how we will act and, more importantly, why. This means that when we meet similar situations in the future they will be less daunting. That is resilience.

Activity 6.6 Reflection

How you feel about an individual that you have to work with or follow is often affected by whether you like him or her as a person and whether you feel s/he cares about you as an individual. This is certainly an important first step in any relationship. When these same people deliver what they promise, when you learn from them what they said you would learn, it generates a feeling of great trust and gratitude. When an individual that you like is unable to deliver what s/he promised, you may not stop liking that person, but you question whether your trust in him or her is well placed and you will think twice before following whatever s/he says in the future.

Further reading

Adair, J (2010) *Develop Your Leadership Skills.* London: Kogan Page.

A really short and useful introduction to leadership as Adair sees it.

Grint, K (2002) Management or Leadership? *Journal of Health Services Research and Policy,* 7 (4): 248–51.

A useful discussion of leadership and management.

Henderson, J and Atkinson, D (eds) (2004) *Managing Care in Context.* London: Routledge.

A good overview of management in health and social care.

Jones, L and Bennett, CL (2012) *Leadership in Health and Social Care: An Introduction for Emerging Leaders.* Banbury: Lantern.

A good primer for people interested in the idea of leadership.

Useful websites

www.kingsfund.org.uk/Leadership

The King's Fund – a good leadership and management resource website.

www.bbc.co.uk/programmes/b00lv0wx

A podcast and explanation of the Hawthorne effect which is worth listening to.

http://www.leadershipacademy.nhs.uk/resources/healthcare-leadership-model

Look here to do the Healthcare Leadership Model activities alluded to in the text.

http://www.england.nhs.uk/tag/6cs

Explanation of the 6 Cs.

Chapter 7
Improving care, change management and entrepreneurial skills

Chapter aims

After reading this chapter you will be able to:

- compare different organisational structures;
- understand the organisation's requirements to maintain standards;
- understand change theory and its use in the change management process;
- evaluate the appraisal tools available to improve work performance;
- appreciate a new approach to changing practice through entrepreneurial skills.

Introduction

This chapter will help you understand how the organisation for which you work is structured and operates to maintain and improve standards. It looks at organisational clinical governance requirements and explores how you can work with others to plan and implement change. Included in this chapter are methods to improve standards of working through performance appraisal, supervision and 360-degree reviews. There is a section on planning, managing and implementing change to improve standards of care and service delivery. The final section looks at how entrepreneurial nurses can adopt a business-minded approach to improving patient care.

Understanding your organisation

Once you have qualified, you will be busy adapting to your new responsibilities and getting to grips with a new working environment. You will have little time to think about the 'powers that be' or the 'upper echelons' of the organisational structure in which you work. But this structure has an impact on your daily working life, so it is worth spending a few minutes figuring out who controls what.

Organisations have a structure that influences the manner in which they operate and perform. The structure, which will vary according to the objectives and culture of the organisation, provides a framework for distributing responsibilities for the different departments and functions. Factors that influence the shape of this structure include size, main purpose and skills of the workforce. The historical origins of a hospital (e.g. as a Victorian workhouse) or location (e.g. in an industrial area, close to a medieval leper colony or monastery), although distant from the modern demands of current NHS or private-sector healthcare, may nevertheless influence the organisation's culture.

Activity 7.1   *Evidence-based practice and research*

1. Ask your mentor if s/he knows the origins of the organisation where you are currently on placement. Consider whether this has had any impact on the functions of the organisation today.
2. Go to the web page of the organisation and look for the welcome page. See if there is a strapline which outlines the main priorities of the organisation. There may be a statement which says 'Our main objective is to …' or 'Our mission is to …'. Finding these key messages helps you understand what the priorities are for the organisation. If there is no web page, each organisation will produce an annual report. Seek this out to see what the main priorities for the organisation are.

As this answer is based on your own research and reflections, there is no specimen answer at the end of the chapter.

An important factor in any organisational structure, whether historically derived, a private healthcare company or small-scale organisation (such as a charitable foundation supporting a hospice), is the **span of control**. Used to describe the number of employees each organisation manager or head of department is responsible for, this can also be expressed in financial terms such as the budget or annual financial turnover of a department. The span of control will determine issues such as the structure, number of departments and managers in an organisation. There will usually be a leading manager, chief executive or similar post and a governing board with a number of board members, some of whom will be external to the organisation to provide expert advice or represent other organisations. In the NHS, for example, these would be patient organisation and local authority representatives from the council or regional government offices.

Activity 7.2   *Evidence-based practice and research*

Find out the structure in the organisation you have a placement in or hope to work in when you qualify. Try to get hold of a copy of the structure or ask your mentor to sketch one out.

Identify who sits on the board of the organisation as this is the main decision-making body with the power to agree or prevent service developments.

Find out if there is a nurse member of the board who represents your professional interests.

As this answer is based on your own research and reflections, there is no specimen answer at the end of the chapter.

Organisation structure

The Learn Management website (**www.learnmanagement2.com**) describes five main organisational structures: tall, flat, hierarchical, matrix and centralised/decentralised. On this website you will find descriptions of each type of structure, along with its advantages and disadvantages. In brief, a *tall* structure is one that has many levels of management, with each line manager having a small number of people reporting directly to him or her, so that the people on the lower levels may have no contact at all with those higher up. This can have implications for accountability and communication, but it does provide employees with a clear management structure with ample opportunities for promotion.

By contrast, a *flat* structure has fewer management layers, but each manager has quite a large number of people (all at more or less the same level) reporting to them. This can encourage team spirit and a sense of collective belonging, but it can be difficult to manage if the organisation is large. A *hierarchical* organisation has much in common with a tall organisation, but there are likely to be more people reporting directly to managers on each different level, particularly at the lower levels (thus giving them a pyramid shape). The most important decisions tend to be taken by the most senior people.

The *matrix* structure could not be more different. In an organisation with this type of structure, the important unit is the team. Each team will be led by a project manager or team leader, and will be responsible for a specific project or aspect of the organisation's work. In some organisations, the team will only exist for the duration of the work required by the project (e.g. a team of engineers working to develop a new type of vacuum cleaner). In others, the team becomes an established department within a whole organisation structure (e.g. with responsibility for distribution of the items being made). In many cases, the matrix organisation would consist of a mixture of permanent teams and project-specific teams.

Tall structures can be contrasted with flat structures, and hierarchical organisations with matrix-based organisations. Another important contrast is between centralised and decentralised structures. In a *centralised* organisation, a small group of senior managers (or a 'head office', which will be in a specific location) retains the major responsibilities and powers. In a *decentralised* organisation, these powers are devolved down to various lower-level managers, perhaps spread over a wide geographical area. Many supermarkets and chain stores are excellent examples of the decentralised structure. Each outlet is a management unit in itself, but, although the manager is relatively autonomous on a day-to-day basis, he or she will be ultimately answerable to the head office – either directly or through an interim (or regional) manager.

Some organisations may find a combination of centralisation and decentralisation to be most effective. For example, functions such as accounting or warehousing may be centralised to save costs. The Department of Health uses a mixture of centralisation and decentralisation, with central policy decisions being made to influence local health services. At the same time, local NHS Trusts have functions and responsibilities to respond to local population health needs and to manage their organisations according to the workforce they require to deliver those services.

Nurses at board level

An influential government report in the early 1980s observed that *If Florence Nightingale were carrying her lamp through the corridors of the NHS today she would almost certainly be searching for the people in charge* (Griffiths, 1983). In the wake of this, the Royal College of Nursing launched a campaign with the slogan 'Nursing should be managed by nurses' and, indeed, the first nurse general managers were appointed shortly afterwards (*Nursing Standard*, 1985). Nurse managers should be well placed to improve the business of caring by helping boards not only to understand the quality of care patients receive on the wards, but also to make positive decisions which improve care.

During the last two decades, the management of NHS organisations has tended to focus on financial measures and performance targets rather than on the quality of clinical care. However, the Darzi report (Darzi, 2008) has reversed this trend, describing the improvement in quality of care as *the basis of everything we do in the NHS*. The business of caring was brought to the forefront in the review and considered just as important as financial management.

The role of nurses at board level in the NHS has changed and more are being appointed. The post of nurse executive (or nursing director) was established alongside the first wave of NHS Trusts in 1991. In 2007 the Burdett Trust commissioned the King's Fund to develop an intensive programme of work to support executive nurses and NHS boards in raising the quality of clinical care and giving a central place to patients and how they experience healthcare.

This work has resulted in two reports:

1. *From Ward to Board* (Machell et al., 2009) sets out the key questions and findings from the first phase of the programme and identifies good practice that can be easily replicated. Key areas to be built on are identified, along with the key skills and qualities nurse executives need to fulfil their role effectively.
2. *Putting Quality First in the Boardroom: Improving the Business of Caring* (Machell et al., 2010) is based on observations of how nurse executives and their boards work together. This report builds on themes that emerged from the previous one, and addresses long-standing concerns about the way in which financial and administrative performance indicators have taken precedence over issues relating to the quality of clinical care.

Commitment to the patient experience and the role of the NHS in the wider community is further recognised in the 2014 *Five Year Forward View* plan published by NHS England which reiterated this position, stating that patients and communities need to be at the heart of care.

Governance

This section examines the regulatory bodies responsible for ensuring quality and good **governance** in health and social care organisations. The White Paper *Equity and Excellence: Liberating the NHS* (Department of Health, 2010) proposed changes to the governance, regulation and accountability arrangements of the NHS in England. The Care Quality Commission (CQC) is a regulatory body with responsibility for monitoring the quality of health and social care provision in England. It was created in 2009 through a merger of the Healthcare Commission, the Mental Health Commission and the Care Service Inspection Service. Scotland, Northern Ireland and Wales have separate governance arrangements.

Activity 7.3   *Evidence-based practice and research*

If you are in placement in an NHS organisation in England there will have been a CQC inspection within recent years. This activity will help you find the most recent report. Go to the website: **http://www.cqc.org.uk**.

In the 'Search whole website' box put a place name or postcode and select a service you wish to find out about. You can also find out about independent nursing homes and social care providers who are registered, and therefore licensed to provide services, with the CQC. Read the most recent report, paying special attention to the elements of quality as identified by the inspectorate, as well as the type of evidence to support the conclusions they have come to about the service.

As this answer is based on your own research, there is no specimen answer at the end of the chapter.

Case study: Investigating quality of care (CQC, 2011)

In February 2010 the CQC investigated Cambridgeshire and Peterborough NHS Foundation Trust and warned it to improve the standards of its mental health services or face enforcement action. In 2011 the CQC published a report which drew attention to its findings and made recommendations for improvements. The inspectors found the Trust was contravening five regulations regarding care and welfare, staffing, safeguarding people, assessing and monitoring service provision and safety and suitability of premises. The Mental Health Act Annual Statement report (2010) presented recommendations as to how the Trust should continue to conform to the Mental Health Act and Codes of Practice when detaining patients (CQC, 2011).

Some concerns identified in the 2011 review had not been fully addressed by the Trust. These were as follows:

- *Care and welfare of people who use services:*
  - o *Not all care plans were person-centred or included information regarding individuals' wider care and inclusion needs.*
  - o *The seclusion suite on one ward is not meeting environmental requirements or the requirements of the Mental Health Act 1983 Code of Practice.*
- *Safeguarding vulnerable people who use services from abuse:*
  - o *Policies in relation to adult safeguarding and incident reporting do not clearly set out arrangements that ensure consistent reporting, investigation and dissemination of learning in relation to matters regarding cases of abuse allegations and incidents.*
  - o *Incident reporting and auditing systems are not robust.*
- *Safety and suitability of premises:*
  - o *Poorly designed fixed furniture and the presence of potential ligature points in some parts of the premises pose a risk to people who use services.*
  - o *The standard of décor and maintenance of one ward does not promote the dignity and well-being of people using services.*
- *Staffing:*
  - o *There are not always sufficient numbers of staff with the right competencies, knowledge, qualifications, skills and experience available to meet the needs of patients.*
- *Assessing and monitoring the quality of service provision:*
  - o *There is a lack of consistency in grading of incidents and no safety mechanism to ensure that inconsistencies are identified and resolved.*
  - o *There are delays in the time it takes between staff reporting incidents and their managers signing off the processes (CQC, 2011).*

Although this Trust has now submitted positive action plans addressing how they plan to meet the essential standards, the CQC will be monitoring the Trust closely and will use enforcement powers if changes are not quickly brought about (CQC, 2011).

This real-life case illustrates the power of the CQC and its ability to act swiftly and responsively if concerns are raised about a regulated service.

Activity 7.4	*Evidence-based practice and research*

It is interesting to note the substantial, but not complete, progress made within the mental health services within the Cambridgeshire and Peterborough NHS Foundation Trust. Go to the website **http://www.cqc.org.uk** and in the 'Search whole website' box put in 'Fulbourn' and follow the links to the October 2013 report. Compare the content of this report to the content of the report above and consider the positive impact the CQC report has had on the development of the service.

As this answer is based on your own research, there is no specimen answer at the end of the chapter.

Changes to regulation

Foundation Trusts are currently regulated by Monitor, an independent regulator. Between April 2012 and April 2013, Monitor's responsibilities widened so that it became an economic regulator with responsibility for all providers of NHS care. All NHS providers have a joint licence overseen by CQC and Monitor, with the CQC responsible for essential levels of safety and quality and Monitor responsible for ensuring continuity of essential services and financial regulation. Meanwhile, the National Institute for Health and Care Excellence (NICE) is developing 150 quality standards which the NHS commissioning board will develop into a comprehensive set of indicators against which quality and progress can be objectively measured. The 2012 Health and Social Care Act identifies the purpose of Monitor as: *to protect and promote the interests of people who use health care services by promoting provision of health care services which is economic, efficient and effective, and maintains or improves the quality of services* (Her Majesty's Government, 2012).

Improving standards

In Chapter 5, we discussed how staff development could enable individuals to develop their skills further. Performance appraisal is one method that managers use to regulate how well individuals carry out their responsibilities. The Chartered Institute of Personnel and Development (CIPD: 2011) claims it is important to distinguish between performance management and performance appraisal. Performance management is undertaken through supervision and achievements are observed against a specific set of objectives or goals, whereas performance appraisal is a dialogue between manager and subordinate to discuss an individual's performance, past and future development and the support required from the organisation and manager to achieve optimum performance. Marquis and Huston (2009) suggest the process of performance appraisal can also be a motivator towards improving performance. In this sense, performance appraisal is a tool to be used in performance management.

The CIPD (2011) recommends five key elements in the process:

1. measurement – assessing the performance against agreed targets and objectives;
2. feedback – providing information to individuals on their performance and progress;

3. positive reinforcement – emphasising what has been done well and making only constructive criticism about what might be improved;
4. exchange of views – a frank exchange of views about what has happened, how appraisees can improve performance, the support they need from their managers to achieve this and their aspiration for their future career;
5. agreement – jointly coming to an understanding by all parties about what needs to be done to improve performance generally and overcome any issues raised in the course of the discussion.

Appraisal tools

There are several tools that can be used for performance appraisal. The simplest is a trait-rating scale where individuals are rated using a numerical score against a set of standards, including their job description, knowledge, behaviours and personal traits – such as attitude to work. This method invites a subjective decision, which is open to potential bias, and, if a point scale is used, a tendency to score to the midline, making the process meaningless.

Self-assessment methods involve individuals submitting a portfolio of achievements and productivity. While introspection and self-awareness can result in growth and achievement, feedback on achievements is essential for a positive result.

Management by objectives is a technique seldom used in healthcare. It incorporates a process that negotiates both the organisation's objectives and the individual's assessments. It is a very specific form of appraisal, with individuals measured against the objectives on a regular basis. In public healthcare organisations the appraisal is usually an annual event, whereas management by objectives is often quarterly and therefore far more intensive and oriented towards action by observable results.

Peer review is, as the name suggests, a process whereby professional colleagues monitor and assess each other's performance. It is used widely in medicine and education, and less widely in wider healthcare. The Nursing and Midwifery Council uses this approach to review nursing and midwifery education. Peer review events take place on an annual basis with a group of colleagues from other, similar organisations or professional groups conducting a review of systems and processes set against publicly available criteria. The process requires data to be collected from a variety of sources, such as charts, patient care plans, information systems, other professionals and patients.

An adaptation of the peer review process is 360-degree feedback. This is an assessment of performance that provides information from a variety of sources and often includes a group of colleagues who work with an individual. Usually, eight to ten people complete questionnaires that can also include a self-assessment, and which are submitted anonymously to an independent observer to collate the responses into a report for the individual. The report should demonstrate a synthesis of information about performance in a role. In healthcare, this could include patients as well as co-workers to provide all-round information, which is where the name originates. This allows the individuals being assessed to understand how other people view them (as in the Johari window, discussed in Chapter 1) and can enable the developing leader to work on areas of their behaviour which they might otherwise not be aware of.

We have previously discussed clinical supervision and coaching (Chapter 5) as a means of supporting individuals to develop new skills. These are also tools that a manager can utilise to improve work performance and standards.

Activity 7.5   *Reflection and critical thinking*

1. How do you feel about being appraised? What are your fears and anxieties about appraisal? Think about the expectations you have. Now put yourself into the shoes of the manager and try to understand his or her expectations of the process.
2. Consider each of the appraisal tools discussed above and draw up a table that compares the advantages and disadvantages of each method. You may need to look again at Chapter 5 on clinical supervision and coaching.

Further guidance is given on this activity at the end of the chapter.

Rewards

Performance appraisal can also be used as a means of assessing an individual's ability to be promoted or moved to another pay band. The Knowledge and Skills Framework, defined in the Agenda for Change (AfC) pay agreement (**www.nhsemployers.org/your-workforce/pay-and-reward/pay/agenda-for-change-pay/how-agenda-for-change-works**), paved the way for a Gateway Policy to be formulated by NHS Trusts to ensure that staff covered by the AfC would obtain a transparent opportunity to move to a higher pay band. Under the AfC, progression from one pay point to another is assessed each year against the skills identified in the Knowledge and Skills Framework bands. At defined points, known as Gateways, management decisions will be made about progression to higher levels of pay and responsibility. There are two Gateways in each of the nine pay bands: Foundation, which takes place no later than 12 months after an individual is appointed to a pay band, and Second Gateway, which is set at a fixed point towards the top of a pay band.

Planning change

You cannot have failed to notice the amount of change that has permeated the health services in recent years. These changes are sometimes driven by policies to restructure organisations, by improvements in medical science such as the development of stem cell research, or advances in society's attitudes to rights, such as with the Human Rights Act (1998). In the day-to-day running of a ward or unit the types of change that take place can be personal (such as when staff change) or organisational (such as changes in shift patterns) or the way in which internal services are delivered (e.g. bed management, portering services, catering services or discharge-planning methods).

There are many forces driving change in healthcare that are not just related to the UK. Rising costs of medical treatments, shortages of skilled workforces, increasing technology, availability of information and a growing elderly population have led, in some cases, to extreme destabilisation and a constant need to upgrade structures, promote better quality and manage workforce constraints. Whatever the changes to the work environment, there are those who embrace the changes and those who find it very difficult to adapt. Nurses in the future will need to be even more adaptable than they have been in the past to keep up with change.

Activity 7.6						*Reflection*

What is your personal perspective on change? Below is a short rating scale for you to self-assess your attitude to change. Place a mark in the score that most fits your perspective: 1 = low agreement; 5 = high agreement.

	1	2	3	4	5
1. I always embrace change					
2. I look for opportunities to change things					
3. I accept change reluctantly					
4. I avoid change at all costs					
5. My response to change is the same as that of my friends and family					
6. Have you always responded to change in this way or have you changed in your lifetime?					
7. What events have altered your views and responses to change?					

As this answer is based on your own experience and reflections, there is no specimen answer at the end of the chapter.

Initiating and co-ordinating change requires well-developed leadership and management skills. It requires vision and expert planning skills because vision alone is not sufficient.

Many of the best ideas for changing practice fail because of inadequate preparation and planning. Poor preparation results in problems during implementation, frustrated staff and lack of successful outcome.

Change theory

Most of the contemporary research into change management originates from the work of social psychologist Kurt Lewin in the mid twentieth century. There are other theories; however, we will concentrate on Lewin's theory in this book and will compare it briefly with newer developments in complexity theory and chaos theory. If you are interested in other theories, please go to the useful websites at the end of this chapter for further information.

Lewin (1951) identified three stages through which change must proceed before any planned change will become embedded in an organisation or system of working. The stages are unfreezing, movement and refreezing.

Unfreezing is when the change agent proposes a convincing plan for change to the team or management. It is also when team members who are not keen on the change can be helped to draw out their anxieties or concerns about the change. At this stage people will become either discontented about the proposal or increasingly aware of the need to change. The skilful leader will be able to work with these conflicting views to build up trust in the change proposal's worth and the value of putting effort into the proposed change. Cummings and McLennan (2005) claim that an essential leadership role is to understand the different perspectives of individuals and **stakeholders** and *to align the changes to be meaningful for them* (page 65).

During unfreezing leaders need to take account of the balance between change and stability, as too much change leads to instability, which results in feelings of lack of control, insecurity and anxiety. A good leader will assess the relative merits of the forces for and against change, such as extent of the proposed change, nature and depth of motivation of stakeholders and the environment in which the change will occur; this last could be physical (e.g. buildings) or political (e.g. local or national policy). The driving forces for change will need to exceed the opposing forces for change to be successful.

In the second stage there is *movement* towards accepting the change, and a plan of action and implementation is instigated. Change takes time as people adjust to the idea, come to understand the benefits of the change and eventually become adopters of the change. Part of the planning process for change management involves including time for recognising, addressing and overcoming resistance to the proposal arising from stakeholders' attitudes, perceptions and personal values.

The final stage, according to Lewin (1951), is *refreezing*. Change needs time before it is accepted as part of the system. This means that, after the change is implemented, support will still be needed to embed the change. The leader's role is to help the continued integration of the change into practice to ensure refreezing – that is, the change becoming part of normal practice; if this does not occur, the previous behaviours will emerge.

One method to ensure the effects of change are perceived as beneficial is to measure the outcomes of change or make improvements to the change as a result of feedback from outcome measures. Thus a plan to evaluate the change should be incorporated in the overall change management plan.

Steps of change

Stage 1: Unfreezing

1. Gather data and information about the planned change.
2. Accurately and objectively describe the issues that are causing the problem or reason for change. Use evidence and hard facts, not supposition or 'finger in the air' tactics.
3. Decide if change is really needed and identify the reasons for change. This could be a pilot for your ideas by testing on your team or one or two close colleagues.
4. Make others aware of the need for change. This also involves highlighting discontent with the current system, i.e. what is wrong or not productive. Progress to the next stage should not happen until sufficient discontent is expressed about the current system.

Stage 2: Movement

1. Develop a change management plan – this could take the form of a project plan (use a **Gantt chart** if it will help you visualise what you want to achieve – see further reading at the end of the chapter).
2. Set goals and objectives.
3. Identify areas of support and resistance.
4. Include everyone who will be affected by the change in its planning; however, you may want to have a small project group or reference group to help manage the project with you.
5. Set target dates and timelines.
6. Develop appropriate strategies.
7. Implement the change.
8. Be available to support others and offer encouragement through the change process.
9. Use strategies for overcoming resistance to change.
10. Evaluate the change.
11. Modify the change if necessary.

Stage 3: Refreezing

Support others so that the change is sustainable and remains in place to achieve improved outcomes.

Source: Adapted from Marquis and Huston (2009), page 171.

Case study: Change management

Cummings and McLennan (2005) outlined four steps in a change management project to introduce advanced practice nurse roles into a traditionally, medically oriented tertiary care oncology centre. Their main aim was to engage stakeholders in the change process and use an evidence-based approach.

Step one was to identify a change model to guide the project. They did this by using Lewin's theoretical change model and adapting it to connect action research and policy drivers for change. The policy drivers challenged stakeholders' values and beliefs (i.e. the value of advanced nursing) and competence, standards of practice, financial savings, medical and nursing workloads.

The second step was to assign a 'champion' or change agent to the project to work closely with staff through the unfreezing stages of the project and enable the final stage, which is beyond the change itself. In the third step a forum was created, involving members from all the professional groups involved in the change, to facilitate open communication between everyone who would be affected by the change and change process. The final stage was to support staff through and beyond the change process to ensure the change became embedded into the working practices of the team.

Cummings and McLennan (2005) found that multidisciplinary team work, already established in the unit, was an important lever to help implement and embed the change. You will have noticed that, all the way through the change process, communication of intentions and plans, which ensures individuals and teams are engaged and informed in the change plan, has been paramount to creating an effective change strategy.

Activity 7.7 — Decision making

Identify a change you would like to make in your personal life. List the driving forces that you think are your reasons for wanting to change. Then list the restraining forces that you think will inhibit you making the change. Work out a plan, utilising all of the steps of change in the box above, to achieve the change.

Hint

Remember the driving forces will need to exceed the restraining forces (Beckhard and Harris, 1987) and you will need to feel sufficient discontent with how things currently are for the change process to tip from unsuccessful to successful. You will also need to plan time for the change to be embedded into your everyday life. This means it will take longer than you originally planned; especially if you were hoping for quick results.

As this answer is based on your own decision making, there is no specimen answer at the end of the chapter.

Complexity theory and chaos theory

Lewin's change theory is a linear approach to change, with an optimistic view that change, once implemented, will be refrozen and equilibrium re-established. In this current world, where science is moving the frontiers of knowledge forward at an increasing pace and organisations respond to change more rapidly, the linear approach has been found wanting. This is particularly evident in UK healthcare, where long-term planning is problematic due to fluctuating economic and political influences. Consequently, non-linear change theories such as complexity theory and chaos theory now influence contemporary thinking about change.

Complexity theory maintains that we inhabit a complex world where individuals are multifaceted and situations are forever dynamic and changing. The theory originates from physics, where the natural order of science is challenged by systems that are constantly adapting because of the interaction between parts and feedback loops that change things and do not maintain the status quo. An example of this is that an individual may have behaved in a certain way in the past but that person's future behaviour may not be predictably the same.

Olson and Eoyang (2001) developed a theory of complex adaptive systems which maintains that we should not focus on the large changes taking place but on the effects of change at a micro level between individuals. It is at the individual level where relationships, and simple expressions of rules, are responsible for change. When applying this theory to changes in healthcare it suggests we should concentrate on the individuals who work in the organisations and understand these relationships before attempting to unfreeze, as in Lewin's theory. They also suggest that continual monitoring and adaptation are needed for refreezing to be achieved.

Research summary: Complexity theory and organisations

Anderson et al. (2004) undertook a study, underpinned by complexity theory, to analyse the effects of organisational climate and communication patterns on high staff turnover in nursing homes. They surveyed 3,449 employees in 164 randomly selected nursing homes in North Carolina, USA, to identify the perceptions of staff about organisational climate and communication. They also asked questions about the characteristics of the homes' facilities, allocation of resources and turnover. The results were analysed statistically using a hierarchical regression technique (to examine the relationship between variables).

They found that there was a lower turnover in the lower-paid staffing groups (which had the highest overall turnover rates) when the climate was viewed positively and communication was open. Where there was a reward-based climate and high levels of open communication, staff performed better than in those homes with unclear and confusing communication methods. They also found that, where there were good levels of staffing, and senior staff who had been in position for a long time, there was more likely to be lower staff turnover. Thus, a stable leadership situation enhanced staff satisfaction with workplace conditions through the influence of the leadership style. A reward-themed climate and open communication were aspects of this style.

Chaos theory was first described in 1963 by Edward Lorenz, a meteorologist working on the problem of weather predictability. It is related to complexity theory in that it refers to the unpredictable and adaptive factors that affect events. Lorenz discovered that a minor change in a part of an experiment could change the whole outcome. A practical example is where a slight rise in the temperature of the ocean in one place in the world may have an effect on the airflow that will eventually lead to a change in temperature in another part of the world.

Chaos theory is a new science that helps us understand why a small change in a situation can alter how a system functions. Chaos theory also suggests that it is impossible to know what this change may be because there are so many different variables that can affect a situation. For example, even if you know everything about football – the players, strategies, ground conditions and everything involved – you still cannot accurately predict the outcome. Yet, if you watch repeated games you would be able to predict some elements of the game.

The application of complexity theory to change management in organisations provides a means of understanding why change does not always go to plan because of unpredictable multifactorial influences and, secondly, that understanding small effects, as chaos theory suggests, can have a big effect in a change management plan. For example, individuals who do not trust the change plan or do not think it can work could jeopardise the change plan. However, if they are brought into the change process and their ideas given a hearing, they may not feel the need to jeopardise the plan. A major lesson for managers is that they cannot completely control a change plan because there will always be some elements that cannot be predicted in advance that will affect it. Managers need to learn how to manage the anxiety that accompanies change as well as flexibility and the ability to think on their feet so that they can manage the unexpected. In Chapter 9 we talk some more about the impact of change on individuals and their self-esteem.

Living in a constantly changing world where there is rapid technological, social, cultural and political change, we have to be prepared to adapt, be willing to learn and test our assumptions. Things that worked in the past may not work in the future and nurses have always been able to find new ways of managing problems and being creative. That is why in the next section we will explore how nurses can use this creativity to improve patient care.

Tools for change: entrepreneurship

In 2004 the International Council of Nurses (ICN) produced a monograph that gives guidance on the scope for nurses to become self-employed using expert skills and knowledge. In the UK there has been limited uptake of independent practitioners of nursing and midwifery; however, the skills of entrepreneurship are now being debated as a potential, valuable contribution to innovative healthcare initiatives. The ICN sets out how this can be understood by describing three different types of nursing entrepreneur:

1. Entrepreneur: an individual who assumes the total responsibility and risk for discovering or creating unique opportunities to use personal talents, skills and energy and who employs a strategic planning process to transfer that opportunity into a marketable service or product.
2. Nurse entrepreneur: a proprietor of a business that offers nursing services of a direct care, educational, research, administrative or consultative nature. The self-employed nurse is

directly accountable to the client, to whom, or on behalf of whom, nursing services are provided.

3. Nurse intrapreneur: a salaried nurse who develops, promotes and delivers an innovative health/nursing programme or project within a given healthcare setting based upon the skills of entrepreneurism (ICN, 2004).

It is this last role that we will be exploring in this chapter. Within these definitions it is clear that the only difference between an intrapreneur and entrepreneur is the setting in which the skills of entrepreneurship are used.

To understand the influence of entrepreneurism on the concept of intrapreneurism, we need to consider its antecedents. There is no commonly accepted definition of the terms 'entrepreneur' and 'entrepreneurship' and furthermore the meaning is shifting as it is applied to healthcare endeavours as intrapreneurism. In business or commercial terms it is someone who has a new idea and wishes to undertake a new venture with a responsibility for the risks that may result and the outcome. There is an implicit sense that the entrepreneur will personally gain from the venture. Entrepreneurs will see opportunities for developments and take advantage of those opportunities; they can act as a catalyst for change and research and innovation, introducing new technologies, increasing efficiency and productivity, and generating new products or services. An intrapreneur will essentially do the same but within the confines of an organisation and will benefit less from the outcomes, but will be exposed to less attendant risk.

Traynor et al. (2006) reported on a research project that investigated the extent and potential for entrepreneurial activity in nursing, midwifery and health visiting (NMHV). In 2007, Drennan et al. published the findings and claimed that, while they found a range of NMHV entrepreneurial activity in the UK, there is very little in relation to the total numbers of nurses, midwives and health visitors registered in the UK. This reflects the international picture. The examples of nurse entrepreneur activity that were found involved nurses being creative and flexible in their working environments to solve problems or substituting for medical roles. The researchers found that nurses in certain fields (such as public health or specialist nursing) were more likely to have carried out entrepreneurial activity. Specific examples of activity were found through knowledge transfer (through training and consultancy), invention of healthcare products and small-business provision of infrastructure services to healthcare and self-employed and small-business provision of direct healthcare services.

The study attempted to find a relationship between entrepreneurial activity and patient choice but found this to be weak, except in the case of independent midwifery. Yet in 20 per cent of the documents they analysed, this was an aspiration, along with seeking autonomous practice and achieving personal and professional accomplishment. Financial incentives were not a prominent feature; however, this was not borne out by seminar participants, who felt that financial gain was a hidden agenda due to the lack of a commercial culture within the NHS.

Activity 7.8　　　　　　　　　　　　　　　　　　　　　*Skills development*

Think of an area of practice, service delivery or patient care that you would like to see improved. Imagine you are going to present this idea to a *Dragons' Den* (BBC TV programme)-type panel of peers. (If you are not familiar with *Dragons' Den*, please generate an idea for presentation to a panel of peers.)

1. Who would you have on the panel? What skills and knowledge would you expect them to have to make a decision about your idea?
2. Design a simple presentation that 'sells' your idea to the panel.

Hint

Go to the BBC web page **http://news.bbc.co.uk/1/hi/business/2943252.stm**, which will give you tips on writing a business plan.

As this answer is based on your own research and reflections, there is no specimen answer at the end of the chapter.

The debate is still open on whether or not entrepreneurialism can drive forward a culture of innovation and creativity, benefiting patient care. There remain several obstacles, such as the prevailing ideology of the NHS as a public-sector organisation and therefore by default a 'not-for-profit industry', and the socialisation of NMHVs that does not include a business frame of reference. As Drennan et al. (2007) point out, there has been no systematic measurement of the outcomes of NMHV enterprise activities to support the effectiveness of entrepreneurial activity. Yet there are examples of where it has made a difference (Drennan et al., 2007).

Chapter summary

In this chapter we have examined different organisational structures that you can map out in your own organisation. You can then identify where the decisions are made in your organisation which will, in turn, help you understand where to find information about the decisions. Nurses are playing an increasingly pivotal role in organisational decisions as government policy recognises that nurses can represent not only their profession but also the patient's point of view. We have studied the governance requirements for NHS institutions to ensure they are meeting the standards required and also looked at the regulatory arrangements starting in 2012. While looking at standards we considered how to improve care on a personal level through performance appraisal and compared some of the methods that can be used.

The chapter has also looked at the theory underpinning change management and contemporary theory developments. Change management is a huge subject and we have only

continued . . . .

briefly touched on the change-planning process to raise your awareness of the methods available. Finally, we looked at the potential for a newer approach to introducing change and improving standards with an emphasis on social enterprise and entrepreneurial skills.

Activity: brief outine answers

Activity 7.5 Reflection and critical thinking

1. Preparation for appraisal is the best method of ensuring levels of anxiety are minimised on the part of both the appraisee and the appraiser. This means ensuring the method and purpose of the appraisal are clearly articulated and agreed beforehand, standards are transparent and evident in the organisation's policies, strengths as well as weaknesses are explored and the paperwork is available and prepared in advance by both parties. Further support for conducting appraisals can be found on the CIPD website listed in the useful websites section below.

2. Comparison of appraisal methods:

	Advantages	Disadvantages
Clinical supervision	Personal and focused Deeper trusting relationship can be established Can specifically match specialty area to improve performance	Could become too intense Personalities may not match More resources required for time
Coaching	Personalised Identifies specific goals Enhances personal motivation	Takes time Needs indepth coaching training to be effective
Trait-rating scales	Uses a set standard that is transparent Incorporates personal behaviours such as attitudes	Can lead to subjective assessments Central tendency in scores 'Halo' or 'horns' effects from rater
Self-appraisal	Collects examples of impact on standards and is achievement-oriented Enables personal growth and awareness	Gives little scope for feedback – positive or negative May have focused on goals that do not correspond to organisational targets for improvement
Management by objectives	Determines individual progress, incorporating both employee and organisation's goals Promotes individual growth and excellence	Authoritarian and directive managers find this approach difficult due to the negotiated nature of the goal setting Some employees may set easily achievable goals
Peer review	Has the potential to increase accuracy of performance appraisal as collects data from wider range of sources	Requires high levels of trust to share data More time consuming than one-to-one appraisals

	Can enhance team working and improve understanding between different teams, especially interdisciplinary teams Provides increased opportunities for professional learning and sharing of good practice	Takes time to orient staff to the process, requires training and has high administration costs Shifts authority away from manager, which can be threatening to the manager, who may feel exposed
360-degree appraisal	Feedback from a variety of sources Provides a broader perspective on an individual's performance	Requires questionnaires to be designed and administered, data collected anonymously and collated into a report, which is costly and time consuming Could be threatening to have such a wide selection of subjective opinions about an individual's performance

Further reading

Dwyer, J, Stanton, P and Thiessen, V (2004) *Project Management in Health and Community.* London: Routledge.

Gantt, HL (1910) *Work, Wages and Profit*, published by *The Engineering Magazine*, New York; republished as *Work, Wages and Profits*. Easton, PA: Hive Publishing Company, 1974.

Kritonis, A (2004) Comparison of Change Theory. *International Journal of Scholarly Academic Intellectual Diversity*, 8 (1).

Marquis, BL and Huston, CJ (2014) *Leadership Roles and Management Functions in Nursing: Theory and Applications* (7th edition). Philadelphia, PA: Lippincott, Williams and Wilkins, Chapter 24: Performance Appraisal.

Traynor, M, Davis, K, Drennan, V, Goodman, C, Humphrey, C, Locke, R, Mark, A, Murray, SF, Banning, M and Peacock, R (2006) *A Report to the National Co-ordinating Centre for NHS Service Delivery and Organisation Research and Development of a Scoping Exercise on 'The Contribution of Nurse, Midwife and Health Visitor Entrepreneurs to Patient Choice'.* London: National Co-ordinating Centre for Service Delivery and Organisation.

Yoder-Wise, PS (2011) *Leading and Managing in Nursing* (5th edition). St Louis, MO: Mosby Elsevier, Chapter 17: Leading Change.

Useful websites

www.cipd.co.uk/hr-resources/factsheets/performance-appraisal.aspx
Performance appraisal: Chartered Institute of Personnel and Development performance appraisal: guidance and processes.

www.learnmanagement2.com
Organisation structures: The Learn Management website gives lots of theory and useful explanatory diagrams.

www.scottlondon.com/interviews/wheatley.html

The New Science of Leadership: an interview with Margaret Wheatley by Scott London.

www.bbc.co.uk/programmes/p00548f6

Chaos theory: BBC broadcast of radio programme chaired by Melvyn Bragg in 2002 with Susan Greenfield, Senior Research Fellow, Lincoln College, Oxford University, David Papineau, Professor of the Philosophy of Science, King's College, London and Neil Johnson, University Lecturer in Physics at Oxford University, discussing chaos theory. The broadcast explains chaos theory and its roots and application to modern-day usage. You will need Realplayer software to listen to the broadcast, which lasts for 45 minutes.

www.nurse-entrepreneur-network.com

US Nurse Entrepreneur Network web page: advice and tips on setting up a nursing business.

www.youtube.com/watch?v=ZxuwVqyyrmM

Wendy Miles, entrepreneurial nurse 'Nurse Joey': Example of a nurse entrepreneur success that has improved nurses' working lives, benefited the organisation and released time for patient care. Wendy developed a handy pocket-like pouch to assist nurses; it saves time for nurses to carry small essential equipment about with them while they work.

www.entreprenurses.net

A website for UK nurses wishing to learn more about developing entrepreneurial skills and links to short learning modules, podcasts and relevant literature.

Chapter 8
Creating a learning environment

NMC Standards for Pre-registration Nursing Education

This chapter will address the following competencies:

Domain 1: Professional values

7. All nurses must be responsible and accountable for keeping their knowledge and skills up to date through continuing professional development. They must aim to improve their performance and enhance the safety and quality of care through evaluation, supervision and appraisal.

Domain 3: Nursing practice and decision-making

1. All nurses must use up-to-date knowledge and evidence to assess, plan, deliver and evaluate care, communicate findings, influence change and promote health and best practice. They must make person-centred, evidence-based judgements and decisions, in partnership with others involved in the care process, to ensure high quality care. They must be able to recognise when the complexity of clinical decisions requires specialist knowledge and expertise, and consult or refer accordingly.

Domain 4: Leadership, management and team working

1. All nurses must act as change agents and provide leadership through quality improvement and service development to enhance people's well-being and experiences of healthcare.
5. All nurses must facilitate nursing students and others to develop their competence, using a range of professional and personal development skills.

Essential Skills Clusters

This chapter will address the following ESCs:

Cluster: Care, compassion and communication

1. As partners in the care process, people can trust a newly registered graduate nurse to provide collaborative care based on the highest standards, knowledge and competence.

continued . . .

At entry to the register

14. Uses professional support structures to develop self awareness, challenge own prejudices and enable professional relationships, so that care is delivered without compromise.

4. People can trust a newly qualified graduate nurse to engage with them and their family or carers within their cultural environments in an acceptable and anti-discriminatory manner free from harassment and exploitation.

At entry to the register

13. Through reflection and evaluation demonstrates commitment to personal and professional development and life-long learning.

Cluster: Organisational aspects of care

12. People can trust the newly registered graduate nurse to respond to their feedback and a wide range of other sources to learn, develop and improve services.

At entry to the register

8. As an individual team member and team leader, actively seeks and learns from feedback to enhance care and own and others' professional development.

18. People can trust a newly registered graduate nurse to enhance the safety of service users and identify and actively manage risk and uncertainty in relation to people, the environment, self and others.

At entry to the register

9. Reflects on and learns from safety incidents as an autonomous individual and as a team member and contributes to team learning.

10. Participates in clinical audit to improve the safety of service users.

Chapter aims

After reading this chapter you will be able to:

- identify what a learning environment is;
- explain why a learning environment is important;
- discuss how a learning environment might be created;
- consider your role in developing a learning environment.

Introduction

Nursing, in common with all health and social care, is evolving. In great part this evolution is driven by the society and culture we live in and by the changing technology we work with, developing understandings of the nature and experience of care. Within this changing environment there is a need for nursing, and individual nurses, to keep pace with developments. The increased professionalisation of nursing, clearly demonstrated by the move to an all-graduate profession, further requires nurses to be engaged with their own development and learning in order to meet the demands of twenty-first-century care provision.

Learning and developing are therefore constant and enduring requirements for all nurses and the need to facilitate this is a key function of nurse leaders and managers. This chapter describes how the creation and maintenance of a learning environment in the clinical setting can contribute to the development of nurses and nursing. You will be challenged within this chapter to consider what this means for you as an individual, as well as how you might take the messages contained in it forward in your career as a leader or manager of nurses. What is important to remember throughout this chapter is that your orientation to learning and the generation of learning environments have a direct, positive impact on patient care. In this respect, environments of care which are 'learning environments' allow us to express some of the values of care we discussed in detail in Chapter 1.

What are 'environments of care'?

Before we go on to consider what is meant by a 'learning environment', it is worth taking a moment to consider what is meant by the term environments in the sense used here. Environments refer to many things, including the physical nature of a building and its surroundings, as well as the meanings different people attach to the same physical space.

Activity 8.1   *Reflection*

To understand the ways in which different people attach different meanings to spaces, let's begin by reflecting on the nature of the work environment. When you are working in the hospital setting, consider the different ways in which people may experience the area in which you work. Consider how you experience the area, how the permanent staff experience it, how visiting staff experience it, how patients experience it and how patient visitors experience it. What are their different interpretations based on? Why is this important?

If you do not work in the hospital setting, consider the same questions in the context of the area in which you do work.

There are some possible answers and thoughts at the end of the chapter.

The interpretation of what an environment is, using the answers to the reflection, very much hinges on the function of the area concerned and your role in relation to that function. Different people experience the same area in a different light and have different views about the nature and workings of the same place. This gives us some clues as to what an environment of care is about, but this is not the whole story.

Environments, especially care environments, are very much the product not only of what goes on there, but of how people behave and interact. In this sense environments can be considered to reflect the psychosocial nature of a place. Many commentators refer to environments as *cultures* (Handy, 1994) and in many ways this term is as useful as environments, if not more so; this is because the word culture conjures up an image of something more ingrained, natural and all-encompassing than the term environment. In this sense a culture is not about nationality, race or ethnicity; it is about a shared sense of the psychosocial nature of a place. This nature of the place is very much tied to the ways in which people interact and behave within the place and is therefore a product of the human interaction and activity which take place there.

The psychosocial feel of a ward, clinical area or team is closely related to the ways in which the people there talk about, and to, each other, and the way in which they interact with people who are visitors to the area – the general ambience, if you like. In many respects, the environment or culture (we will use the terms interchangeably) created in a care area reflects the *values* of the people who work there.

As nurses, and especially as leaders or managers, we have the ability to affect the environment in which we work. Understanding the impact we have as individuals and as leaders and managers is essential to understanding how to manage environments; you may find it useful to revisit the Johari window discussed in Chapter 1 at this stage to remind yourself about how others see us and how we see ourselves and what impact this has on relationships.

As a leader of people, the tone and nature of your interactions with others will set the benchmark by which others act. If you are seen not to care about where you work, or the people who work there, neither will the team. If you are brash, loud or condescending, then members of the team will be too. It is almost impossible to overestimate the impact that leaders have on their immediate environment. The message about the impact of leaders on the environment of the team they lead is therefore clear – in most instances leaders create the culture. It is perhaps worth thinking about the values you identified in Chapter 1 and how you might see these influencing the way you work and the way in which you, in a leadership role, can influence the people around you.

The Nursing and Midwifery Council (NMC, 2002) states that lifelong learning *requires an enquiring approach to the practice of nursing and midwifery, as well as to issues which impact on that practice.* The role of the manager and leader in developing environments of care that support such learning development is critical. Creating a learning culture is something that leaders must therefore do by setting an example, not only in undertaking formal education, but by learning from their team, their clients, from complaints and from their own practice. The action of learning from others is an example of the exercise of the value of being 'other-regarding'.

Lee et al. (2010, page 475) state: *By practising the knowledge builder role, leaders create opportunities and processes that stimulate and encourage knowledge sharing amongst team members.* This knowledge-building role is achieved by offering new ideas and solutions to problems and by encouraging dialogue in the team. The key message here is that, for a team to develop a learning culture, the leader or manager must take the lead in that learning by role modelling learning behaviour.

What a learning environment is

A learning environment is essentially a set of attitudes, values and their corresponding actions that creates a culture in which learning and development can take place. Quinn (1995) suggests that the learning that takes place in the clinical setting is more meaningful to nursing students than that which occurs in the classroom setting. The proposal here is that the opportunities for learning and development which occur in the clinical setting are invaluable to the development of students. We would argue this point can be stretched further to include all of the staff who work in a particular setting.

A ward, clinic or community team whose members are empowered to learn and develop will be able to provide meaningful care which not only reflects current clinical trends but which puts the patient at the heart of care. A team which operates in a learning environment will seize every opportunity to grow and develop and as a result, their ability to care will be enhanced. In this sense, a learning environment is one which fosters positive development and change.

Bersin (2010, page 16) argues that a learning environment is *the collective practices that encourage sharing of information and all forms of people development.* This idea further supports the idea that learning is more than an optional extra within the team; it is fundamental to the development of all members of the team and therefore the improvement of what they do. As such the creation, adoption and maintenance of a learning environment is a fundamental approach to addressing the standards of proficiency highlighted at the start of the chapter. What this means for you as an individual student or nurse will be discussed later in the chapter.

Why learning environments are important

Increasing emphasis is being placed on the benefits associated with work-based learning in today's health and social care provision. In some part, this is evidenced by the increase in the number and range of foundation degrees available and in the increasing provision of workplace learning modules in post-registration continuing professional development programmes for health and social care professionals.

The emphasis on work-based learning has been described by Spouse (2001) as arising from the need to generate workers who have moved on from being skilled and technically competent to becoming active problem solvers who are able to adapt and develop in tandem with their environment. Think of it this way; someone who is trained to change a dressing will do just that, while someone who understands how to change a dressing and what to look for in the way of healing will both change the dressing and be aware of alternative ways of doing the dressing, what infection might look like and what the nutritional needs of the patient might be. This latter way of working is an example of the activity which takes place in a learning environment where care is constantly evolving. Care which is the best it can be allows the nurse to exercise the values of providing high-quality, holistic care and in this sense, at least, the generation of a learning environment is a fulfilment of nursing values.

Developing a learning environment in the workplace also has the potential to bring many benefits to the team and to the individuals within the team. A team established in a learning culture can rapidly adapt to change and develop new ways of working that are consistent with best practice. Staff who work in and adopt the values of a learning organisation both feel, and are, more empowered to do their job and as a consequence have the ability to be more effective at what they do.

Activity 8.2   *Reflection*

Reflect on the times in the classroom setting when you have engaged with the conversation around whatever it is you were learning. How did your engagement in the debate around the topic affect your learning? Did your contribution have an impact on what you learnt and how you felt about what you learnt?

There are some possible answers and thoughts at the end of the chapter.

Your answers to the above reflection probably demonstrate that on the occasions you engaged in what was happening in the classroom you learnt more, felt happier and were clearer about the subject matter. What is more important is that engaging in what is going on probably helped you to feel more involved, part of something if you like, as well as feeling you contributed to the learning and development of the group as a whole.

Certainly the same ideas translate into the practice setting, where engaging in learning, rather than being the passive recipient of knowledge, will greatly affect the learning which you are able to take from a situation. Consider this scenario:

Case study: The same mentor

Paul is a student nurse in his first year of training. Paul has a clinical placement on a care of the elderly ward and is not at all happy with it as there is not enough high-tech care going on. Paul comes into work each shift, as he knows he must, and goes through the motions of caring for the elderly patients. He washes and helps to feed patients but does little in the way of communication and does not attempt to understand the care needs of those he nurses. Paul's mentor offers little in the way of teaching, support or advice to Paul. Overall, it is a pretty poor experience and Paul does little more than endure it.

Mary, also a first-year student, is placed on the same ward as Paul. Mary is keen to understand the care she is giving and what it means for the patients. She too would prefer to work somewhere more exciting but has decided to get what she can in the way of learning from her experience. Mary talks to her patients and asks them about their lives. She observes them closely when washing and dressing them and takes note of issues such as the development of pressure areas. Mary listens when patients explain their symptoms and makes mental notes to look things up when she is off duty. Mary asks questions of

---

> *her mentor and explores ideas and tries to understand the new experiences she is having. Mary's mentor is the same person mentoring Paul, but offers Mary different learning opportunities and looks for ways to enhance her learning experience. Mary quite quickly starts to enjoy her placement and learns a lot about good-quality nursing care provision.*

This case study may reflect some of the experiences you have had either as a student or a mentor. What is important to understand in this case study is that the learning opportunities for both Mary and Paul are the same. What makes the difference is their approach to learning. Mary adopts a positive and open approach to learning. You might say she embodies a learning culture in herself, and as a result she gets a lot from her experience. Paul, on the other hand, closes himself off to learning and therefore gets little from his placement.

The reward for Mary in adopting this positive approach to her own development is enjoyment of the placement and enhanced learning. It is clear her mentor also gained something from mentoring Mary and therefore sought opportunities to support her development. Again, this is all about attitude. Mary shows her mentor that she is engaged and values the experience. The extra effort the mentor makes for her is in recognition of this.

As well as the opportunities that arise for self-development, learning cultures bring other rewards to the team and the organisation at large. Consider again the case study above. In being more diligent about her care provision and in seeking not only to provide care but to understand the care she is giving, Mary has the opportunity to identify and prevent some potential complications arising in the patients she cares for. Such proactive nursing will benefit Mary, her patients, the team and the wider organisation in reducing complication rates and the time patients stay in hospital.

From the perspective of the ward manager, the constructive approach to learning Mary has adopted demonstrates benefits for the team in the creation of a positive environment. For the team leader or ward manager the fostering of a positive learning culture will benefit the team in helping with staff recruitment and retention as well as the potential reduction in absences from work.

What is fascinating about this is the impact that allowing people to ask and answer questions can have on both morale and clinical outcomes. It seems so insignificant a thing to do, but clearly the effect is great.

Elements of the learning environment

So far we have identified a definition of a learning culture and have explored some of the benefits for the individual, team and organisation. In order to understand better the notion of learning environments it is now worth exploring the elements which go towards creating and sustaining them.

Peter Senge (1990), one of the leading writers on learning organisations, identifies five key elements – he calls them disciplines – which need to be in place for a learning organisation to be generated and maintained.

> ## The five disciplines needed to create a learning environment
>
> 1. Systems thinking – this is essentially the ability to see the bigger picture. Seeing the big picture is an important element of nursing and leadership because of the complex nature of caring for people. Jackson and Ellis (2010) argue that whole-systems thinking in complex environments requires us to: identify all of the components of the system (people) and their roles as well as the nature of the interrelationships between them; recognise that working in a whole system is beneficial; and understand the risks of whole-systems working. The idea is that we see the interconnectedness of what each component (individual) of the system does and work to maximise its input (in much the same way as we explored team working in Chapter 2 and when we explored systems theory in Chapter 7).
> 2. Personal mastery – this is about the commitment of the people in the system to self-development. Self-development in this sense is about realising our potential and striving to be the best that we can be through constant and consistent self-development – clearly this relates to the exercise of our personal values, as we explored in Chapter 1.
> 3. Mental models – this requires us to identify and acknowledge the values, issues and beliefs that prevent us from being all we can be. This process involves reflection on ourselves and our motivations and becoming open and receptive to new ideas and ways of working; this often requires a change in both personal and team cultures.
> 4. Building shared visions – for the leader or manager, this is about gaining consensus on the view of how things should be from all of the members of the team. When the team can agree to a vision of how things should be, they can work consistently and supportively to achieve it. As well as understanding your values, as a leader you will need to understand and acknowledge the values of the team.
> 5. Team learning – this is the final and fundamental aspect of creating a learning culture. One person does not make a culture alone. Nursing involves the co-operative working of nurses and other care professionals. Learning together facilitates the creation of relationships which enable the wider team to work together more effectively.
>
> Source: Adapted from Senge (1990).

What Senge's model demonstrates is that the creation of learning cultures requires the ability to see how things fit together, personal commitment, a change in thinking, shared drive and a willingness to learn together. So some of the messages here are about us as individuals and others about us and the way we interact in, or lead, teams.

Senge (1996) further identifies that the first step on the road to becoming a learning team or organisation is a willingness to allow people of all levels to lead in different ways. This requirement points to the need for each individual within the learning environment to commit to the values and practice of learning together.

What this means for you

The teams that work within a learning environment are made up of many individuals. As we have discussed, to a great extent the culture of the team derives from the actions and values of the leader or manager. The message is therefore clear for the leader or manager who wants to create a learning culture: lead by example. But what if you are not the manager or leader? What do the messages of this chapter hold for you?

As with all aspects of leading and managing, the first port of call is self. We saw in Chapter 4 that to deal with conflict effectively you must first of all ensure you are not the problem; we saw in Chapter 1 that to be an effective leader you must first know yourself and what drives and motivates you. Similarly, if you want to develop into the sort of leader who can promote learning and development, you must first of all develop yourself. Such development is not all about learning new things and ideas: it is more about your attitude to learning and development – the exercise of your values. For the student nurse this may mean adopting a more proactive approach to learning. You have made an important first step in choosing to read books such as this. If you are a trained nurse your attitude to your own continuing professional development is equally important.

Not only is your attitude to self-development important, but so too is your attitude to the learning and development of others. Are you happy to share what you know? Do you support colleagues and friends who need to understand something that you already know? Are you willing to listen to and learn from others, perhaps even those you consider to be more junior to yourself? Are you comfortable in asking questions?

Activity 8.3 — *Critical thinking*

In order to develop as a nurse learner and to contribute to the development of learning environments of care, it is important that you understand your journey as a nurse. In order to understand better what you need to do to develop, you must first reflect on your learning journey to date. Write a short biography of your learning as a person and a nurse to date. What have you learnt, where have you learned it and how has what you have learnt changed you as a person? You should write this as if you are explaining who you are to someone meeting you for the first time.

As this is based on your own observations, there is no specimen answer at the end of the chapter.

There are some key challenges here about the way in which you present yourself to others as well as understanding what truly motivates you and your practice. There are multiple influences on what and how we learn; reflecting on these may start to tell us something about the type of environment we might want to create in order to promote learning. Certainly the culture of the place in which you work now will impact on how you answer Activity 8.3 as well as how you feel about learning, but once again the onus rests with you as to how you will react to new learning opportunities. For the leader, again, the message about leading by example is clear: if you are comfortable about asking questions and developing your learning, so will your staff be; if you make people feel valued when they ask questions, then they will ask questions and with questioning will come learning and development.

Developing a learning environment: the challenge

Now we have some understanding of the nature of learning environments, their benefits to the individual, team and wider organisation, the challenge is to understand for ourselves how we might create and develop such an environment. For the remainder of this chapter, this challenge takes the form of a series of activities which set out to help you identify your orientation to learning environments, your experience of learning environments to date and your understanding of how a learning environment might be created.

It is important that you explore these issues in order to address the requirement of the 2010 NMC Standard of proficiency: Leadership, management and team working, number 5: *All nurses must facilitate nursing students and others to develop their competence, using a range of professional and personal development skills.*

Activity 8.4   *Reflection*

Reflecting on how you feel about learning in general and learning within the practice setting in particular will say something about your orientation to learning environments. Consider these questions and answer truthfully. You may find that some of the comments from mentors in your practice assessment document will help you to identify how others perceive your learning behaviours: you might like to reflect on the learning biography you wrote in Activity 8.3.

- How do you feel about new situations in the practice setting?
- Do you like new experiences or are you only comfortable with things that you know?
- How do you feel about asking questions?
- Does it matter who you are asking the questions of?
- Are you comfortable asking questions in front of others?
- When a patient asks you a question that you do not know the answer to, do you make up an answer, say you don't know and find someone else or tell the patient that you will find out?
- When you come across something that you do not understand, do you ignore it, ask questions of people who do, go away and look it up for yourself, ask questions and look it up?

As this is based on your own observations, there is no specimen answer at the end of the chapter.

What these questions will help you to appreciate is what you value in the way of learning and understanding in the clinical setting. While there are no wrong answers as such, primarily because these questions do not ask you what is the right thing to do but ask you what it is *you* do, there are some states of behaviour and responses which are perhaps more in line with the values needed to engage in a learning environment.

What is needed from you in terms of engaging in self-development which makes you fit for life-long learning and engagement in, and potentially future creation of, learning environments is: keenness to engage in and understand new situations and ways of working; a willingness to admit when you do not know something; a willingness to ask questions and a desire to increase your understanding and the understanding of others when you are in a position to do so.

When we fail to embrace these key values as individual nurses, or nursing students, it is not only ourselves that we fail, but also the wider team, organisation and ultimately our patients.

Activity 8.5   *Critical thinking*

Your orientation to learning environments will influence your understanding and feelings about learning environments. Think about how the environments in the various clinical areas that you have worked in have affected your learning. Consider how you have responded to the various learning opportunities presented to you:

- What have you done when the learning opportunities appear poor?
- Do you ask questions?
- Do you try to supplement this with your own reading and finding out?
- When faced with a poor learning environment, do you try to help more junior staff or students with their learning?
- What factors in the ward environment affect the learning opportunities available?
- Can you identify personal or group behaviours which appear to make a difference?

As this is based on your own observations, there is no specimen answer at the end of the chapter.

The questions in this activity point to the role you might play in creating your own learning opportunities regardless of the culture of the place in which you are working. They ask questions about whether you role model positive learning behaviours and take a proactive stance in your own learning and that of others.

You are also asked to reflect on individual and group behaviours which impact on your learning and that of others in the area. Reflecting on and being aware of the behaviours and attitudes that promote, or hinder, learning equip you with ideas about how you might behave in order to promote a positive learning environment. What is important is that you realise that issues you have reflected on as a student or junior member of staff become action points for your future career. When you see good practice you might choose to mirror it when you are a leader or manager and when you see poor practice, or practices which do not work very well, you learn from these and do not repeat the same mistakes when you are in a position of influence.

Activity 8.6   *Critical thinking*

Given your orientation to learning environments and your experience of them to date, consider how you might go about creating a learning environment in the clinical setting:

- What strategies might you use to promote the change?
- How will you sell the idea to others?
- What strategies for learning might you promote to others?

The project management template below might help you plan your answer to this activity in a constructive manner.

Project management template
What is the purpose of the project? What do we do now and what is it we are trying to achieve?
Who is responsible for what aspect of the project? What skills and resources do we have available to us?
Who are our stakeholders? Who will this project affect and how will we get people on board with the idea?
How will we make a start? What do we need to do to start the change process?
What are the possible outcomes, both positive and negative? Consider here personal, team, organisational and patients.
What things might hinder the project and what might help it progress? What are the personnel and financial costs attached?
What should we have achieved by when and how will we know we have achieved these goals?
What will this look like when it is implemented? How will we know we have achieved our ultimate goals?
How and how often will we audit what we have done and maintain impetus, assuming we achieve our goals? What measure, both direct and indirect, might there be of our success?

As this is based on your own observations, there is no specimen answer at the end of the chapter.

The purpose of this activity is to demonstrate the thinking, planning, communicating and team working that need to go into the initiation of a change project. Committing to becoming more learning-oriented for yourself and developing a learning culture in a team require commitment, time, effort and good communication. By working through the template you should now be more familiar with the sorts of processes required to make such an important change.

Learning environments and values

One of the fundamental messages of this book has been about how we can develop as managers and leaders who exercise the values which brought us into nursing in the first place. As we have seen throughout the book, there are many values which we need to exercise as leaders of care. As we saw in Chapter 6, the most famous current example of these values are Cummings' (2012) 6 Cs: care, compassion, competence, communication, courage and commitment.

The development of a learning environment which is underpinned by the values of good care, compassion and communication requires us as leaders to exercise courage and commitment in developing ourselves to become more competent at what we do and in supporting the developing competency of others. In this sense we can see that learning environments contribute strongly to enabling nurses to express their values.

Chapter summary

In this chapter we have seen that environments or cultures of care are important in the functioning of health and social care teams. We have identified that learning cultures are important for the sustained development of nursing teams, and the wider healthcare system. We have identified that for learning cultures to succeed there is a need for engagement of all of the members of the team. The role of the individual nurse or nursing student within the team has been identified as being fundamental to the success of any culture.

We have also seen how developing learning environments serves to develop environments in which nursing values, as embodied in the 6 Cs, can thrive, to the benefits of staff, individual nurses and, most importantly, patients.

The challenge that has been presented in this chapter has been one of engaging in self-development as a learner for yourself before considering taking on the extended task of creating a learning environment in your place of work.

Activities: brief outline answers

Activity 8.1 Reflection

As a student transiting through an area as part of your training, you may see the area as a place of learning while having a feeling of being an outsider. Permanent staff may be comfortable with the area and regard it very much as a place of work. Visiting staff, such as physiotherapists and social workers, may experience the area as an extension of a bigger area of work. Patients may experience the environment as one in which they do not belong and which is somewhere they can at least leave.

When working in the community, your place of work is often someone else's home, a place where you are both at work and a visitor, and where your patient is both patient and home owner.

Activity 8.2 Reflection

When we engage in open conversation about a topic, we become involved. Being involved in something brings a sense of belonging and worth. This sense of worth helps us to understand our place in contributing to something bigger than ourselves, in this case the collective understanding of the topic. This reflects nicely the concept of the learning environment, where people feel that they belong because they are not only learning together, they are also contributing to that learning.

Further reading

Clarke, A (2001) *Learning Organisations: What They Are and How to Become One.* Leicester: National Institute of Adult Continuing Education.

A comprehensive guide to learning organisations.

Handy, C (1994) *Understanding Organizations.* London: Penguin.

A great and classic text on organisational cultures.

Mullins, LJ (2011) *Essentials of Organisational Behaviour* (3rd edition). London: Prentice Hall.

A comprehensive guide to understanding organisations.

Useful websites

www.cipd.co.uk/helpingpeoplelearn/_lrncltre.htm

An interesting selection of case studies about learning cultures from the Chartered Institute of Personnel and Development.

www.pmis.co.uk/free-project-management-templates.htm

A wide collection of interesting and adaptable project templates.

www.investorsinpeople.co.uk/About/PolicyDevelopment/Pages/Engagingemployees.aspx

A useful website about strategies for employee engagement and people development. This page has a link to the report *Employee Engagement,* which is a good primer for any aspiring leader of people.

Chapter 9
Developing confidence as a manager and leader

continued . . .

At entry to the register

1. Inspires confidence and provides clear direction to others.
2. Bases decisions on evidence and uses experience to guide decision-making.
3. Acts as a positive role model for others.

Chapter aims

After reading this chapter you will be able to:

- discuss the practice–leadership continuum;
- demonstrate an awareness of some of the issues with transition to leadership and management roles;
- discuss some of the key challenges which face new leaders and managers;
- explain how confidence might be developed in the new manager.

Introduction

Throughout this book we have introduced you to ideas and theories about leadership and management and some of the tasks that leaders and managers undertake; you may have formed the impression there is a lot to learn, and indeed there is. You will also have noted many of the tasks of management start with understanding yourself and your orientation to a situation, role or task as well as having a clear appreciation of your values and those of the organisation in which you work. Clearly understanding yourself and being aware of your strengths and weaknesses are as important for succeeding as a leader or manager as for nursing in general.

This chapter will look at some of the issues facing the new leader or manager and identify and focus on some strategies that might be used to help develop ability and confidence. Other issues which commonly confront the new manager will also be addressed, with some ideas about how these might be handled both proactively and reactively. As with all of the chapters in this book it is important that you engage with the activities as they represent tools for self-development which may help to enhance both your learning and your development as a manager as well as your confidence to lead.

The transition to leadership

When you first thought about being a nurse and when you were interviewed for your nurse training, it is likely you thought and talked about all of the ways you could help people as a practising nurse. As you progress through your training and into your nursing career you may start to aspire to leadership and management and start to see this as a way of extending the scope of what you can do for and with patients.

It is worth reflecting here on the different stages of professional life we adopt as we move from practising nurse through to leadership and management roles. Causer and Exworthy (2003) identify six stages on the path from practice to management which they regard as being stages on a continuum of roles which health and social care professionals may find themselves on.

Roles within the professional–management continuum

1. The practising professional: The main task of the practising professional is the provision of care. Within this definition there are two groups of people:

    (a) the pure practitioner – who undertakes professional roles but has no supervisory role;
    (b) the quasi-managerial practitioner – who undertakes a professional caring role, and has some responsibility for supervising others or allocating resources.

2. The managing professional: The main function of these professionally trained managers is the supervision of other professionals and the allocation and management of resources. Again, this group is split into two groups:

    (a) the practising managing professional – who still works in the delivery of care as well as managing others and resources;
    (b) the non-practising managing professional – who does not deliver care, but supervises other professionals and manages resources.

3. General managers: These are managers who manage others who are involved in the delivery of professional care, but not at the day-to-day (**operational**) level. Again, these are subdivided into two categories:

    (a) non-professionally grounded general managers – who are not part of the profession they are managing;
    (b) professionally grounded general managers – who are part of the profession they are managing.

Source: Adapted from Causer and Exworthy (2003).

What Causer and Exworthy (2003) identify is that the transition from being a practitioner to being a manager can be one that is subtle and takes place over a series of stages. The move from practice to management is therefore not a stark one, whereby one day you are a nurse practising on the ward and the next day you are a general manager, far removed from the realities of day-to-day care. The process identified here will most certainly allow for some adaptation and personal and professional development to take place. This notion links well with the ideas around being a learning organisation and individual, identified in Chapter 8.

Activity 9.1   *Critical thinking*

Taking the categories of professionals and managers that Causer and Exworthy identify, consider all of the people who work in the team in the clinical area in which you are, or were last, placed. Which of the roles identified in the model do they fit into, if any? What characteristics of Causer and Exworthy's descriptions do they display? What was their previous role? You may want to take this activity a step further and discuss the changing nature of the individual roles with them.

As this is based on your own observations, there is no specimen answer at the end of the chapter.

Undertaking this activity will help you to discover that there are layers of responsibility, leadership and management in the clinical setting. The degree of certainty people have in the roles they undertake can grow and develop as they move from one position to another within the team, or between teams, and as they learn from their own practice and from those around them. What is important in the transition from practice to management remains the focus on the values which you came into nursing with (see Chapter 1) and a willingness to develop both yourself and others around you (see Chapter 8).

Self-esteem and transition

As with all development, the changes which need to occur for you to move from school, or from another job, to becoming a nursing student, to qualifying and beyond, require some psychological adjustment. Even when we are excited about something, there are adjustments to make to the ways in which we think and behave as we move on to something new. Sometimes the adjustments we have to make are in response to whatever it was we aspired to not quite living up to what we expected from it. Either way, it is worth considering the nature of change and transition from being a practising nurse to being a leader.

Activity 9.2   *Reflection*

Think about how you felt during your first few weeks in a care environment. One day you were a member of the public and the next a carer or a student nurse. Taking responsibility for the welfare of other human beings requires some adjusting to and is the cause for some soul searching; reflect on your feelings at this time and think about how you managed to cope with this transition.

There are some possible answers and thoughts at the end of the chapter.

Some of your answers to the above reflection will show that the emotions experienced during a change can be quite overwhelming, even if it is a change which we want and are on the whole excited about. What this tells us for planning to make the change from practitioner to leader or manager is that there are a host of normal emotions and responses to change that we need to prepare for.

Perhaps the first lesson is that an emotional response to change is normal and not something we should be shy or embarrassed about. You should therefore not be surprised if you are a little stressed by a promotion or when you are given a leadership role; it is normal!

It is worth stopping again here and considering the nature of the emotional responses that people have as they adapt and evolve.

Bridges (2003), a leading thinker and writer about the change process, reminds us that things change, but people go through transitions. A fundamental tenet of Bridges' position is that transition involves loss and letting go, as well as developing a new understanding of how things are. In the case of the nurse making the transition from practising nurse to leader or manager, this involves a redefining of his or her professional and personal identity. Bridges' model of transition captures these ideas in a three-stage process.

Three-phase process of transition

1. Ending, losing, letting go: at this stage people have to make the adjustment to not being who they were before. For example, a student nurse on the point of qualifying must adjust to being a qualified and accountable nurse; or a staff nurse being promoted to being a junior sister may have to adapt to being more visible to others and the hub of questions and responsibility.
2. The neutral zone: at this stage people try to make sense of who they are now and how things are going to be. Student nurses start to accept they are now qualified and begin to adopt the persona of someone who is accountable for what s/he is doing; junior charge nurses start to understand they have to be the one to find solutions to problems and act as a role model to the team.
3. The new beginning: a new identity is forming and there is increased clarity about what is expected in the new role. There is a sense of urgency and of wanting to get on with the job. New staff nurses start to feel confident in their own ability and what they are doing; the new sister or charge nurse feels comfortable about being a role model and overseeing the work of the team.

Source: Adapted from Bridges (2003).

While progressing through the process of changing identity – what we h~
is norma' ~ ~ ~hole range of d:ff
discusse

- Ellis

emotions and recognising them in yourself, as well as others, is a good way of helping maintain and develop your confidence as you progress through your nursing career. When these emotional responses feel like they might become overwhelming, it is worth harking back to our discussion of values in Chapter 1; what is important about the values of caring and of leading care is that they are the same values. All that changes, and therefore what healthcare leaders and managers have left of their caring identity, is how the values are expressed. You may find it useful here to revisit the case study from Chapter 1, 'The newly qualified nurse', in which Deirdre, the ward sister, explains to Julius, the newly qualified nurse, how what she has to do as the ward manager supports the ward staff in the delivery of care, which she is often unable to participate in because of the various other roles she must perform.

Hopson and Adams (1976) propose a useful, and enduring, model which helps identify some of the stages people go through when they are subject to transition. This model, presented below, is not a linear one (people move through it in different directions at different rates and may skip stages), nor does it necessarily apply to all transitions people go through; nevertheless, it is a useful model for helping us to understand the emotional response to transition.

Changes in self-esteem during transitions

- Immobilisation: the feeling of being unable to act and being overwhelmed because of a transition. Transitions for which people are unprepared and ones associated with negative expectations may intensify this stage.
- Minimisation: a coping mechanism. People often deny the change is happening. This reaction is common in a crisis which is too difficult to face head-on.
- Depression: some people become depressed when they have to face the reality of change.
- Accepting reality: occurs when a person going through a transition begins to let go of how things were and starts to accept the reality of the change.
- Testing: begins when the reality of the change has been accepted. At this stage people start to try out new behaviours to cope with the new situation.
- Seeking meaning: a reflective stage, during which people try to work out how and why things are different.
- Internalisation: the final stage of the process, during which the new situation becomes accepted. The new understanding then becomes part of the person's behaviour.

Source: Adapted from Hopson and Adams (1976).

When making the transition from student nurse to trained nurse and then on to leader and manager it is useful for us to be aware of the ways in which we react to change as individuals. Being aware of our own responses enables us to make sense of and progress through the various stages of emotional response to change as well as managing how we behave around and towards other people.

Being aware of the range of emotions experienced during times of transition also allows us to provide appropriate support to staff during periods of change and transition in their lives. Change and transition are not only confined to the workplace: changes in home circumstances, bereavement and ill health will all impact on how managers and their staff feel and behave. Being aware of this and maintaining good channels of communication will allow the leader or manager to develop skills and confidence in people management which are closely associated with emotional intelligence.

Activity 9.3   *Critical thinking*

Now that you have seen Hopson and Adams' model of the changes in self-esteem during change, can you relate to any of the stages identified for yourself, or in others? Now that you understand something more of the ways in which people respond to transition, what strategies do you think you can employ as an individual or as a leader to help people adjust to change?

There are some possible answers and thoughts at the end of the chapter.

Clearly, being prepared for the emotional response which you may have to a change in your role or work circumstances means you will be able to reflect on what is happening and better prepare yourself mentally for the challenges ahead. As a leader or manager, providing support to your team through supervision, information giving and being generally supportive will mean you can help reduce some of the impact of negative emotional responses to transition.

Activity 9.4   *Evidence-based practice and research*

To understand better the nature of the emotional responses to change people have, look up the **Holmes–Rahe Life Event Rating Scale** (see the useful websites at the end of the chapter) and read the categories of change that people find most stressful in their lives; some of the listed changes may surprise you.

As this is based on your own observations, there is no specimen answer at the end of the chapter.

Having a growing understanding of your own responses to change will enable you to face the transitions required to progress throughout your career in nursing with a renewed degree of confidence. Preparing yourself mentally and emotionally for the impact of transition will mean you are better prepared for some of the challenges of leadership and management.

Developing yourself as a leader

The purpose of this book has been to prepare you for some of the challenges being a leader or manager can present. This section will present and examine some of the strategies you can use to prepare yourself better for a leadership or management role whilst being aware of, and managing, your own emotional response to change. All of the ideas presented here are tools and tactics that can be used while a student or junior staff nurse in order to improve and enhance your own confidence, understand yourself better and develop some self-discipline in your approach to managing yourself.

Williams (2007, page 51) tells us: *exceptional leaders have the ability to honestly assess their leadership skills – and the discipline to improve their weaknesses and build upon their strengths.* Only you can truly know whether you are willing to put effort into your self-development.

Set incremental goals

Target setting is a key factor in self-motivation. If you cannot be bothered to write an essay or to complete an application form, then whatever it is you are aiming to do will not happen. Motivation is an interesting tool, both in personal and professional development as well as from the point of view of the leader or manager. Herzberg (1959), the most enduring and famous theorist in this area, proposed the motivation-hygiene theory of job satisfaction. In essence, Herzberg's theory suggests that people will work hard in order to achieve the hygiene needs, as without them they are unhappy. Once the hygiene factors are achieved, people are happy, but only for a short time. It is only the true motivators which keep people happy and motivate them and offer a true sense of meaning for individuals.

Motivation-hygiene theory of job satisfaction

Hygiene factors

- Quality of relationships with supervisors
- Working conditions
- Salary
- Status
- Job security
- Quality of relationship with subordinates
- Personal life

True motivators

- Achievement
- Recognition
- Opportunity for advancement

- Work itself
- Responsibility
- Sense of personal growth

Source: Adapted from Herzberg (1959).

What we can see both for ourselves and for others is that motivation lies in taking responsibility and improving on what we do and therefore who we are. For the student this may mean getting better at writing essays, by learning from feedback to achieve better marks and hence recognition. For the leader it may be important to ensure the hygiene factors are all in place before worrying too much about the motivators.

Case study: Recognising the value of motivation

Jacinta had recently been promoted to Modern Matron in the surgical care team. Jacinta had worked her way up through the team over a period of years and was very much aware of the issues which preoccupied the staff. She knew that staff morale was very low as the team felt overworked, understaffed, poorly cared for and generally neglected. Jacinta understood the team felt the need for further professional development as well as some clarity about promotion opportunities. Jacinta was also aware that the whole team were fed up with the state of their coffee room, which had been allowed to deteriorate over time. She knew she needed to do something fast to raise the morale of the whole team and to consolidate her position as the team leader, but she also knew she had limited funds with which to do anything.

Jacinta considered her options and decided there were some things she could do collectively for the team as well as some things she needed to do for individuals within the team in order to raise morale, gain trust and improve motivation. Jacinta decided to spend some of the capital budget available to her to buy new furniture for the coffee room. By doing so she improved working conditions for the whole team and addressed a hygiene need.

Jacinta quickly realised she could not provide the motivation the staff needed purely by spending money (which was not available to her anyway), so she identified new roles for various members of the team as link nurses for infection control, diabetes and wound management, providing some of the junior staff with a sense of increased responsibility, recognition and personal growth. Furthermore, Jacinta took it upon herself to try to make sure staff went home when their shifts ended. She praised effort and cultivated her relationships within the team, addressing key hygiene and motivational needs.

This case study, which is based on a real-life experience, demonstrates how easy it can be to grow as a leader or manager in the eyes of the team by making small but important changes. Facilitating and bringing about the changes meant that not only did the team feel happier, but Jacinta's confidence as a manager grew as she started to notice a change in the morale of the team and that the team had started to trust her as someone who both cared about them and was able to get things done.

Trust is an important element of the role of the manager, ensuring the work which the team needs to get done is actually done. We saw in Chapter 4 how the meta-analysis by Dirks and Ferrin (2002) demonstrated that trust is important in the prevention and management of conflict; their work also showed two other important findings pertinent to goal setting and motivation in the personal and team setting. The first is about attitude to work, where attitude is seen as contributing both to achieving your goals and to the exercise of values. Having a positive attitude as a leader will reflect in your orientation to work, the *manner* by which you achieve goals, and this in turn leads to the other important observation, which is about citizenship.

Because the team learn to trust you in the way you work and in the types of goals you set yourself, they start to feel responsibility towards the things you find important. This citizenship is in essence about the ways in which we behave towards each other and how we share some common values and aspirations. In turn this means that the leader can be confident the members of the team will also work toward achieving the goals the leader has set not because they have to, but because they want to.

Learn to listen

For the nurse as much as the leader or manager, listening is a fundamental skill. When we learn to listen to others, be it in a formal context or by listening to informal sources of information, then we can understand the true context of situations. Listening also enables us to find solutions to problems which we may not have identified for ourselves.

Listening is a key skill for the leader or manager in understanding what the team are thinking and what is important to them. Managing information was identified in Chapter 6 as one of Mintzberg's (1975) roles of the manager. Information allows us to make decisions which are well grounded and learning to listen and to be enquiring will enhance your ability both to understand what is going on around you and to make sound decisions.

In this context listening is more about taking the time to hear what people are saying and trying to understand it while placing what we are hearing in the context of what we know. As an active skill, listening is important for personal growth and for professional development within healthcare, which is a complex and evolving environment within which to work (Jackson and Ellis, 2010). For the developing leader, listening means you can be confident you understand what is going on around you.

Understand, then communicate

The ultimate aim of listening properly and effectively is to understand. Understanding situations and new ideas is a good way of developing your confidence. Part of understanding is the ability to ask the right questions at the right time as well as being able to communicate your ideas in an effective way. Communicating effectively hinges on your ability to understand what other people know as well as what it is they want.

As a leader or manager your confidence will develop as people become aware that you are able to communicate clearly. Clear communication will mean members of the team understand what it is you want from them; it allows you to delegate effectively and explain ideas. Learning to think and understand before speaking is a key skill for the aspiring leader or manager; we have all been in situations when individuals have made themselves look silly because they have said something or asked a question which clearly demonstrates they have not been listening; being thought of as silly is not a good place to be for the new leader or manager!

Concept summary: Active listening

Active listening is about listening to, understanding and responding appropriately to what other people are saying. Becoming an active listener requires the leader to engage fully in a number of activities:

1. Give the person speaking your undivided attention: use your body language to show you are listening to what s/he is saying. Eye contact and responses, such as smiles and nods, help here.
2. Give feedback on what is being said from time to time. This can be used to demonstrate understanding and/or to check things you have not understood
3. Learn when to be quiet. Sometimes being quiet when someone is in full flow will allow you to find the answer to a question without frustrating the person through interruptions.
4. Be clear in your responses. This will include agreeing or disagreeing with what you have heard and putting across your own opinion in an unambiguous but respectful way.

Believe in yourself

Self-belief is not the same as arrogance or being egocentric. Self-belief is having the confidence you can do something well and doing it. Self-belief comes only from practice, from exercising your leadership muscles by developing and maintaining good relationships with staff and understanding yourself. When you believe in what you are doing as well as believe you have the ability to do it, other people will see this self-belief and feel able to follow your lead.

Leaders and managers who are confident in their own abilities are better able to develop their team and are comfortable with members of the team having better skills and knowledge in certain areas than they do. The manager who has self-belief will recognise that the team is more important than self and this team-focused attitude will help develop trust within the team.

Don't be afraid to make mistakes

Making mistakes is part of life. This is as true for the leader or manager as it is for individual team workers. Learning to reflect enables us to make sense of what has happened as well as learning how to do something better in the future (see Howatson-Jones, 2013, *Reflective Practice in Nursing*, also in this series). Learning from our mistakes can make us stronger as individuals and as leaders as we develop new ways of working which take account of what we have learnt as well as where we want to be. Failure often precedes success, as it is through trying new ways of working that we are able to be innovative (Farson and Keyes, 2002).

Part of the process of growing as a person and a leader is the ability to accept responsibility for the things we get wrong. When, as leaders, we develop the ability to accept responsibility for our own actions we can role model responsibility and accountability to our team.

Within the team context, supporting others who make mistakes empowers them to make decisions and take actions with the confidence that they will be supported; again, this is a key element of trust. SanFacon (2008) reminds leaders that in order to achieve success they need to trust in their staff and allow them to make mistakes. So being brave enough to try new things and new ways of working is useful in developing your confidence in yourself and in your ability to lead others.

Learn to manage your time effectively

As a leader or manager how you use time is important. The pressures on time as a leader of people come in all shapes and forms and can quite easily disrupt your working day. Time management is the art of getting the most from your time by developing an awareness of what time is and how it is used. Understanding the importance of time and how to use it wisely will help you understand what you can achieve and in what time frame. This will translate into the confidence to take on new roles and tasks or allow you to explain why you cannot.

John Adair (1990), whose model of action-centred leadership we looked at in Chapter 6, suggests leaders and managers need to learn to manage time before they can manage anything else. In Adair's view good time management is a requirement for allowing us to focus on what we do and achieve our goals. Time management is therefore about being focused on attaining our goals and achieving results and, in Adair's view, there are ten principles by which good time management can be achieved by a leader or manager.

Theory summary: Adair's ten principles of good time management

1. Develop a personal sense of time: this is about understanding where your time goes and therefore understanding where it is wasted and where it could be better used. For the leader it may also uncover areas of work which might be better delegated to someone else.
2. Identify long-term goals: this is about knowing what it is you want to achieve in life and work. Adair recognises values as being a key driving force behind setting such goals.
3. Make medium-term plans: understand what things you need to do in order to prepare you to achieve your long-term goals and plan what you need to do now to achieve them. Medium-term plans involve setting realistic goals which are measurable.

4. Plan the day: without planning what you will achieve today, you cannot know whether you have used your time wisely at the end of the day. Learning to say no to things which are a poor use of your time or which interfere with you achieving your goals is important here.
5. Make the best use of your best time: understand what times of day you work best and work during them. Take time to think about issues and ideas which need planning while doing other more mundane activities.
6. Organise office work: make sure that you organise your life and your working space so things you need are at hand when you need them.
7. Manage meetings: understand what you want from a meeting or other period of communication with other people and stick to the time available for this.
8. Delegate effectively: consider what things you need to do and what might be better done by someone else.
9. Make use of committed time: plan to use time that is usually wasted waiting or travelling and be prepared to use this to good effect, perhaps reading something, making phone calls or thinking constructively about an issue.
10. Manage your health: things are easier to achieve when we are well, so look after yourself and make time to do things that are necessary for your physical and mental well-being.

Source: Adapted from Adair (1990).

For Adair, understanding and being aware of time and how we use it is key to personal success. Making good use of time and being aware of what we can achieve in a given time frame are key to developing confidence in ourselves both as individuals and as leaders or managers. When you know what you achieved and why it is a great motivator.

Activity 9.5 — *Evidence-based practice and research*

Keep a diary of all the things you do for 1 week. Split the time into 15-minute slots and record what you do: be careful to record wasted time as well as activities. After 1 week review the diary and identify times during which you could have done something useful if you were prepared. Consider how you might adapt some of your ways of working and habits to allow you to achieve more in the time available to you.

You may wish to use this exercise as a springboard for planning your personal development and planning what you want to achieve, how and by when. Understanding how you use time will enable you to plan this more effectively.

As this is based on your own observations, there is no specimen answer at the end of the chapter.

Once you understand how you use time and where you can fit in tasks to make your use of time more efficient, you will start to see that it is possible to fit more into your day. When you free up

159

time you can decide how you are going to use it, perhaps undertaking more work or engaging in a hobby or other interest.

Know your values

You may feel that we have discussed values too much in this book; however, since our values shape the ways we behave, their importance cannot be overestimated. Knowing what your values are as a human, as a nurse and ultimately as a leader or manager will mean there is some consistency in the ways in which you act. Sticking to your values will not only mean you are happier in whatever you do; it will mean the team will know what to expect from you and, perhaps more importantly, what you expect from them. In part trust, which is the means by which leaders get things done, relies on leaders demonstrating their integrity to their followers (Lawton, 1998).

One of the issues which face nurses as they move from practice to leadership and management roles is their lack of clarity about their identity. It is easy to forget the things which mattered to you as a student or staff nurse, the values which guided your desire to be a nurse and your subsequent practice as you become more engaged with leadership and management roles. Understanding what your values are now and being able to discuss them in a meaningful way will help you remain grounded and focused as you prepare for leadership.

Activity 9.6   *Reflection*

Take some time now to consider the things which you value as a human being and as a nurse. Think about the things you might have said at interview about why you wanted to train as a nurse or the skills and attributes which you bring to your current role. Consider the issues in practice which cause you frustration and the behaviours which you think are unacceptable from your colleagues. Write these things down and keep them safe. Spend some time over the next few weeks thinking about and observing these issues in practice and considering what you might do to change poor practice and role model good leadership values when you are in a position to do so.

As this is based on your own observations, there is no specimen answer at the end of the chapter.

Issues such as fairness, treating people as equals, being polite and treating people with care and compassion might feature on your list. These are all basic values which are easily forgotten in the milieu of the busy working day. Practising these values and ensuring they become part of who you are and how you act will allow you to establish a reputation not only as someone who knows what s/he is doing but also as someone who knows who s/he is and what s/he is about. In common with all of the activities in this book, this is an important issue to think about. It is all too simple when you become a leader to forget how it feels to be led, so instead of addressing and rejecting the negative leadership behaviours you have witnessed, you adopt the same negative leadership behaviours.

Develop resilience

One of the hallmarks of the strong leader or manager is the ability to be resilient. Resilience is the ability to take criticism constructively, listen to what people are saying about your organisation and team without taking it personally and to understand the meaning of situations.

Resilience is not all about developing a thick skin, not least of all because a thick skin prevents effective empathy. Resilience is more about having the ability to deal with stressful situations. It is important here again to understand yourself. If you understand what things you find stressful and why, you can learn to manage them.

Case study: Developing resilience

Mee-Onn was a newly appointed junior sister on a general medical ward. She had come from a different hospital to take on the new role and did not know any of the team. Mee-Onn found that the staff and the patients on the ward were very free and easy about making complaints, grumbling and suggesting how things might be done better.

As the junior sister, Mee-Onn was often the target of these suggestions and gripes. Mee-Onn found it hard to cope with all of the information and after a few weeks in post started to take all of the negative comments personally, as if they were a reflection on her. She started to feel very stressed and did not want to go to work any more. Mee-Onn discussed her feelings with the medical matron. The matron, who had come up through the ranks in the hospital, suggested to Mee-Onn that she stopped taking all of the criticism as personal and that she turned issues back to the staff, with questions like 'how would you see this progressing?' or 'what would you suggest we do to improve this?' The matron also suggested Mee-Onn did not accept some of the unfair things people were saying and that she should tell them what they were saying was unfair.

Asking these simple questions reminded Mee-Onn that the problems were not hers alone. She developed the strength to confront some of the situations and issues which plagued the team and started to be seen as someone with solutions. She also developed a reputation for being fair-minded and not someone who would tolerate unreasonable behaviour.

This study, again based on a real-life story, demonstrates that one of the skills of being a leader or manager is learning what a gripe or moan means and who it is aimed at. It also demonstrates how taking on board issues which are not personal, and are not purely your own problem, may lead to a sense of helplessness and futility. Taking charge of such situations by being brave enough to ask for a solution, rather than saying something like 'I know what you mean', can help you as the leader develop delegation skills and demonstrate trust. It can also help you move away from being weak and downtrodden.

So in part resilience is about developing strategies to deflect and reflect problems back to where they really belong; although, of course, this does not mean every problem which comes your way!

Confront challenging situations

Developing resilience leads us nicely into the next skill, which is about not being afraid to get involved. There are times as a nurse when situations arise and people behave in ways which we feel are less than acceptable. Such situations need confronting and learning to communicate your point in a way which links in with your expressed values is a good place to start. Certainly as a manager or leader there is nowhere to hide and learning to confront difficult situations early is a good idea. One strategy for the novice is to accompany more experienced staff who are, for example, breaking bad news; ask questions about what they did after the event and reflect on the answers.

The other sort of challenging situation is one which you do not understand or about which you are uncertain. The key to developing the ability to confront such a situation is developing the ability to ask questions. Asking questions allows for understanding and should not be mistaken for weakness. As an aspiring leader it is important you develop a reputation for being enquiring and that you support others in their efforts to achieve self-awareness and self-development.

Develop your emotional intelligence

Perhaps many of the messages which are contained in this book can be boiled down to one key message: develop your emotional intelligence. Throughout the book we have suggested there is a need to understand yourself and the part you play in many situations before you look at what other people are doing or saying. You also need to understand where other people are coming from and what motivates their actions.

Emotional intelligence requires you to be able to use this understanding of the emotional motivation which you and other people have in order to communicate effectively. Emotional intelligence and awareness of motivations as well as the ability and desire to help others achieve their goals reflect strongly on many of the standards of proficiency and essential skills highlighted at the start of this chapter.

Activity 9.7   *Reflection*

Consider the standards of proficiency and Essential Skill Clusters identified at the start of the chapter and how these relate to the ability of individual nurses to understand themselves and others. Reflect on how being emotionally literate will enable you to achieve many of the standards and skills identified and what you will do in order to demonstrate you have the necessary skills and values in place to achieve them.

As this is based on your own reflections, there is no specimen answer at the end of the chapter.

You will notice many of the skills, attributes and roles which nurses undertake require them to be self-aware and aware of the needs of others. This awareness, which you are required to develop as a student nurse, will most certainly be a big part of the suite of skill competencies which we have suggested in this book go towards creating effective managers and leaders. What is important for you as you develop from student nurse to staff nurse, sister and beyond is that you conscientiously continue to develop these capabilities in such a way that they become part of who you are and therefore how you behave. Nurse leaders and managers are entrusted with the management and leadership of people delivering care to some of the most vulnerable in society. By becoming a good role model you can be more certain the care you and your team deliver lives up to the lofty ideals of modern nursing practice.

Chapter summary

In this chapter we have explored the journey from student nurse to nurse manager and what this might mean for us in managing our emotional responses to change and transition. We have identified a number of important strategies, skills, tactics and values which, taken together, can better prepare you for the responsibilities that leadership and management bring. We have demonstrated how developing trust can have a positive impact on the development of self and of the wider team.

We have identified that the core values and skills of nursing translate well into leadership and management roles and hence the need for student nurses and junior staff nurses to develop, practise and hone these skills from an early point in their career.

Activities: brief outline answers

Activity 9.2 Reflection

The emotions that people feel as they experience different changes and transitions in their lives are not purely tied to the sort of change they are experiencing. All change can bring fear and trepidation, even the changes that are wanted and exciting. The move into a caring role requires some thought about who you put first, how you behave, what impact the emotional investment will have on you as a person and how you will adapt.

Activity 9.3 Critical thinking

Being aware of people's responses to change will mean you are prepared for and can understand the emotions you experience as you go through transitions for yourself. You will also be able to identify and provide support for staff and colleagues subject to change by responding appropriately to their needs as they progress through the transition. Failure to recognise that someone is depressed or seeking new meaning may mean as a leader or manager we misinterpret their behaviours and perhaps treat them in a less than supportive manner.

Further reading

Bennis, WG (2004) The Seven Ages of the Leader. *Harvard Business Review*, 82 (1): 46–53.
An inspiring and informational look at leadership development.

Davis, N (2011) *Learning Skills for Nursing Students.* Exeter: Learning Matters.
Gives helpful advice for gaining knowledge and confidence.

Howatson-Jones, L (2013) *Reflective Practice in Nursing* (2nd edition). London: SAGE.
Essential advice on how to understand yourself and grow in professionalism.

Jones, L and Bennett, CL (2012) *Leadership in Health and Social Care: An Introduction for Emerging Leaders.* Banbury: Lantern.
An easy-to-read general introduction to growing yourself as a leader.

Useful websites

www.businessballs.com/self-confidence-assertiveness.htm
A useful and interesting take on developing self-confidence.

http://changingminds.org/disciplines/change_management/psychology_change/ psychology_change.htm
A quirky but informative look at the psychology of change and transition.

www.learnmanagement2.com/managementconcepts.htm
Some good pages on motivational theories can be found here.

www.cipd.co.uk/subjects/lrnanddev/selfdev/emotintel.htm?IsSrchRes=1
The Chartered Institute of Personnel and Development's synopsis of emotional intelligence.

www.mindtools.com/CommSkll/ActiveListening.htm
Some insights into active listening.

www.mindtools.com/pages/article/newTCS_82.htm
The Holmes and Rahe stress scale.

Glossary

active listening   listening to, understanding and responding appropriately to what other people are saying.

binary thinking   in the sense used here it refers to a way of defining your identity with reference to the differences between you and someone else.

charisma/charismatic   a facet of personality which is compelling to other people and inspires others to follow the individual who is charismatic

clinical supervision   a process of guided group reflection facilitated by a third party.

emotional intelligence   being aware of your own emotions, the emotions in others and how these modify behaviours and being able to talk about this in a meaningful way with others.

Gantt chart   the most common format for displaying project outlines and progress. Named after Henry Gantt, who developed it in the early 1900s, the chart is a form of bar chart which displays activities or events plotted against time.

governance   the methods by which organisations follow regulations stipulated by higher governing bodies to ensure standards are met through their authoritative structures.

group think   a phenomenon that occurs when the members of a group make a collective decision based on seeking unanimity rather than encouraging individual reasoning or critical evaluation of ideas.

Hawthorne effect   changes which occur in people's behaviour because they know they are being observed.

Holmes–Rahe Life Event Rating Scale   a scale of 43 life events which are scored by the amount of stress they can cause. A high score means more stress. Some of the changes are positive ones but still cause significant stress.

integrity   staying true to your own moral and ethical principles.

learning cultures/organisations/teams   groups of people who learn from, and with, each other in the workplace and use this learning to enhance what they do.

legitimate power   the power to lead and manage that an individual has by virtue of his or her position within an organisation as well as the ability to use that power in a reasonable, perhaps ethical, manner.

mediation   resolution of conflict through the facilitation of an impartial third party.

negotiation/negotiate   the process of reaching a compromise agreement through talking.

operational   referring to the management of the day-to-day tasks of an organisation or team.

othering   the process whereby anyone who does not share the same characteristics as us is seen to be 'other'. If we are nurses, non-nurses are 'other'.

outcomes   in the sense they are used in this book, outcomes refer not only to the result of a care episode but also the individual's experience of care. Quality is therefore seen as achieving health goals as well as providing healthcare in a manner acceptable to and involving the client.

person-centred   referring to care which is provided with the needs and wants of the patients at its core. This is the opposite of providing care which is dictated by what health and social care professionals want to provide or which is rigidly dictated by policy.

skill mix   an appropriate number of people of various levels of ability on duty at the same time in order to be able to undertake the tasks required during a shift.

social capital   building up a bank of good will that can be called on later when you need a favour or support.

span of control   the number of employees for which each organisation manager or head of department is responsible.

stakeholders   individuals who will be affected directly or indirectly as a result of the organisation's actions, objectives, outcomes.

terms of reference   the purposes and powers of a committee, usually contained within a written document.

total quality management   an approach to quality management that takes account of both the outcome of the care episode and the ways in which the care episode was experienced by the patient or client.

values   the personal rules and understandings we have about what is right and what is wrong in human behaviour.

whistle blowing   the process of raising the alarm about some poor practice, usually through an established channel.

References

Adair, J (1990) *How to Manage Your Time*. Guildford: Talbot Adair Press.

Adair, J (2010) *Develop Your Leadership Skills*. London: Kogan Page.

Aiken, LH, Clarke, SP, Sloane, DL, Sochalski, J and Silber, JH (2002) Hospital Nurse Staffing and Patient Mortality, Nurse Burnout and Job Dissatisfaction. *Journal of American Medical Association*, 23/30, 288 (16): 1987–93.

Anderson, RA, Corazzini, KN and McDaniel, RR (2004) Complexity Science and the Dynamics of Climate and Communication: Reducing Nursing Home Turnover. *The Gerontologist*, 44: 378–88.

Antai-Otong, D (1997) Team Building in a Health Care Setting. *American Journal of Nursing*, 97 (7): 48–51.

Bach, S and Grant, A (2015) *Communication and Interpersonal Skills in Nursing* (3rd edition). London: SAGE/Learning Matters.

Barrick, MR and Mount, MK (1991) The Big Five Personality Dimensions and Job Performance: A Meta Analysis. *Personnel Psychology*, 44 (41): 1–26.

Bass, BM (1985) *Leadership and Performance*. New York: Free Press.

Beckhard, RF and Harris, RT (1987) *Organisation Transitions: Managing Complex Change*. Boston: Addison Wesley.

Belbin, MR (2010) *Management Teams: Why They Succeed or Fail* (3rd edition). Oxford: Butterworth Heinemann.

Bennis, WG (1989) *On Becoming a Leader*. New York: Addison Wesley.

Bersin, J (2010) Create a High-Impact Learning Culture. *Chief Learning Officer*, 9 (10): 16.

Bondas, T (2006) Paths to Nursing Leadership. *Journal of Nursing Management*, 14: 332–9.

Bray, L and Nettleton, P (2007) Assessor or Mentor? Role Confusion in Professional Education. *Nurse Education Today*, 27 (8): 848–55.

Bridges, W (2003) *Managing Transitions: Making the Most of Change*. London: Nicholas Brearley.

Butterworth, T, Bell, L, Jackson, C and Majda, P (2007) Wicked Spell or Magic Bullet? A Review of the Clinical Supervision Literature 2001–2007. *Nurse Education Today*, 28 (3): 264–72.

Care Quality Commission (2011) *Care Quality Commission Demands Action After Report Identifies Failings at Cambridgeshire and Peterborough NHS Trust*. Available online at: www.cqc.org.uk/newsandevents/pressreleases.cfm?cit_id=37178&FAArea1=customWidgets.content_view_1&usecache=false

Causer, G and Exworthy, M (2003) Professionals as Managers Across the Public Sector, in Bullman, A, Charlesworth, J, Henderson, J, Reynolds, J and Seden, J (eds) *The Managing Care Reader* (pages 213–19). London: Routledge.

Chartered Institute of Personnel and Development (2007) *Managing Conflict at Work: Survey Report.* London: CIPD.

Chartered Institute of Personnel and Development (2011) *Performance Appraisal Factsheet.* Available online at: www.cipd.co.uk/hr-resources/factsheets/performance-appraisal.aspx

Clews, G (2010) *Lack of Support for Nurses Blamed for Mid Staffs Failings.* Available online at: www.nursingtimes.net/whats-new-in-nursing/acute-care/lack-of-support-for-nurses-blamed-for-mid-staffsfailings/5011861.article

Croskerry, P and Norman, G (2008) Overconfidence in Clinical Decision Making. *American Journal of Medicine*, 121: S24–9.

Cummings, G and McLennan, M (2005) Advanced Practice Nursing: Leadership to Effect Policy Change. *Journal of Nursing Administration*, 35 (2): 61–6.

Cummings, J (2012) *Leadership: What's in a Word?* Available online at: http://www.england.nhs. uk/tag/6cs

Daft, R (2001) *The Leadership Experience* (2nd edition). Florence, Kentucky: South-Western Educational Publishing.

Darzi, A (2008) *High-Quality Care for All: NHS Next Stage Review Final Report.* London: Department of Health.

Davies, C (2004) Workers, Professions and Identity, in Henderson, J and Atkinson, D (eds) *Managing Care in Context* (pages 189–210). London: Routledge.

Dawson, A and Butler, I (2004) The Morally Active Manager, in Henderson, J and Atkinson, D (eds) *Managing Care in Context* (pages 237–58). London: Routledge.

Department of Health (2010) *Equity and Excellence: Liberating the NHS.* Available online at: https://www.gov.uk/government/uploads/system/uploads/attachment_data/file/213823/dh_117794.pdf

Dirks, KT and Ferrin, DL (2002) Trust in Leadership: Meta-Analytic Findings and Implications for Research and Practice. *Journal of Applied Psychology*, 87 (4): 611–28.

Drennan, V, Davis, K, Traynor, M, Goodman, C, Mark, A, Peacock, R, Humphrey, C and Fairley-Murray, S (2007) Entrepreneurial Nurses and Midwives in the United Kingdom: An Integrative Review. *Journal of Advanced Nursing*, 60 (5): 459–69.

Edwards, D, Burnard, P, Hannigan, B, Cooper, L, Adams, J, Juggessur, T, Fothergil, A and Coyle, D (2006) Clinical Supervision and Burnout: The Influence of Clinical Supervision for Community Mental Health Nurses. *Journal of Clinical Nursing*, 15: 1007–10.

Ellis, P (2013) *Understanding Research for Nursing Students* (Transforming Nursing Practice) (2nd edition). London: SAGE.

Ellis, P (2014) *Understanding Ethics for Nursing Students* (Transforming Nursing Practice). London: SAGE.

Ellis, P and Abbott, J (2010) How to Learn to Delegate Effectively in the Renal Unit. *Journal of Renal Nursing*, 2 (2): 38–40.

Farson, R and Keyes, R (2002) The Failure Tolerant Leader. *Harvard Business Review*, 80 (8): 64–71.

Fowler, A (1996) How to Provide Effective Feedback. *People Management*, 2 (14): 44–5.

Francis, R (2013) *Report of the Mid Staffordshire NHS Foundation Trust Public Inquiry*. Available online at: http://www.midstaffspublicinquiry.com/report

Frankel, A (2008) What Leadership Styles Should Senior Nurses Develop? *Nursing Times*, 104 (35): 23–4.

French, JPR Jr and Raven, B (1960) The Bases of Social Power, in Cartwright, D and Zander, A (eds) *Group Dynamics* (pages 607–23). New York: Harper and Row.

Gainsborough, S (2009) Risks and Benefits: Changing the Nursing Skill Mix. *Nursing Times*, 22 (September). Available online at: www.nursingtimes.net/whats-new-in-nursing/acute-care/risks-and benefits-changing-the-nursing-skill-mix/5006399.article

Gallway, T (1974) *The Inner Game of Tennis*. New York: Random House.

Gallway, T (2000) *The Inner Game of Work*. New York: Random House.

Goleman, D (1996) *Emotional Intelligence: Why It Can Matter More Than IQ*. London: Bloomsbury.

Goleman, D (1998) *Working with Emotional Intelligence*. New York: Bantam Books.

Grant, AM (2001) *Towards a Psychology of Coaching*. Sydney: Coaching Psychology Unit, University of Sydney.

Griffin, RW (1999) *Management* (6th edition). New York: Houghton Mifflin.

Griffiths, R (1983) *NHS Management Inquiry: Report to the Secretary of State of Social Services*. London: HMSO.

Grivas, C and Puccio, G (2012) *The Innovative Team: Unleashing Creative Potential for Breakthrough Results*. San Francisco: Jossey Bass

Handy, C (1994) *Understanding Organizations*. London: Penguin.

Her Majesty's Government (2010) *Equality Act 2010*. Available online at: http://www.legislation.gov.uk/ukpga/2010/15/contents

Her Majesty's Government (2012) *Health and Social Care Act*. Available online at: http://www.legislation.gov.uk/ukpga/2012/7/contents/enacted

Hersey, P, Blanchard, K and Johnson, D (2007) *Management of Organisational Behaviour* (9th edition). Oxford: Pearson Education.

Herzberg, F (1959) *The Motivation to Work*. New York: John Wiley.

Hewison, A and Sim, J (1998) Managing Interprofessional Working: Using Codes of Ethics as a Foundation. *Journal of Interprofessional Care*, 12 (3): 309–21.

Hocking, BA (2006) Using Reflection to Resolve Conflict. *Journal of the Association of Operating Room Nurses*, 84 (2): 249–59.

Homans, GC (1961) *Social Behavior: Its Elementary Forms*. New York: Harcourt Brace.

Hopson, B and Adams, J (1976) *Transition: Understanding and Managing Personal Change.* London: Martin Robertson.

House, RJ (2004) *Culture, Leadership, and Organizations: The GLOBE Study of 62 Societies.* Thousand Oaks: SAGE.

Howatson-Jones, L (2004) The Servant Leader. *Nursing Management,* 11 (3): 20–4.

Howatson-Jones, L (2013) *Reflective Practice in Nursing* (Transforming Nursing Practice). London: SAGE.

International Council of Nurses (2004) *Guidelines on the Nurse Entre/Intrapreneur Providing Nursing Service.* Geneva: ICN Publications. Available online at: www.crnns.ca/documents/Self%20 Emp%20Practice/Guidelines%20for%20Nurse%20Entrepreneurs%20(ICN).pdf

Jackson, C and Ellis, P (2010) Creative Thinking for Whole Systems Working, in Standing, M (ed.) *Clinical Judgement and Decision Making in Nursing and Interprofessional Healthcare* (pages 54–79). Maidenhead: Open University Press.

Johnson, M (1994) Conflict and Nursing Professionalization, in McCloskey, J and Grace, H (eds) *Current Issues in Nursing* (4th edition) (pages 643–9). St Louis: Mosby.

Kohn, S and O'Connell, V (2005) *6 Secrets of Highly Effective Bosses.* Richmond: Crimson.

Kotter, J (1990) *A Force for Change: How Leadership Differs from Management.* New York: Free Press.

Lawton, A (1998) *Ethical Management for the Public Services.* Buckingham: Open University Press.

Lee, P, Gillespie, N, Mann, L and Wearing, A (2010) Leadership and Trust: Their Effect on Knowledge Sharing and Team Performance. *Management Learning,* 41 (4): 473–91.

Lewin, K (1951) *Field Theory in Social Sciences.* New York: Harper and Row.

Lorenz, E N (1963) Deterministic Nonperiodic Flow. *Journal of the Atmospheric Sciences,* 20 (2): 130–41.

Luft, J and Ingham, H (1955) The Johari Window, a Graphic Model of Interpersonal Awareness, in *Proceedings of the Western Training Laboratory in Group Development.* Los Angeles: UCLA.

Machell, S, Gough, P and Steward, K (2009) *From Ward to Board: Identifying Good Practice in the Business of the Caring.* London: King's Fund Publications.

Machell, S, Gough, P, Naylor, D, Nath, V, Steward, K and Williams, S (2010) *Putting Quality First in the Boardroom: Improving the Business of Caring.* London: The King's Fund and the Burdett Trust for Nursing. Available online at: www.kingsfund.org.uk/publications/putting-quality-first-boardroom

Mahoney, J (2001) Leadership Skills for the 21st Century. *Journal of Nursing Management,* 9 (5): 269–71.

Marquis, BL and Huston, CJ (2009) *Leadership Roles and Management Functions in Nursing: Theory and Applications.* Philadelphia, PA: Lippincott, Williams and Wilkins.

Maslach, C (2003) Job Burnout: New Directions in Research and Intervention. *Current Directions in Psychological Science,* 12 (5): 189–92.

Mayer, JD and Salovey, P (1993) The Intelligence of Emotional Intelligence. *Intelligence,* 17 (4): 433–42.

Mintzberg, H (1975) The Manager's Job: Folklore and Fact. *Harvard Business Review,* July/August: 66–75.

Mumford, A (1999) *Effective Learning.* London: Chartered Institute of Personnel Development.

NHS Employers (2013) *Briefing Note: Issues Highlighted by the 2013 NHS Staff Survey in England.* London: NHS Employers. Available online at: http://www.nhsstaffsurveys.com/Caches/Files/NHS%20staff%20survey_nationalbriefing_2013_FINAL-1.pdf

NHS England (2014) *Five Year Forward View.* Available online at: www.england.nhs.uk/wp-content/uploads/2014/10/5yfv-web.pdf

NHS Leadership Academy (2013) *The Healthcare Leadership Model.* Available online at: www.leadershipacademy.nhs.uk/discover/leadershipmodel

Northam, S (2009a) Conflict in the Workplace: Part 1. Sex, Age, Hierarchy, and Culture Influence the Nursing Environment. *American Journal of Nursing,* 109 (6): 70–3.

Northam, S (2009b) Conflict in the Workplace: Part 2. Strategies to Resolve Conflict and Restore Collegial Working Relationships. *American Journal of Nursing,* 109 (7): 65–7.

Nursing and Midwifery Council (2002) *Supporting Nurses and Midwives through Lifelong Learning.* London: NMC.

Nursing and Midwifery Council (2010) *Standards for Pre-registration Nursing Education.* London: NMC.

Nursing and Midwifery Council (2015) *The Code: Professional Standards of Practice and Behaviour for Nurses and Midwives.* London: NMC.

Nursing Standard (1985) Editorial: First Nurses Appointed DHA General Managers. *Nursing Standard,* 385 (21 February): 1.

Olson, EE and Eoyang, GH (2001) *Facilitating Organization Change: Lessons from Complexity Science.* San Francisco: Jossey Bass/Pfeiffer.

Parsloe, E and Leedham, M (2009) *Coaching and Mentoring: Practical Conversations to Improve Learning.* London: Kogan Page.

Pascale, R (1990) *Managing on the Edge.* London: Penguin.

Patterson, C (2005) *Generational Diversity: Implications for Consultation and Teamwork.* Paper presented at the meeting of the Council of Directors of School Psychology Programs on generational differences. Deerfield Beach, Florida.

Quinn, F (1995) *Principles and Practice of Nurse Education.* London: Chapman Hall.

Redshaw, G (2008) Improving the Performance Appraisal System for Nurses. *Nursing Times,* 104 (18): 30–1. Available online at: www.nursingtimes.net/nursing-practice-clinical-research/improving-theperformance-appraisal-system-for-nurses/1314790.article

SanFacon, G (2008) *A Conscious Person's Guide to the Workplace.* Bloomington: Trafford Publishing.

Scholtes, PR (1998) *The Leader's Handbook: A Guide to Inspiring Your People and Managing the Daily Workflow.* New York: McGraw-Hill.

Schuetze, H and Inman, P (2010) *The Community Engagement and Service Mission of Universities.* Leicester: National Institute of Adult and Continuing Education (NIACE).

Schwartz, SH (1994) Are There Universal Aspects in the Structure and Contents of Human Values? *Journal of Social Issues*, 50 (4): 19–45.

Senge, P (1990) *The Fifth Discipline: The Art and Practice of the Learning Organization.* New York: Doubleday.

Senge, P (1996) Leading Learning Organizations. *Training and Development*, 50 (12): 36–7.

Smola, KW and Sutton, CD (2002) Generational Differences in Working Age Women. *Journal of Organizational Behavior*, 23 (4): 363–82.

Spouse, J (2001) Work-Based Learning in Health Care Environments. *Nurse Education in Practice*, 1: 12–18.

Sullivan, EJ and Decker, PJ (2009) *Effective Leadership and Management in Nursing* (7th edition). Harlow: Pearson International Edition.

Swansburg, RC and Swansburg, RJ (2002) *Introduction to Management and Leadership for Nurse Managers* (3rd edition). Boston: Jones and Bartlett.

The Work Foundation (2008) *Work–Life Balance.* Available online at: www.theworkfoundation. com/research/health/worklifebalance.aspx

Thomas, J (2006) *Survival Guide for Ward Managers, Sisters and Charge Nurses.* London: Churchill Livingstone, Elsevier.

Thomas, KW and Kilmann, RH (1974) *Thomas–Kilmann Conflict Mode Instrument.* Sterling Forest, New York: Xicom.

Traynor, M, Davis, K, Drennan, V, Goodman, C, Humphrey, C, Locke, R, Mark, A, Murray, SF, Banning, M and Peacock, R (2006) *A Report to the National Co-ordinating Centre for NHS Service Delivery and Organisation Research and Development of a Scoping Exercise on 'The Contribution of Nurse, Midwife and Health Visitor Entrepreneurs to Patient Choice'.* London: National Co-ordinating Centre for Service Delivery and Organisation.

von Bertalanffy, L (1968) *General System Theory: Foundations, Developments, Applications.* New York: Braziller.

Ward, A (2003) Managing the Team, in Seden, J and Reynolds, J (eds) *Managing Care in Practice* (pages 33–56). London: Routledge.

Williams, J (2007) Follow the Leader. *Healthcare Financial Management*, 61 (1): 50–5.

Wright, P (1996) *Managerial Leadership.* London: Routledge.

Yoder-Wise, P (2007) *Leading and Managing in Nursing* (4th edition). Amsterdam: Elsevier.

Index